Jane with love

for

many a good laugh

Buck to Jack

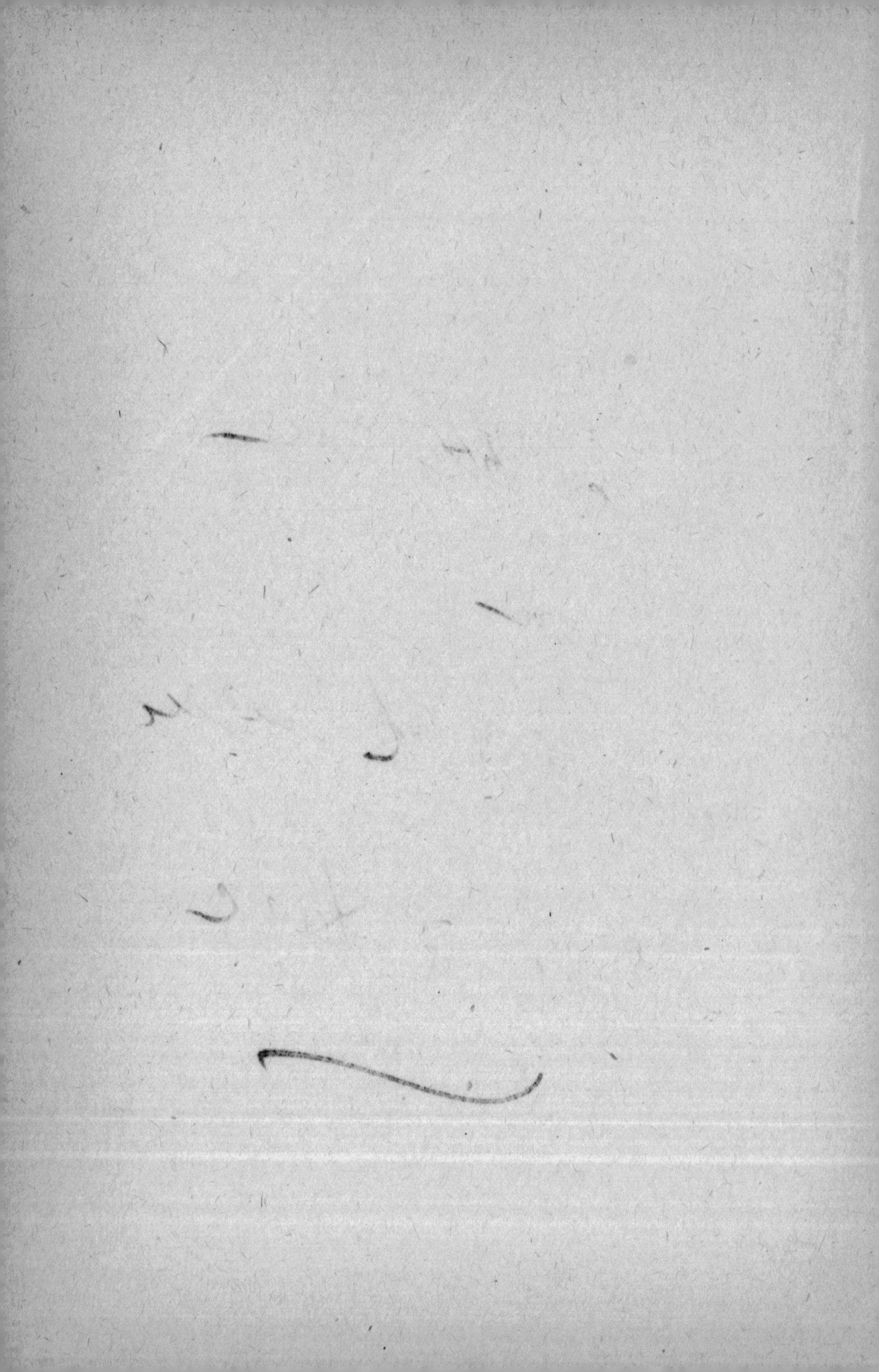

GEO. W. PECK

PECK'S BAD BOY

AND HIS PA

COMPLETE EDITION

BY

GEORGE W. PECK

WITH

100 ILLUSTRATIONS

BY

TRUE WILLIAMS

PHILADELPHIA
DAVID McKAY COMPANY
WASHINGTON SQUARE

PECK'S BAD BOY AND HIS PA.

CONTENTS

CHAPTER V

CHAPTER VI

CHAPTER VII

CHAPTER VIII

CHAPTER IX

CHAPTER X

HIS PA HAS GOT RELIGION

CHAPTER XI

HIS PA TAKES A TRICK

CHAPTER XII

HIS PA GETS PULLED

CHAPTER XIII

HIS PA GOES TC THE EXPOSITION

CHAPTER XIV

HIS PA CATCHES ON

CHAPTER XV

HIS PA AT THE REUNION

PAGE

CHAPTER XVI

THE BAD BOY IN LOVE

CHAPTER XVII

HIS PA FIGHTS HORNETS

CHAPTER XVIII

HIS PA GOES HUNTING

CHAPTER XIX

HIS PA IS "NISHIATED"

CHAPTER XX

HIS GIRL GOES BACK ON HIM

CHAPTER XXI

HE AND HIS PA IN CHICAGO

CHAPTER XXII

HIS PA IS DISCOURAGED

CHAPTER XXIII

HE BECOMES A DRUGGIST

CHAPTER XXIV

HE QUITS THE DRUG BUSINESS

CHAPTER XXV

HIS PA KILLS HIM

CHAPTER XXVI

HIS PA MORTIFIED

CHAPTER XXVII

HIS PA BROKE UP

CHAPTER XXVIII

HIS PA GOES SKATING

CHAPTER XXIX

HIS PA GOES CALLING

CHAPTER XXX

HIS PA DISSECTED

CHAPTER XXXI

HIS PA JOINS A TEMPERANCE SOCIETY

CHAPTER XXXII

HIS PA'S MARVELOUS ESCAPE

CHAPTER XXXIII

HIS PA JOKES HIM

CHAPTER XXXIV

HIS PA GETS MAD

CHAPTER XXXV

HIS PA AN INVENTOR

CHAPTER XXXVI

HIS PA GETS BOXED

CONTENTS

VOL. II

CHAPTER V

HIS PA AND DYNAMITE

CHAPTER VI

HIS PA AN ORANGEMAN

CHAPTER VII

HIS MA DECEIVED HIM

CHAPTER VIII

THE BABY AND THE GOAT

CHAPTER IX

A FUNERAL PROCESSION

CHAPTER X

THE OLD MAN MAKES A SPEECH

PAGE

CHAPTER XI

GARDENING UNDER DIFFICULTIES

CHAPTER XII

THE OLD MAN SHOOTS THE MINISTER

CHAPTER XIII

THE BAD BOY A THOROUGHBRED

CHAPTER XIV

ENTERTAINING Y. M. C. A. DELEGATES

CHAPTER XV

HE TURNS SUPE

CHAPTER XVI

UNCLE EZRA PAYS A VISIT

CHAPTER XVII

HE DISCUSSES THEOLOGY

CHAPTER XVIII

THE DEPARTED ROOSTER

CHAPTER XIX

ONE MORE JOKE ON THE OLD MAN

CHAPTER XX

FOURTH OF JULY MISADVENTURES

PAGE

CHAPTER XXI

WORKING ON SUNDAY

CHAPTER XXII

THE OLD MAN AWFULLY BLOATED

CHAPTER XXIII

THE GROCERY MAN AND THE GHOST

CHAPTER XXIV

THE CRUEL WOMAN AND THE LUCKLESS DOG

CHAPTER XXV

THE BAD BOY GROWS THOUGHTFUL

CHAPTER XXVI

FARM EXPERIENCES

CHAPTER XXVII

DRINKING CIDER IN THE CELLAR

LIST OF ILLUSTRATIONS

A CARD FROM THE AUTHOR

OFFICE OF "PECK'S SUN."
Milwaukee.

GENTS—If you have made up your minds that the world will cease to move unless these "Bad Boy" articles are given to the public in book form, why go ahead, and peace to your ashes. The "Bad Boy" is not a "myth," though there may be some stretches of imagination in the articles. The counterpart of this boy is located in every city, village and country hamlet throughout the land. He is wide awake, full of vinegar and is ready to crawl under the canvas of a circus or repeat a hundred verses of the New Testament in Sunday School. He knows where every melon patch in the neighborhood is located, and at what hours the dog is chained up. He will tie an oyster can to a dog's tail to give the dog exercise, or will fight at the drop of the hat to protect the smaller boy or a school girl. He gets in his work everywhere there is a fair prospect of fun, and his heart is easily touched by an appeal in the right way, though his coat-tail is oftener touched with a boot than his heart is by kindness. But he shuffles through life until the time comes for him to make a mark in the world, and then he buckles on the harness and goes to the front, and becomes successful, and then those who said he would bring up in State Prison, remember that he always *was* a mighty smart lad, and they never tire of telling of some of his deviltry when he was a boy, though they thought he was pretty tough at the time. This book is respectfully dedicated to boys, to the men who have been boys themselves, to the girls who like the boys, and to the mothers, bless them, who like both the boys and the girls.

Very respectfully,
GEO. W. PECK.

PECK'S BAD BOY

AND HIS PA

CHAPTER I

THE BOY WITH A LAME BACK

The boy couldn't sit down—A practical joke on the Old Man—A letter from "Daisy"—Guarding the four corners—The Old Man is unusually generous—Ma asks awkward questions—The boy talked to with a bed-slat—No encouragement for a boy.

A YOUNG fellow who is pretty smart on general principles, and who is always in good humor, went into a store the other morning limping and seemed to be broken up generally. The proprietor asked him if he wouldn't sit down, and he said he couldn't very well, as his back was lame. He seemed discouraged, and the proprietor asked him what was the matter. "Well," says he, as he put his hand on his pistol pocket and groaned: "There is no encouragement for a boy to have any fun nowadays. If a boy tries to play an innocent joke he gets kicked all over the house." The store keeper asked him what had happened to disturb his hilarity. He said he had played a joke on his father and he had been limping ever since.

"You see, I thought the old man was a little spry. You know he is no spring chicken yourself; and though his eyes are not what they used to be, yet he can see a pretty girl further than I can. The other day I wrote a note in a fine hand and addressed it to him, asking him to meet me on the corner of Wisconsin and Milwaukee streets, at 7:30 on Saturday evening, and signed the name of 'Daisy' to it. At supper time Pa he was all shaved up and had his hair plastered over the bald spot, and he got on some clean cuffs, and said he was going to the Consistory to initiate some candidates from the country, and he might not be in till late. He didn't eat much supper, and hurried off with my umbrella. I winked at Ma, but didn't say anything. At 7:30 I went down town and he was standing there by the postoffice corner, in a dark place. I went by him and said, 'Hello, Pa, what are you doing there?' He said he was waiting for a man. I went down street and pretty soon I went up on the other corner by Chapman's and he was standing there. You see, he didn't know what corner 'Daisy' was going to be on, and he had to cover all four corners. I saluted him and asked him if he hadn't found his man yet, and he said no, the man was a little late. It is a mean boy that won't speak to his Pa when he sees him standing on a corner. I went up street and saw Pa cross over by the drug store in a sort of a hurry, and I could see a girl going by with a waterproof on, but she skited right along and Pa looked kind of solemn, the way he does when I ask him for new clothes. I turned and came back and he was standing in the doorway, and I said, 'Pa, you will catch cold if you stand around waiting for a man. You go down to the Consistory and let me lay for the man.' Pa said, 'never you mind, you go about your business and I will attend to the man.'

THE GROCERYMAN.

"Well, when a boy's Pa tells him to never you mind, and looks spunky, my experience is that a boy wants to go right away from there, and I went down street. I thought I would cross over, go up the other side, and see how long he would stay. There was a girl or two going up ahead of me, and I see a man hurrying across from the drug store to Van Pelt's corner. It was Pa, and as the girls went along and never looked around Pa looked mad and stepped into the doorway.

PA LOOKED MAD AND STEPPED INTO THE DOORWAY.

It was about eight o'clock then, and Pa was tired, and I felt sorry for him and I went up to him and asked him for half a dollar to go to the Academy. I never knew him to shell out so freely and so quick. He gave me a dollar, and I told him I would go and get it changed and bring him back the half dollar, but he said I needn't mind the change. It is awful mean of a boy that has always been treated well to play it on his Pa that way, and I felt ashamed. As I turned the corner and saw him standing there shivering, waiting for the man, my conscience troubled me, and I told a policeman to go and tell Pa that 'Daisy' had been suddenly taken with worms, and would not be there that evening. I peeked around the corner and Pa and the policeman went off to get a drink. I was glad they did, cause Pa needed it, after standing around so long. Well, when I went home the joke was so good I told Ma about it, and she was mad. I guess she was mad at me for treating Pa that way. I heard Pa come home about eleven o'clock, and Ma was real kind to him. She told him to warm his feet, cause they were just like chunks of ice. Then she asked him how many they initiated in the Consistory, and he said six, and then she asked him if they initiated 'Daisy' in the Consistory, and pretty soon I heard Pa snoring. In the morning he took me into the basement, and gave me the hardest talking to that I ever had, with a bed slat. He said that he knew that I wrote that note all the time, and he thought he would pretend that he was looking for 'Daisy,' just to fool me. It don't look reasonable that a man would catch epizootic and rheumatism just to fool his boy, does it? What did he give me the dollar for? Ma and Pa don't seem to call each other pet any more, and as for me, they both look at me as though I was a hard citizen. I am going to Missouri to take Jesse James' place. There is no encouragement for a boy here. Well, good morning. If Pa comes in here asking for me tell him that you saw an express wagon going to the morgue with the remains of a pretty boy who acted as though he died from concussion of a bed slat on the pistol pocket. That will make Pa feel sorry. O, he has got the awfulest cold, though."

And the boy limped out to separate a couple of dogs that were fighting.

GROCERIES.

CHAPTER II

THE BAD BOY AT WORK AGAIN

The best boys full of tricks—The Old Man lays down the law about jokes—Rubber-hose macaroni—The Old Man's struggles—Chewing vigorously but in vain—An inquest held—Revelry by night—Music in the woodshed—"'Twas ever thus."

Of course all boys are not full of tricks, but the best of them are. That is, those who are readiest to play innocent jokes, and who are continually looking for chances to make Rome howl, are the most apt to turn out to be first-class business men. There is a boy in the Seventh Ward who is so full of fun that sometimes it makes him ache. He is the same boy who not long since wrote a note to his father and signed the name "Daisy" to it, and got the old man to stand on a corner for two hours waiting for the girl. After that scrape the old man told the boy that he had no objection to innocent jokes, such as would not bring reproach upon him, and as long as the boy confined himself to jokes that would simply cause pleasant laughter, and not cause the finger of scorn to be pointed at a parent, he would be the last one to kick. So the boy has been for the three weeks trying to think of some innocent joke to play on his father. The old man is getting a little near sighted, and his teeth are not as good as they used to be, but the old man will not admit it. Nothing that anybody can say can make him own up that his eyesight is failing, or that his teeth are poor, and he would bet a hundred dollars that he could see as far as ever. The boy knew the failing, and made up his mind to demonstrate to the old man that he was rapidly getting off his base. The old person is very fond of macaroni, and eats it about three times a week. The other day the boy was in a drug store and noticed in a show case a lot of small rubber hose, about the size of sticks of macaroni, such as is used on nursing bottles, and other rubber utensils. It was white and nice, and the boy's mind was made up at once. He bought a yard of it, and took it home. When the macaroni was cooked and ready to be served, he hired the table girl to help him play it on the old man. They took a pair of shears and cut the rubber hose in pieces about the same length as the pieces of boiled macaroni, and put them in a saucer with a little macaroni over the rubber pipes, and placed the dish at the old man's plate. Well, we suppose if ten thousand peo-

HE WAS MAD AND GLAD.

ple could have had reserved seats and seen the old man struggle with the India rubber macaroni, and have seen the boy's struggle to keep from laughing, they would have had more fun than they would at a circus. First the old delegate attempted to cut the macaroni into small pieces, and failing, he remarked that it was not cooked enough. The boy said his macaroni was cooked too tender, and that his father's teeth were so poor that he would have to eat soup entirely pretty soon. The old man said, "Never you mind my teeth, young man," and decided that he would not complain of anything again. He took up a couple of pieces of rubber and one piece of macaroni on a fork and put them in his mouth. The macaroni dissolved easy enough, and went down perfectly easy, but the fiat macaroni was too much for him. He chewed on it for a minute or two, and talked about the weather in order that none of the family should see that he was in trouble, and when he found the macaroni would not down, he called their attention to something out of the window and took the rubber slyly from his mouth, and laid it under the edge of his plate. He was more than half convinced that his teeth were played out, but went on eating something else for awhile, and finally he thought he would just chance the macaroni once more for luck, and he mowed away another fork full in his mouth. It was the same old story. He chewed like a seminary girl chewing gum, and his eyes stuck out and his face became red, and his wife looked at him as though afraid he was going to die of apoplexy, and finally the servant girl burst out laughing, and went out of the room with her apron stuffed in her mouth, and the boy felt as though it was unhealthy to tarry too long at the table, and he went out.

Left alone with his wife the old man took the rubber macaroni from his mouth and laid it on his plate, and he and his wife held an inquest over it. The wife tried to spear it with a fork, but couldn't make any impression on it, and then she saw it was rubber hose, and told the old man. He was mad and glad, at the same time; glad because he had found his teeth were not to blame, and mad because the grocer had sold him boarding house macaroni. Then the girl came in and was put on the confessional, and told all, and presently there was a sound of revelry by night, in the wood shed, and the still, small voice was saying, "O, Pa, don't! you said you didn't care for innocent jokes. Oh!" And then the old man, between the strokes of the piece of clap-board would say, "Feed your father a hose cart next, won't ye? Be firing car springs and clothes wringers down me next, eh? Put some gravy on a rubber overcoat, probably, and serve it to me for salad. Try a piece of overshoe, with a bone in it, for my beefsteak, likely. Give your poor old father a slice of rubber bib in place of tripe to-morrow, I expect. Boil me a rubber water bag for apple dumplings, pretty soon, if I don't look out. There! You go and split the kindling wood." 'Twas ever thus. A boy can't have any fun now days.

CHAPTER III

THE BAD BOY GIVES HIS PA AWAY.

Pa is a hard citizen—Drinking sozodont—Making up the spare bed—The midnight war-dance—An appointment by the coal bin.

THE bad boy's mother was out of town for a week, and when she came home she found every thing topsy turvy. The beds were all mussed up, and there was not a thing hung up anywhere. She called the bad boy and asked him what in the deuce had been going on, and he made it pleasant for his Pa about as follows:

"Well, Ma, I know I will get killed, but I shall die like a man. When Pa met you at the depot he looked too innocent for any use, but he's a hard citizen, and don't you forget it. He hasn't been home a single night till after eleven o'clock, and he was tired every night, and he had somebody come home with him."

"O, heavens, Hennery," said the mother, with a sigh, "are you sure about this?"

"Sure!" says the bad boy, "I was on to the whole racket. The first night they came home awful tickled, and I guess they drank some of your Sozodont, cause they seemed to foam at the mouth. Pa wanted to put his friend in the spare bed, but there were no sheets on it, and he went to rummaging around in the drawers for sheets. He got out all the towels and table-cloths, and made up the bed with table-cloths, the first night, and in the morning the visitor kicked because there was a big coffee stain on the table-cloth sheet. You know that table-cloth you spilled the coffee on last spring, when Pa scared you by having his whiskers cut off. O, they raised thunder around the room. Pa took your night-shirt, you know the one with the lace work all down the front, and put a pillow in it, and set it on a chair, and then took a burned match and marked eyes and nose on the pillow, and put your bonnet on it, and then they had a war dance. Pa hurt the bald spot on his head by hitting it against the gas shandelier, and then he said dammit. Then they throwed pillows at each other. Pa's friend didn't have any night shirt, and Pa gave his friend one of your'n, and the friend

PA MARKED EYES AND NOSE ON THE PILLOW.

took that old hoop-skirt in the closet, the one Pa always steps on when he goes in the closet after a towel and hurts his bare foot, you know, and put it under the night shirt, and they walked around arm in arm. O, it made me tired to see a man Pa's age act so like a darned fool."

"Hennery," says the mother, with a deep meaning in her voice, "I want to ask you one question. Did your Pa's friend *wear a dress?"*

"O, yes," said the bad boy, coolly, not noticing the pale

face of his Ma, "the friend put on that old blue dress of yours, with the pistol pocket in front, you know, and pinned a red cloth on for a train, and they danced the can-can."

Just at this point Pa came home to dinner, and the bad boy said, "Pa, I was just telling Ma what a nice time you had the first night she went away, with the pillow, and—"

"Hennery!" says the old gentleman severely, "you are a confounded fool."

"Izick," said the wife more severely, "Why did you bring a female home with you that night? Have you got no—"

"O, Ma," says the bad boy, "it was not a woman. It was young Mr. Brown, Pa's clerk at the store, you know."

"O!" said Ma, with a smile and a sigh.

"Hennery," said the stern parent, "I want to see you there by the coal bin for a minute or two. You are the gaul durndest fool I ever see. What you want to learn the first thing you do is to keep your mouth shut," and then they went on with the frugal meal, while Hennery seemed to feel as though something was coming.

CHAPTER IV.

THE BAD BOY'S FOURTH OF JULY

Pa is a Pointer not a Setter—Special arrangements for the Fourth of July—A grand supply of fire works—The explosion—The air full of Pa and dog and rockets—The new Hell—A Scene that beggars description.

"How long do you think it will be before your father will be able to come down to the office?" asked the druggist of the bad boy as he was buying some arnica and court plaster.

"O, the doc. says he could come down now if he would, on some street where there were no horses to scare," said the boy as he bought some gum, "but he says he ain't in no hurry to come down till his hair grows out, and he gets some new clothes made. Say, do you wet this court plaster and stick it on?"

The druggist told him how the court plaster worked, and then asked him if his Pa couldn't ride down town.

"Ride down? well, I guess nix. He would have to set down if he rode down town, and Pa is no setter this trip, he is a pointer. That's where the pin wheel struck him."

"Well how did it happen?" asked the druggist as he wrapped a yellow paper over the bottle of arnica, and twisted the ends, and then helped the boy stick the strip of court plaster on his nose.

"Nobody knows how it happened but Pa, and when I come near to ask him about it he feels around his nightshirt where his pistol pocket would be if it was pants he had on, and tells me to leave his sight forever, and I leave too quick. You see he is afraid I will get hurt every Fourth of July, and he told me if I wouldn't fire a fire-cracker all day, he would let me get four dollars' worth of nice fire-works and he would fire them off for me in the evening in the back yard. I promised, and he gave me the money and I bought a dandy lot of fire-works, and don't you forget it. I had a lot of rockets and Roman candles, and six-pin wheels, and a lot of nigger chasers, and some of these cannon fire-crackers, and torpedoes, and a box of parlor matches. I took them home and put the package in our big stuffed chair and put a newspaper over them.

Pa always takes a nap in that stuffed chair after dinner, and he went into the sitting room and I heard him driving our poodle dog out of that chair, and heard him ask the dog what he was a-chewing, and just then the explosion took place, and we all rushed in there. I tell you what I honestly think. I think that dog was chewing that box of parlor matches. This kind that pops so when you step on them. Pa was just going to set down when the whole air was filled with dog, and Pa, and rockets, and everything. When I got in there Pa had a sofa pillow trying to put the dog out. In the meantime Pa's linen pants were afire. I grabbed a pail of this indigo water that they had been rinsing clothes with and throwed it on Pa, or there wouldn't have been a place on him bigger'n a six-pence that wasn't burnt, and then he threw a camp chair at me and told me to go to Gehenna. Ma says that's the new hell they have got up in the revised edition of the Bible for bad boys. When Pa's pants were out his coat-tail blazed up and a Roman candle was firing blue and red balls at his legs, and a rocket got in to his white vest. The scene beggared description, like that Racine fire. A nigger chaser got after Ma and treed her on top of the sofa, and another one took after a girl that Ma invited to dinner, and burnt one of her stockings so she had to wear one of Ma's stockings, a good deal too big for her, home. After things got a little quiet, and we opened the doors and windows to let out the smoke and smell of burnt dog hair and Pa's whiskers, the big fire crackers began to go off, and a policeman came to the door and asked what was the matter, and Pa told him to go along with me

A NIGGER CHASER GOT AFTER MA AND TREED HER ON TOP OF THE SOFA.

to Gehenna, but I don't want to go with a policeman. It would give me dead away. Well, there was nobody hurt much but the dog and Pa. I felt awful sorry for the dog. He hasn't got hair enough to cover hisself. Pa didn't have much hair anyway, except by the ears, but he thought a good deal of his whiskers, cause they wasn't very gray. Say, couldn't you send this anarchy up to the house? If I go up there Pa will say I am the damest fool on record. This is the last Fourth of July you catch me celebrating. I am going to work in a glue factory, where nobody will ever come to see me."

And the boy went out to pick up some squib fire crackers that had failed to explode, in front of the drug store.

CHAPTER V

THE BAD BOY'S MA COMES HOME

No deviltry, only a little fun—The bad boy's chum—Alady's wardrobe in the Old Man's room—Ma's unexpected arrival—Where is the huzzy?—Damfino!—The bad boy wants to travel with a circus.

"WHEN is your Ma coming back?" asked the grocery man, of the bad boy, as he found him standing on the sidewalk when the grocery was opened in the morning, taking some pieces of brick out of his coat tail pockets.

"O she got back at midnight, last night," said the boy as he eat a few blue berries out of a case. "That's what makes me up so early. Pa has been kicking at these pieces of brick with his bare feet, and when I came away he had his toes in his hand and was trying to go back up-stairs on one foot. Pa haint got no sense."

"I am afraid you are a terror," said the grocery man, as he looked at the innocent face of the boy. "You are always making your parents some trouble, and it is a wonder to me they don't send you to some reform school. What deviltry were you up to last night to get kicked this morning?"

"No deviltry, just a little fun. You see, Ma went to Chicago to stay a week, and she got tired, and telegraphed she wou'' be home last night, and Pa was down town and I forgot to give him the dispatch, and after he went to bed, me and a chum of mine thought we would have a Fourth of July.

"You see, my chum has got a sister about as big as Ma, and we hooked some of her clothes and after Pa got to snoring we put them in Pa's room. O, you'.. a laffed. We put a pair of number one slippers with blue stockings, down in front of the rocking chair, beside Pa's boots, and a red corset on a chair, and my chum's sister's best black silk dress on another chair, and a hat with a white feather on, on the bureau, and some frizzes on the gas bracket, and everything we could find that belonged to a girl in my chum's sister's room. O, we got a red parasol too and left it right in the middle of the floor. Well, when I looked at the layout, and heard Pa snoring, I thought I should die. You see, Ma knows Pa is a darn good feller, but she is easily excited. My chum slept with me that night, and when we heard the door-bell ring, I stuffed a pillow in my mouth. There was nobody to meet Ma at the depot, and she hired a hack and came right up. Nobody heard the bell but me, and I had to go down and let Ma in. She was pretty hot, now you bet, at not being met at the depot.

THEN I SLIPPED UP-STAIRS AND LOOKED OVER THE BANISTERS.

"Where's your father?" said she, as she began to go up stairs.

"I told her I guessed Pa had gone to sleep by this time, but I heard a good deal of ıoise in the room about an hour ago, and may be he was taking a bath. Then I slipped up stairs and looked over the banisters. Ma said something about heavens and earth, and 'where is the huzzy,' and a lot of things I couldn't hear, and Pa said 'damfino' and 'its no such thing,' and the door slammed and they talked for two hours. I s'pose they finally laid it to me, as they always do, 'cause Pa called me very early this morning, and when I came down stairs he came out in the hall and his face was redder'n a beet, and he tried to stab me with his big toe-nail, and if it hadn't been for these pieces of brick he would have hurt my feelings. I see they had my chum's sister's clothes all pinned up in a newspaper; and I s'pose when I go back I shall have to carry them home, and then she will be down on me. I'll tell you what, I have got a good notion to take some shoemakers' wax and stick my chum on my back and travel with a circus as a double-headed boy from Borneo. A fellow could have more fun, and not get kicked all the time."

And the boy sampled some strawberries in a case in front of the store and went down the street whistling for his chum, who was looking out of an alley to see if the coast was clear.

CHAPTER VI

HIS PA IS A DARN COWARD

His Pa has been a major—How he would deal with burglars—His bravery put to the test—The ice revolver—His Pa begins to pray—Tells where the change is—"Please, Mr. Burglar, spare a poor man's life!"—Ma wakes up—The bad boy and his chum run—Fish-pole sauce—Ma would make a good chief of police.

"I SUPPOSE you think my Pa is a brave man," said the boy to the grocer, as he was trying a new can opener on a tin biscuit box in the grocery, while the grocer was putting up some canned goods for the boy, who said the goods were for the folks to use at a picnic, but which was to be taken out camping by the boy and his chum.

"O, I suppose he is a brave man," said the grocer as he charged the goods to the boy's father. "Your Pa is called a major, and you know at the time of the re-union he wore a veteran badge, and talked to the boys about how they suffered during the war."

"Suffered nothing," remarked the boy, with a sneer; "unless they suffered from the peach brandy and leather pies Pa sold them. Pa was a suttler, that's the kind of a veteran he was, and he is a coward."

"What makes you think your Pa is a coward?" asked the grocer, as he saw the boy slipping some sweet crackers into his pistol pocket.

"Well, my chum and me tried him last night, and he is so sick this morning that he can't get up. You see, since the burglars got into Magie's, Pa has been telling what he would do if the burglars got into our house. He said he would jump out of bed and knock one senseless with his fist, and throw the other over the banister. I told my chum Pa was a coward, and we fixed up like burglars, with masks on, and I had Pa's long hunting boots on, and we pulled caps down over our eyes, and looked fit to frighten a policeman. I took Pa's meerchaum pipe case and tied a little piece of ice over the end the stem goes in, and after Pa and Ma was asleep we went into the room, and I put the cold muzzle of the ice revolver to Pa's temple, and when he woke up I told him if he moved a muscle or said a word I would

THEN I STOOD OFF AND TOLD HIM TO HOLD UP HIS HANDS.

spatter the wall and the counterpane with his brains. He closed his eyes and began to pray. Then I stood off and told him to hold up his hands, and tell me where the valuables was. He held up his hands, and sat up in bed, and sweat and trembled, and told us the change was in his left hand pants pocket, and that Ma's money purse was in the bureau drawer in the cuff box, and my chum went and got them. Pa shook so the bed fairly squeaked and I told him I was a good notion to shoot a few holes in him just for fun, and he cried and said, 'Please Mr. Burglar, take all I have got, but spare a poor old man's life who never did any harm!' Then I told him to lay down on his stomach and pull the clothes over his head, and stick his feet over the foot board, and he did it, and I took a shawl strap and was strapping his feet together, and he was scared, I tell you. It would have been all right if Ma hadn't woke up. Pa trembled so Ma woke up and thought he had the ager, and my chum turned up the light to see how much there was in Ma's purse, and Ma seen me, and asked me what I was doing and I told her I was a burglar, robbing the house. I didn't know whether Ma tumbled to the racket or not, but she threw a pillow at me, and said 'get out of here or I'll take you across my knee,' and she got up and we run. She followed us to my room, and took Pa's jointed fish pole and mauled us both until I don't want any more burglaring, and my chum says he will never speak to me again. I didn't think Ma had so much sand. She is as brave as a lion, but Pa is a regular squaw. Pa sent for me to come to his room this morning, but I ain't well, and am going out to Pewaukee to camp out till the burglar scare is over. If Pa comes around here talking about war times, and how he faced the enemy on many a well fought field you ask him if he ever threw any burglars down a banister. He is a fraud, Pa is, but Ma would make a good chief of police, and don't you let it escape you."

And the boy took his canned ham and lobster, and tucking some crackers inside the bosom of his blue flannel shirt, started for Pewaukee, while the grocer looked at him as though he were a hard citizen.

CHAPTER VII

HIS PA GETS A BITE

His Pa gets too much water—The doctors disagree—How to spoil boys—His Pa goes to Pewaukee in search of his son—Anxious to fish—"Stop 'er, I've got a whale!"—Overboard—His Pa is saved—Goes to cut a switch—A dollar for his pants.

"So the doctor thinks your Pa has ruptured a blood vessel, eh?" says the street car driver to the bad boy, as the youngster was playing sweet on him to get a free ride down town.

"Well, they don't know. The doctor at Pewaukee said Pa had dropsy, until he found the water that they wrung out of his pants was lake water, and there was a doctor on the cars belonging to the Insane Asylum, when we put Pa on the train, who said from the looks of his face, sort of red and blue, it was apoplexy, but a horse doctor that was down at the depot when we put Pa in the carriage to take him home, said he was off his feed, and had been taking too much water when he was hot, and got foundered. O, you can't tell anything about doctors. No two of 'em guesses alike," answered the boy, as he turned the brake for the driver to stop the car for a sister of charity, and then punched the mule with a fish pole, when the driver was looking back, to see if he couldn't jerk her off the back step.

"Well, how did your Pa happen to fall out of the boat? Didn't he know the lake was wet?"

"He had a suspicion that it was damp, when his back struck the water, I think. I'll tell you how it was. When my chum and I run away to Pewaukee, Ma thought we had gone off to be piruts, and she told Pa it was a duty he owed to society to go and get us to come back, and be good. She told him if he would treat me as an equal, and laugh and joke with me, I wouldn't be so bad. She said kicking and pounding spoiled more boys than all the Sunday schools. So Pa came out to our camp, about two miles up the lake from Pewaukee, and he was just as good natured as though we had never had any trouble at all. We let him stay all night with us, and gave him a napkin with a red border to sleep on under a tree, cause there was not blankets enough to go around, and in the morning I let him have one of the soda crackers I had in my shirt bosom and he wanted to go fishing with us. He said he would show us how to fish. So he got a piece of pork rind at a farm house for bait, and he put it on a hook, and we got in an old boat, and my chum rowed and Pa and I trolled. In swinging the boat around Pa's line got under the boat, and come right up near me. I don't know what possessed me, but I took hold of Pa's line and gave it a 'yank,' and Pa jumped so quick his hat went off in the lake. 'Stop 'er,' says Pa, 'I've got a whale.' It's mean in a man to call his chubby faced little boy a whale, but the whale yanked again and Pa began to pull him in. I hung on, and let the line out a little at a time, just zackly like a fish, and he pulled, and sweat, and the bald spot on his head was getting sun burnt, and the line cut my hand, so I wound it around the oar-lock, and Pa pulled hard enough to tip the boat over. He thought he had a forty pound musculunger, and he stood up in the boat and pulled on that oar-lock as hard as he could. I ought not to have done it, but I loosened the line from the oar-lock, and when it slacked up Pa went right out over the side of the boat, and struck on his pants, and split a hole in the water as big as a wash tub. His head went down under water and his boot heels hung over the boat. 'What you doin'? Diving after the fish?' says I as Pa's head came up and he blowed out the water. I thought Pa belonged to the church, but he said 'youdamidyut.' I guess he was talking to the fish. Well, sir, my chum took hold of my Pa's foot and the collar of his coat, and held him in the stern of the boat, and I paddled the boat to the shore, and Pa crawled out and shook himself. I never had no ijee a man's pants could hold so much water. It was just like when they pull the thing on a street sprinkler. Then Pa took off his pants and my chum and me took hold of the legs and Pa took hold of the summer kitchen and we wrung the water out. Pa wan't so sociable after that, and he went back into the woods with his knife, with nothing on but a linen duster and a neck-tie, while his pants were drying on a tree, to cut a switch, and we hollered to him that a party of picnicers from Lake Side were coming ashore right where his pants were, to pic-nic, and Pa he run into the woods. He was afraid there would

THEN PA CRAWLED OUT AND SHOOK HIMSELF.

be some wimmen in the pic-nic that he knowed, and he coaxed us to come in the woods where he was, and he said he would give us a dollar apiece and not be mad any more if we would bring him his pants. We got his pants, and you ought to see how they was wrinkled when he put them on. They looked as though they had been ironed with waffle irons. We went to the depot and came home on the freight train, and Pa sneezed all the way in the caboose, and I don't think he has ruptured any blood vessel. Well, I get off here at Mitchell's bank," and the boy turned the break and jumped off without paying his fare.

CHAPTER VIII

HE IS TOO HEALTHY

An empty Champagne bottle and a black eye—He is arrested—Oconomowoc for health—His Pa is an old masher—Danced till the cows came home—The girl from the Sunny South—The bad boy is sent home.

"THERE, I knew you would get into trouble," said the grocery man to the bad boy, as a policeman came along leading him by the ear, the boy having an empty champagne bottle in one hand, and a black eye. "What has he been doing Mr. Policeman?" asked the grocery man, as the policeman halted with the boy in front of the store.

"Well, I was going by a house up here when this kid opened the door with a quart bottle of champagne, and he cut the wire and fired the cork at another boy, and the champagne went all over the sidewalk, and some of it went on me, and I knew there was something wrong, cause champagne is too expensive to waste that way, and he said he was running the shebang and if I would bring him here you would say he was all right. If you say so I will let him go."

The grocery man said he had better let the boy go, as his parents would not like to have their little pet locked up. So the policeman let go his ear, and he throwed the empty bottle on a coal wagon, and after the policeman had brushed the champagne off his coat, and smelled of his fingers, and started off, the grocery man turned to the boy, who was peeling a cucumber, and said:

"Now, what kind of a circus have you been having, and what do you mean by destroying wine that way? And where are your folks?"

"Well, I'll tell you. Ma has got the hay fever and has gone to Lake Superior to see if she can't stop sneezing, and Saturday Pa said he and me would go out to Oconomowoc and stay over Sunday, and try and recuperate our health. Pa said it would be a good joke for me not to call him Pa, but to act as though I was his younger brother, and we would have a real nice time. I knowed what he wanted. He is an old masher, that's what's the matter with him, and he was going to play himself for a bachelor. O, thunder, I got on to his racket in a minute. He was introduced to

"IF YOU SAY SO I'LL LET HIM GO," SAID THE POLICEMAN.

some of the girls and Saturday evening he danced till the cows come home. At home he is awful 'fraid of rheumatiz, and he never sweats, or sits in a draft; but the water just poured off'n him, and he stood in the door and let a girl fan him till I was afraid he would freeze, and just as he was telling a girl from Tennessee, who was joking him about being an old bach, that he was not sure as he would always hold out a woman hater if he was to be thrown into contact with the charming ladies of the Sunny South, I pulled his coat and said, 'Pa how do you spose Ma's hay fever is to-night?

I'll bet she is just sneezing the top of her head off.' Wall, sir, you just oughten see that girl and Pa. Pa looked at me as if I was a total stranger, and told the porter if that freckled face boot-black belonged around the house he had better be fired out of the ball-room, and the girl said 'the disgustin' thing,' and just before they fired me I told Pa he had better look out or he would sweat through his liver-pad.

"I went to bed and Pa staid up till the lights were put out. He was mad when he came to bed, but he didn't lick me, cause the people in the next room would hear him, but the next morning he talked to me. He said I might go back home Sunday night, and he would stay a day or two. He sat around on the verandah all the afternoon, talking with the girls, and when he would see me coming along he would look cross. He took a girl out boat riding, and when I asked him if I couldn't go along, he said he was afraid I would get drowned, and he said if I went home there was nothing there too good for me, and so my chum and me got to firing bottles of champane, and he hit me in the eye with a cork, and I drove him out doors and was going to shell his earth works, when the policeman collared me. Say, what's good for a black eye?"

The grocery man told him his Pa would cure it when he got home. "What do you think your Pa's object was in passing himself off for a single man at Oconomowoc?" asked the grocery man, as he charged up the cucumber to the boy's father.

"That's what beats me. Aside from Ma's hay fever she is one of the healthiest women in town. O, I suppose he does it for his health, the way they all do when they go to a summer resort, but it leaves a boy an orphan, don't it, to have such kitteny parents."

CHAPTER IX

HIS PA HAS GOT 'EM AGAIN

His Pa is drinking hard—He has become a terror—A jumping dog—The Old Man is shamefully assaulted—"This is a hellish climate, my boy!"—His Pa swears off—His Ma still sneezing at Lake Superior.

"If the dogs in our neighborhood hold out I guess I can do something that all the temperance societies in this town have failed to do," says the bad boy to the grocery man, as he cut off a piece of cheese and took a handful of crackers out of a box.

"Well for Heaven's sake, what have you been doing now, you little reprobate?" asked the grocery man, as he went to the desk and charged the boy's father with a pound and four ounces of cheese and two pounds of crackers. "If you was my boy and played any of your tricks on me I would maul the everlasting life out of you. Your father is a cussed fool that he don't send you to the reform school. The hired girl was over this morning and says your father is sick, and I should think he would be. What you done? Poisoned him I suppose."

"No, I didn't poison him; I just scared the liver out of him, that's all."

"How was it?" asked the groceryman, as he charged up a pound of prunes to the boy's father.

"Well, I'll tell you, but if you ever tell Pa I won't trade here any more. You see, Pa belongs to all the secret societies, and when there is a grand lodge or anything here, he drinks awfully. There was something last week, some sort of a leather apron affair, or a sash over the shoulder, and every night he was out till the next day, and his breath smelled all the time like in front of a vinegar store, where they keep yeast. Ever since Ma took her hay fever with her up to Lake Superior, Pa has been a terror, and I thought something ought to be done. Since that variegated dog trick was played on him he has been pretty sober till Ma went away, and I happened to think of a dog a boy in the Third Ward has got, that will do tricks. He will jump up and take a man's hat off, and bring a handkerchief, and all that. So I got the boy to come up on our street, and Monday night, about dark, I got in the house and told the boy when Pa came along to make the dog take his hat,

THE DOG GAVE ONE BARK AND WENT FOR PA'S DUSTER.

and to pin a handkerchief to Pa's coat tail and make the dog take that, and then for him and the dog to light out for home. Well, you'd a died. Pa came up the street as dignified and important as though he had gone through bankruptcy, and tried to walk straight, and just as he got near the door the boy pointed to Pa's hat and said, 'Fetch it.' The dog is a big Newfoundland, but he is a jumper, and don't you forget it. Pa is short and thick, and when the dog struck him on the shoulder and took his hat Pa almost fell over, and then he said, 'Get out,' and he kicked and backed up toward the step, and then turned around and the boy pointed to the handkerchief and said, 'fetch it,' and the dog gave one bark and went for it, and got hold of it and part of Pa's duster, and Pa tried to climb up the steps on his hands and feet, and the dog pulled the other way, and it is an old last year's duster anyway, and the whole back breadth come out, and when I opened the door there Pa stood with the front of his coat and the sleeves on, but the back was gone, and I took hold of his arm, and he said, 'Get out,' and was going to kick me, thinking I was a dog, and I told him I was his own little boy, and asked him if anything was the matter. 'M(hic)atter enough. New F(hic)land dog chawing me last hour'n a half. Why didn't you come and k(hic)ill 'em?' I told Pa there was no dog at all, and he must be careful of his health or I wouldn't have no Pa at all. He looked at me and asked me, as he felt for the place where the back of his linen duster was, what had become of his coat tail and hat if there was no dog, and I told him he had probably caught his coat on that barbed wire fence down street, and he said he saw the dog and a boy just as plain as could be, and for me to help him up stairs and go for the doctor. I got him in the bed, and he said, 'this is a hellish climate, my boy,' and I went for the doctor. Pa said he wanted to be cauterised, so he wouldn't go mad. I told the doc. the joke, and he said he would keep it up, and he gave Pa some powders, and told him if he drank any more before Christmas he was a dead man. Pa says it has learned him a lesson and they can never get any more pizen down him, but don't you give me away, will you, cause he would go and complain to the police about the dog, and they would shoot it. Ma will be back as soon as she gets through sneezing, and I will tell her, and she will give me a chromo, cause she don't like to have Pa drink only between meals. Well, good day. There's an Italian got a bear that performs in the street, and I am going to find where he is showing, and feed the bear a cayenne pepper lozenger, and see him clean out the Polack settlement. Good bye." And the boy went to look for the bear.

CHAPTER X

HIS PA HAS GOT RELIGION

The bad boy goes to Sunday school—Promises reformation— The Old Man on trial for six months—What Ma thinks—Ants in Pa's liver-pad—The Old Man in church—Religion is one thing—Ants another.

"WELL, that beats the devil," said the grocery man, as he stood in front of his grocery and saw the bad boy coming along on the way home from Sunday school, with a clean shirt on, and a testament and some dime novels under his arm. "What has got into you, and what has come over your Pa? I see he has braced up, and looks pale and solemn. You haven't converted him, have you?"

"No, Pa has not got religion enough to hurt yet, but he has got the symptoms. He has joined the church on probation, and is trying to be good so he can get in the church for keeps. He said it was hell living the way he did, and he has got me to promise to go to Sunday school. He said if I didn't he would maul me so my skin wouldn't hold water. You see, Ma said Pa had got to be on trial for six months before he could get in the church, and if he could get along without swearing and doing anything bad, he was all right, and we must try him and see if we could cause him to swear. She said she thought a person, when they was on probation, ought to be a martyr, and try and overcome all temptations to do evil, and if Pa could go through six months of our home life, and not cuss the hinges off the door, he was sure of a glorious immortality beyond the grave. She said it wouldn't be wrong for me to continue to play innocent jokes on Pa, and if he took it all right he was a Christian, but if he got a hot box, and flew around mad, he was better out of church than in it. There he comes now," said the boy as he got behind a sign, "and he is pretty hot for a

Christian. He is looking for me. You had ought to have seen him in church this morning. You see, I commenced the exercises at home after breakfast by putting a piece of ice in each of Pa's boots, and when he pulled on the boots he yelled that his feet were all on fire, and we told him that it was nothing but symptoms of gout, so he left the ice in his boots to melt, and he said all the morning that he felt as though he had sweat his boots full. But that was not the worst. You know, Pa he wears a liver-pad. Well, on Saturday my chum and me was out on the lake shore and we found a nest of ants, these little red ants, and I got a pop bottle half full of the ants and took them home. I didn't know what I would do with the ants, but ants are always handy to have in the house. This morning, when Pa was dressing for church, I saw his liver-pad on a chair, and noticed a hole in it, and I thought what a good place it would be for the ants. I don't know what possessed me, but I took the liver-pad into my room, and opened the bottle, and put the hole over the mouth of the bottle and I guess the ants thought there was something to eat in the liver-pad, cause they all went into it, and they crawled around in the bran and condition powders inside of it, and I took it back to Pa, and he put it on under his shirt, and dressed himself, and we went to church. Pa squirmed a little when the minister was praying, and I guess some of the ants had come to view the landscape o'er. When we got up to sing the hymn Pa kept kicking, as though he was nervous, and he felt down his neck and looked sort of wild, the way he did when he had the jim-jams. When we sat down Pa couldn't keep still, and I like to dide when I saw some of the ants come out of his shirt bosom and go racing around his white vest. Pa tried to look pious and resigned, but he couldn't keep his legs still, and he sweat mor'n a pail full. When the minister preached about 'the worm that never dieth,' Pa reached into his vest and scratched his ribs, and he looked as though he would give ten dollars if the minister would get through. Ma she looked at Pa as though she would bite his head off, but Pa he just squirmed, and acted as though his soul was on fire. Say, does it bite, or just crawl around? Well, when the minister said amen, and prayed the second round, and then said a brother who was a missionary to the heathen would like to make a few remarks about the work of the missionaries in Bengal, and take up a collection, Pa told Ma they would have to excuse *him,* and he lit out for home, slapping himself on the legs and on the arms and on the back, and he acted crazy. Ma and me went

THE LIVER PAD WAS ON THE FLOOR AND PA STAMPING ON IT.

home, after the heathen got through, and found Pa in his bed room, with part of his clothes off, and the liver-pad was on the floor, and Pa was stamping on it with his boots, and talking offul.

" 'What is the matter,' says Ma. 'Don't your religion agree with you?'

" 'Religion be dashed,' says Pa, as he kicked the liver-pad. 'I would give ten dollars to know how a pint of red ants got into my liver-pad. Religion is one thing, and a million ants walking all over a man, playing tag, is another.

I didn't know the liver-pad was loaded. How in Gehenna did they get in there?' and Pa scowled at Ma as though he would kill her.

" 'Don't swear, dear,' says Ma, as she threw down her hymn book, and took off her bonnet. 'You should be patient. Remember Job was patient and he was afflicted with sore boils.'

"I don't care," says Pa, as he chased the ants out of his drawers, 'Job never had ants in his liver-pad. If he had he would have swore the shingles off a barn. Here you,' says Pa, speaking to me, 'you head off them ants running under the budeau. If the truth was known I believe you would be responsible for this outrage.' And Pa looked at me kind of hard.

" 'O, Pa,' says I, with tears in my eyes. 'Do you think your little Sunday school boy would catch ants in a pop bottle on the lake shore, and bring them home, and put them in the hole of your liver-pad, just before you put it on to go to church? You are too bad.' And I shed some tears. I can shed tears now any time I want to, but it didn't do any good this time. Pa knew it was me, and while he was looking for the shawl strap I went to Sunday school, and now I guess he is after me, and I will go and take a walk down to Bay View."

The boy moved off as his Pa turned a corner, and the grocery man said, "Well, that boy beats all I ever saw. If he was mine I would give him away."

CHAPTER XI

HIS PA TAKES A TRICK

Jamaica rum and cards—The bad boy possessed of a devil—The kind deacon—At prayer meeting—The Old Man tells his experience—The flying cards—The prayer meeting suddenly closed.

"WHAT is it I hear about your Pa being turned out of prayer meeting Wednesday night?" asker the grocer of the bad boy, as he came over after some canteloupes for breakfast, and plugged a couple to see if they were ripe.

"He wasn't turned out of prayer meeting at all. The people all went away and Pa and me was the last ones out of the church. But Pa was mad, and don't you forget it."

"Well, what seemed to be the trouble? Has your Pa become a backslider?"

"O, no, his flag is still there. But something seems to go wrong. You see, when we got ready to go to prayer meeting last night, Pa told me to go up stairs and get him a handkerchief, and to drop a little perfumery on it, and put it in the tail pocket of his black coat. I did it, but I guess I got hold of the wrong bottle of fumery. There was a label on the fumery bottle that said 'Jamaica Rum,' and I thought it was the same as Bay Rum, and I put on a whole lot. Just afore I put the handkerchief in Pa's pocket, I noticed a pack of cards on the stand, that Pa used to play hi-lo-jack with Ma evenings when he was so sick he couldn't go down town, before he got 'ligion, and I wrapped the handkercher around the pack of cards and put them in his pocket. I don't know what made me do it, and Pa don't, either, I guess 'cause he told Ma this morning I was possessed of a devil. I never owned no devil, but I had a pair of pet goats onct, and they played hell all around, Pa said. That's what the devil does, ain't it? Well, I must go home with these melons, or they won't keep."

"But hold on," says the grocery man as he gave the boy a few raisins with worms in, that he couldn't sell, to keep him, "what about the prayer meeting?"

"O, I like to forgot. Well, Pa and me went to prayer meeting, and Ma came along afterwards with a deakin that is mashed on her, I guess, 'cause he says she is to be pitted for havin' to go through life yoked to such an old prize ox as Pa. I heard him tell Ma that, when he was helping her put on her rubber waterprivilege to go home in the rain the night of the sociable, and she looked at him just as she does at me when she wants me to go down to the hair foundry after her switch, and said, 'O, you dear brother,' and all the way home he kept her waterprivilege on by putting his arm on the small of her back. Ma asked Pa if he didn't think the deakin was real kind, and Pa said, 'yez, dam kind,' but that was afore he got 'ligion. We sat in a pew, at the prayer meeting, next to Ma and the deakin, and there was lots of pious folks all around there. After the preacher had gone to bat, and an old lady had her innings, a praying, and the singers had gone out on first base, Pa was on deck, and the preacher said they would like to hear from the recent convert, who was trying to walk in the straight and narrow way, but who found it so hard, owing to the many crosses he had to bear. Pa knowed it was him that had to go to bat, and he got up and said he felt it was good to be there. He said he didn't feel that he was a full sized Christian yet, but he was getting in his work the best he could. He said at times everything looked dark to him, and he feared he should falter by the wayside, but by a firm resolve he kept his eye sot on the future, and if he was tempted to do wrong he said, 'Get thee behind me, Satan,' and stuck in his toe-nails for a pull for the right. He said he was thankful to the brothers and sisters, particularly the sisters, for all they had done to make his burden light, and hoped to meet them all in—. When Pa got as far as that he sort of broke down. I spose he was going to say heaven, though after a few minutes they all thought he wanted to meet them in a saloon. When his eyes began to leak, Pa put his hand in his tail pocket for his handkerchief, and got hold of it, and gave it a jerk, and

HE HOPED TO MEET THEM ALL IN——.

out came the handkercher, and the cards. Well, if he had shuffled them, and Ma had cut them, and he had dealt six hands, they couldn't have been dealt any better. They flew into everybody's lap. The deakin that was with Ma got the jack of spades and three aces and a deuce, and Ma got some nine spots and a king of hearts, and Ma nearly fainted, cause she didn't get a better hand, I spose. The preacher got a pair of deuces, and a queen of hearts, and he looked up at Pa as though it was a misdeal, and a old woman who sat across the isle, she only got two cards, but that was enough. Pa didn't see what he had done at first, cause he had the handkerchief over his eyes, but when he smelt the rum on it, he took it away, and when he saw everybody discarding, and he thought he had struck a poker game, and he looked around as though he was mad cause they didn't deal him a hand. The minister adjourned the prayer meeting and whispered to Pa, and everybody went out holding their noses on account of Pa's fumery, and when Pa came home he asked Ma what he should do to be saved. Ma said she didn't know. The deakin told her Pa seemed wedded to his idols. Pa said the deakin better run his own idols, and Pa would run his. I don't know how it is going to turn out, but Pa says he is going to stick to the church."

CHAPTER XII

HIS PA GETS PULLED

The Old Man studies the Bible—Daniel in the lion's den—The mule and the mule's father—Murder in the Third Ward—The Old Man Arrested—The Old Man fans the dust out of his son's pants.

"WHAT was you and your Ma down at the police station for so late last night?" asked the grocery man of the bad boy, as he kicked a dog away from a basket of peaches standing on the sidewalk. "Your Ma seemed to be much affected."

"That's a family secret. But if you will give me some of those rotten peaches I will tell you, if you won't ever ask Pa how he came to be pulled by the police."

The grocery man told him to help himself out of the basket that the dog had been smelling of, and he filled his pockets, and the bosom of his flannel shirt, and his hat, and said:

"Well, you know Pa is studying up on the Bible, and he is trying to get me interested, and he wants me to ask him questions, but if I ask him any questions that he can't answer he gets mad. When I asked him about Daniel in the den of lions, and if he didn't think Dan was traveling with a show, and had the lions chloroformed, he said I was a scoffer, and would go to Gehenna. Now I don't want to go to Gehenna just for wanting to get posted in the show business of old times, do you? When Pa said Dan was saved from the jaws of the lions because he prayed three times every day, and had faith, I told him that was just what the duffer that goes into the lions' den in Coup's circus did because I saw him in the dressing room, when me and my chum got in for carrying water for the elephant, and he was exhorting with a girl in tights who was going to ride two horses. Pa said I was mistaken, cause they never prayed in circus, 'cept the lemonade butchers. I guess I know when I hear a man pray. Coup's Daniel talked just like a deacon at class meeting, and told the girl to go to the place where the minister says we will all go if we don't do different. Pa says it is wicked to speak of Daniel in the same breath that you speak of a circus, so I am wicked I spose. Well, I couldn't help it and when he wanted me to ask him questions about Elijah going up in a chariot of fire, I asked him if he believed a chariot like the ones in the circus, with eight horses, could carry a man right up to the clouds, and Pa said of course it could. Then I asked him what they did with the horses after they got up there, or if the chariot kept running back and forth like a bust to a pic-nic, and whether they had stalls for the horses and harness-makers to repair harnesses, and wagon-makers, 'cause a chariot is liable to run off a wheel, if it strikes a cloud in turning a corner. Pa said I made him tired. He said I had no more conception of the beauties of scripture than a mule, and then I told Pa he couldn't expect a mule to know much unless the mule's father had brought him up right, and where a mule's father had been a regular old bummer till he got the jim jams, and only got religion to keep out of the inebriate asylum, that the little mule was entitled to more charity for his shortcomings than the mule's Papa. That seemed to make Pa mad, and he said the scripture lessons would be continued some other time, and I might go out and play, and if I wasn't in before nine o'clock he would come after me and warm my jacket. Well, I was out playing, and me and my chum heard of the murder in the Third Ward, and went down there to see the dead and wounded, and it was after ten o'clock, and Pa was searching for me, and I saw Pa go into an alley, in his shirt sleeves and no hat on, and the police were looking for the murderer, and I told the policeman there was a suspicious looking man in the alley, and the policeman went in there and jumped on his back, and held him down, and the patrol wagon came, and they loaded Pa in, and he gnashed his teeth, and said they would pay dearly for this, and they held his hands and told him not to talk, as he would commit himself, and they tore off his suspender buttons, and I went home and told Ma the police had pulled Pa for being in a suspicious place, and she said she had always been afraid he would come to some bad end, and we went down to the station and

HE WAS EXHORTING A GIRL IN TIGHTS.

the police let Pa go on promise that he wouldn't do so again, and we went home and Pa fanned the dust out of my pants. But he did it in a pious manner and I can't complain. He was trying to explain to Ma how it was that he was pulled, when I came away, and I guess he will make out to square himself. Say, don't these peaches seem to have a darn queer taste? Well, good bye, I am going down to the morgue to have some fun."

CHAPTER XIII

HIS PA GOES TO THE EXPOSITION

The bad boy acts as guide—The circus story—The Old Man wants to sit down—Tries to eat pancakes—Drinks some mineral water—The Old Man falls in love with a wax woman—A policeman interferes —The lights go out—The grocery man don't want a clerk.

"WELL, everything seems to be quiet over to your house this week," says the grocery man to the bad boy as the youth was putting his thumb into some peaches through the mosquito netting over the baskets, to see if they were soft enough to steal, "I suppose you have let up on the old man, haven't you?"

"O, no. We keep it right up. The minister of the church that Pa has joined says while Pa is on probation it is perfectly proper for us to do everything to try him, and make him fall from grace. The minister says if Pa comes out of his six months' probation without falling by the wayside he has got the elements to make the boss christian, and Ma and me are doing all we can."

"What was the doctor at your house for this morning?" asked the grocery man. "Is your Ma sick?"

"No, Ma is worth two in the bush. It's Pa that ain't well. He is having some trouble with his digestion. You see he went to the exposition with me as guide, and that is enough to ruin any man's digestion. Pa is near-sighted, and said he wanted me to go along and show him things. Well, I never had so much fun since Pa fell out of the boat. First we went in by the fountain, and Pa had never been in the exposition building before. Last year he was in Yourip and he was astonished at the magnitude of everything. First I made him jump clear across the aisle there, where the stuffed tigers are, by the fur place. I told him the keeper was just coming along with some meat to feed the animals, and when they smelled the meat, they just chawed things. He run against a show-case, and then wanted to go away.

He said he traveled with a circus when he was young, and nobody knew the dangers of fooling around wild animals better than he did. He said once he fought with seven tigers and two Nubian lions for five hours, with Mabee's old show. I asked him if that was afore he got religion, and he said, 'Never you mind.' He is an old liar, even if he is converted. Ma says he never was with a circus, and she has known him ever since he wore short dresses. Wall, you would a dide to see Pa there by the furniture place, where they have got beautiful beds and chairs. There was one blue chair under a glass case, all velvet, and a sign was over it, telling people to keep their hands off. Pa asked me what the sign was, and I told him it said ladies and gentlemen are requested to sit in the chairs and try them. Pa climbed over the railing and was just going to sit down on the glass show-case over the chair, when one of the walk-around fellows, with imitation police hats, took him by the collar and yanked him back over the railing, and was going to kick Pa's pants. Pa was mad to have his coat collar pulled up over his head, and have the set of his coat spoiled, and was going to sass the man, when I told Pa the man was a lunatic from the asylum, that was on exhibition, and Pa wanted to go away from there. He said he didn't know what they wanted to exhibit lunatics for. We went up stairs to the pancake bazar, where they broil pancakes out of self rising flour, and put butter and sugar on them and give them away. Pa said he could eat more pancakes than any man out of jail, and wanted me to get him some. I took a couple of pancakes and tore out a piece of the lining of my coat and put it between the pancakes and handed them to Pa, with a paper around the pancakes. Pa didn't notice the paper nor the cloth, and it would have made you laff to see him chew on them. I told him I guessed he didn't have as good teeth as he used to, and he said, 'Never you mind the teeth,' and he kept on until he swallowed the whole business, and he said he guessed he didn't want any more. He is so sensitive about his teeth that he would eat a leather apron if anybody told him he couldn't. When the Doctor said Pa's digestion was bad, I told him if he could let Pa swallow a seamstress or a sewing machine, to sew up the cloth, he would get well, and the doc. says I am going to be the death of Pa some day. But I thought I should split when Pa wanted a drink of water. I asked him if he would druther have mineral water, and he said he guessed it would take the strongest kind of mineral water to wash down them pancakes, so I took him to where the fire extinguishers are, and got him to take the nozzle of the extinguisher in his mouth, and I turned the faucet. I don't think he got more than a quart of the stuff out of the saleratus machine down him, but he rared right up and said he be condamed if he believed that water was ever intended to drink, and he felt as though he should bust, and just then the man who kicks the big organ struck up and the building shook, and I guess Pa thought he *had* busted. The most fun was when we came along to where the wax woman is. They have got a wax woman dressed up to kill, and she looks just as natural as if she could breathe. She had a handkerchief in her hand, and as we came along I told Pa there was a lady that seemed to know him. Pa is on the mash himself, and he looked at her and smiled and said good evening and asked me who she was.

"I told him it looked to me like the girl that sings in the choir at our church, and Pa said course it is, and he went right in where she was and said 'Pretty good show, isn't it?' and put out his hand to shake hands with her, but the woman who tends the stand came along and thought Pa was drunk and said, 'Old gentleman, I guess you had better get out of here. This is for ladies only.'

"Pa said he didn't care nothing for her ladies only, all he wanted was to converse with an acquaintance, and then one of the policemen came along and told Pa he had better go down to the saloon where he belonged. Pa excused himself to the wax woman, and said he would see her later, and told the policeman if he would come out to the sidewalk he would knock leven kinds of stuffing out of him. The policeman told him that would be all right, and I led Pa away. He was offul mad. But it was the best fun when the lights went out. You see this electric light machine slipped a cog or lost its cud and all of a sudden the lights went out

THIS IS FOR LADIES ONLY.

and it was as dark as a squaw's pocket. Pa wanted to know what made it so dark, and I told him it was not dark. He said, 'Boy, don't you fool me.' You see I thought it would be fun to make Pa believe he was struck blind, so I told him his eyes must be wrong. He said, 'Do you mean to say you can see?' and I told him everything was as plain as day, and I pointed out the different things, and explained them and walked Pa along, and acted just as though I could see, and Pa said it had come at last. He had felt for years as though he would some day lose his eyesight and now it had come and he said he laid it all to the condamned mineral water. After a little they lit some of the gas burners, and Pa said he could see a little, and wanted to go home, and I took him home. When we got out of the building he began to see things, and said his eyes were coming around all right. Pa is the easiest man to fool ever I saw."

"Well, I should think he would kill you," said the grocery man. "Don't he ever catch on, and find out you have deceived him?"

"O, sometimes. But about nine times in ten I can get away with him. Say, don't you want to hire me for a clerk?"

The grocery man said that he had rather have a spotted hyena, and the boy stole a melon and went away.

CHAPTER XIV

HIS PA CATCHES ON

Two days and nights in the bath room—Religion cakes the old man's breast—The bad boy's chum—Dressed up as a girl—The old man deluded—The couple start for the court house park—His Ma appears on the scene—"If you love me kiss me"—Ma to the rescue—"I am dead, am I?"—His Pa throws a chair through the transom.

"Where have you been for a week back?" asked the grocery man of the bad boy, as the boy pulled the tail board out of the delivery wagon accidentally and let a couple of bushels of potatoes roll out into the gutter. "I haven't seen you around here, and you look pale. You haven't been sick, have you?"

"No, I have not been sick. Pa locked me up in the bath room for two days and two nights, and didn't give me nothing to eat but bread and water. Since he has got religious he seems to be harder than ever on me. Say, do you think religion softens a man's heart, or does it give him a caked breast? I 'spect Pa will burn me at the stake next."

The grocery man said that when a man had truly been converted his heart was softened, and he was always looking for a chance to do good and be kind to the poor, but if he only had this galvanized religion, this roll plate piety, or whitewashed reformation, he was liable to be a harder citizen than before. "What made your Pa lock you up in the bath-room on bread and water?" he asked.

"Well, says the boy, as he eat a couple of salt pickles out of a jar on the sidewalk, "Pa is not converted enough to hurt him, and I knowed it, and I thought it would be a good joke to try him and see if he was so confounded good, so I got my chum to dress up in a suit of his sister's summer clothes. Well, you wouldn't believe my chum would look so much like a girl. He would fool the oldest inhabitant, You know how fat he is. He had to sell his bicycle to a slim fellow that clerks in a store, cause he didn't want it any more. His neck is just as fat and there are dimples in it, and with a dress low in the neck, and long at the trail he looks as tall as my Ma. He busted one of his sisters slipper's getting them on, and her stockings were a good deal too big for him, but he tucked his drawers down in them and tied a suspender around his leg above the knee, and they stayed on all right. Well, he looked killin', I should prevaricate, with his sister's muslin dress on, starched as stiff as a shirt, and her reception hat with a white feather as big as a Newfoundland dog's tail. Pa said he had to go down town to see some of the old soldiers of his regiment, and I loafed along behind. My chum met Pa on the corner and asked him where the Lake Shore Park was. 'She' said she was a stranger from Chicago, that her husband had deserted her and she didn't know but she would jump into the lake. Pa looked into my chum's eye and sized her up, and said it would be a shame to commit suicide, and asked if she didn't want to take a walk. My chum said he should titter, and he took Pa's arm and they walked up to the lake and back. Well, you may talk about joining the church on probation all you please, but they get their arm around a girl all the same. Pa hugged my chum till he says he thought Pa would break his sister's corset all to pieces, and he squeezed my chum's hand till the ring cut right into his finger and he has to wear a piece of court plaster on it. They started for the Court House park, as I told my chum to do, and I went and got Ma. It was about time for the soldiers to go to the exposition for the evening bizness, and I told Ma we could go down and see them go by. Ma just throwed a shawl over her head and we started down through the park. When we got near Pa and my chum I told Ma it was a shame for so many people to be sitting around lally-gagging right before folks, and she said it was disgustin', and then

I pointed to my chum who had his head on Pa's bosom, and Pa was patting my chum on the cheek, while he held his other arm around his waist. They was on the iron seat, and we came right up behind them and when Ma saw Pa's bald head I thought she would bust. She knew his head as quick as she sot eyes on it. My chum asked Pa if he was married, and he said he was a widower. He said his wife died fourteen years ago, of liver complaint. Well, Ma shook like a leaf, and I could hear her new teeth rattle just like chewing strawberries with sand in them. Then my chum put his arms around Pa's neck and said, 'If you love me kiss me in the mouth.' Pa was just leaning down to kiss my chum when Ma couldn't stand it any longer, and she went right around in front of them, and she grabbed my chum by the hair and it all came off, hat and all, and my chum jumped up and Ma scratched him in the face, and my chum tried to get his hands in his pants pockets to get his handkerchief to wipe off the blood on his nose, and Ma she turned to Pa and he turned pale, and then she was going

"MA COULDN'T STAND IT ANY LONGER."

for my chum again when he said, 'O let up on a feller,' and he see she was mad and he grabbed the hat and hair off the gravel walk and took the skirt of his sister's dress in his hand and lifted out for home on a gallop, and Ma took Pa by the elbow and said, 'You are a nice old party ain't you? I am dead, am I? Died of liver complaint fourteen years ago, did I? You will find an animated corpse on your hands. Around kissing spry women out in the night, sir.' When they started home Pa seemed to be as weak as a cat, and couldn't say a word, and I asked him if I could go to the exposition, and they said I could. I don't know what happened after they got home, but Pa was setting up for me when I got back and he wanted to know what I brought Ma down there for, and how I knew he was there.

"I thought it would help Pa out of the scrape and so I told him it was not a girl he was hugging at all, but it was my chum, and he laughed at first, and told Ma it was not a girl but Ma said she knew a darn sight better. She guessed she could tell a girl.

"Then Pa was mad and he said I was at the bottom of the whole bizness, and he locked me up, and said I was enough to paralyze a saint. I told him through the key-hole that a saint that had any sense ought to tell a boy from a girl, and then he throwed a chair at me through the transom. The worst of the whole thing is my chum is mad at me cause Ma scratched him, and he says that lets him out. He don't go into any more schemes with me. Well, I must be going. Pa is going to have my measure taken for a raw hide, he says, and I have got to stay at home from the sparring match and learn my Sunday school lesson."

CHAPTER XV

HIS PA AT THE RE-UNION

The old man in military splendor—Tells how he mowed down the rebels—"I and Grant"—What is a sutler?—Ten dollars for pickles!—"Let us hang him!"—The old man on a run—He stands up to supper—The bad boy is to die at sunset.

"I SAW your Pa wearing a red, white, and blue badge, and a round red badge, and several other badges, last week, during the re-union," said the grocery man to the bad boy, as the youth asked for a piece of codfish skin to settle coffee with. "He looked like a hero, with his old black hat, with a gold cord around it."

"Yes, he wore all the badges he could get, the first day, but after he blundered into a place where there were a lot of fellows from his own regiment, he took off the badges, and he wasn't very numerous around the boys the rest of the week. But he was lightning on the sham battle," says the boy.

"What was the matter? Didn't the soldiers treat him well? Didn't they seem to yearn for his society?" asked the grocery man, as the boy was making a lunch on some sweet crackers in a tin canister.

"Well, they were not very much mashed on Pa. You see, Pa never gets tired telling us about how he fit in the army. For several years I didn't know what a sutler was, and when Pa would tell about taking a musket that a dead soldier had dropped, and going into the thickest of the fight, and fairly mowing down the rebels in swaths, the way they cut hay, I thought he was the greatest man that ever was. Until I was eleven years old I thought Pa killed men enough to fill the Forest Home cemetery. I thought a sutler was something higher than a general, and Pa used to talk about

'I and Grant,' and what Sheridan told him, and how Sherman marched with him to the sea, and all that kind of rot, until I wondered why they didn't have pictures of Pa on a white horse, with epaulets on, and a sword. One day at school I told a boy that my Pa killed more men than Grant, and the boy said he didn't doubt it, but he killed them with commissary whisky. The boy said his Pa was in the same regiment that my Pa was a sutler of, and his Pa said my Pa charged him five dollars for a canteen of pepper sauce and alcohol and called it whisky. Then I began to inquire into it, and found out that a sutler was a sort of liquid peanut stand, and that his rank in the army was about the same as a chestnut roaster on the sidewalk here at home. It made me sick, and I never had the same respect for Pa after that. But Pa don't care. He thinks he is a hero, and tried to get a pension on account of losing a piece of his thumb, but when the officers found

THE SOLDIER STARTED AFTER PA WITH SABER DRAWN.

he was wounded by the explosion of a can of baked beans they couldn't give it to him. Pa was down town when the veterans were here, and I was with him, and I saw a lot of old soldiers looking at Pa, and I told him they acted as though they knew him, and he put on his glasses, and said to one of them, 'How are you Bill?' The soldier looked at Pa and called the other soldiers, and one said, 'That's the old duffer that sold me the bottle of brandy peaches at Chickamauga for three dollars, and they eat a hole through my stummick.' Another said, 'He's the cuss that took ten dollars out of my pay for pickles that were put up in *aqua fortis*. Look at the corps badges he has on.' Another said, 'The old whelp! He charged me fifty cents a pound for onions when I had the scurvy at Atlanta.' Another said, 'He beat me out of my wages playing draw poker with a cold deck, and the aces up his sleeve. Let us hang him.' By this time Pa's nerves got unstrung and began to hurt him, and he said he wanted to go home, and when we got around the corner he tore off his badges and threw them in the sewer, and said it was all a man's life was worth to be a veteran nowadays. He didn't go down town again till next day, and when he heard a band playing he would go around a block. But at the sham battle where there were no veterans hardly, he was all right with the militia boys, and told them how he did when he was in the army. I thought it would be fun to see Pa run, and so when one of the cavalry fellows lost his cap in the charge, and was looking for it, I told the dragoon that the pussy old man over by the fence had stolen his cap. That was Pa. Then I told Pa that the soldier on the horse said he was a rebel, and he was going to kill him. The soldier started after Pa with his sabre drawn, and Pa started to run, and it was funny, you bet. The soldier galloped his horse, and yelled, and Pa put in his best licks, and run up to the track to where there was a board off the fence, and tried to get through, but he got stuck, and the soldier put the point of his sabre on Pa's pants and pushed, and Pa got through the fence and I guess he ran all the way home. At supper time Pa would not come to the table, but stood up and ate off the sideboard, and Ma said Pa's shirt was all bloody, and Pa said mor'n fifty of them cavalry men charged on him, and he held them at bay as long as he could, and then retired in good order. This morning a boy told him that I set the cavalry men onto him, and he made me wear two mouse straps on my ears all the forenoon, and he says he will kill me at sunset. I ain't going to be there at sunset, and don't you remember about it. Well, good bye. I have got to go down to the morgue and see them bring in the man that was found on the lake shore, and see if the morgue keeper is drunk this time."

CHAPTER XVI

THE BAD BOY IN LOVE

Are you a Christian?—No getting to Heaven on small potatoes!—The bad boy has to chew cobs—Ma says its good for a boy to be in love—Love weakens the bad boy—How much does it cost to get married?—Mad dog!—Never eat ice cream.

"ARE you a Christian?" asked the bad boy of the grocery man, as that gentleman was placing vegetables out in front of the grocery one morning.

"Well, I hope so," answered the grocery man, "I try to do what is right, and hope to wear the golden crown when the time comes to close my books."

"Then how is it that you put out a box of great big sweet potatoes, and when we order some, and they come to the table, they are little bits of things, not bigger than a radish? Do you expect to get to heaven on such small potatoes, when you use big ones for a sign?" asked the boy, as he took out a silk handkerchief and brushed a speck of dust off his nicely blacked shoes.

The grocery man blushed and said he did not mean to take any such advantage of his customers. He said it must have been a mistake of the boy that delivers groceries.

"Then you must hire the boy to make mistakes, for it has been so every time we have had sweet potatoes for five years," said the boy. "And about green corn. You have a few ears stripped down to show how nice and plump it is, and if we order a dozen ears there are only two that have got any corn on at all, and Pa and Ma gets them, and the rest of us have to chew cobs. Do you hope to wear a crown of glory on that kind of corn?"

"O, such things will happen," said the grocery man with a laugh. "But don't let's talk about heaven. Let's talk about the other place. How's things over to your house? And say, what's the matter with you? You are all dressed up, and have got a clean shirt on, and your shoes blacked, and I notice your pants are not raveled out so at the bottoms of the legs behind. You are not in love are you?"

"Well, I should smile," said the boy, as he looked in a small mirror on the counter, covered with fly specks. "A girl got mashed on me, and Ma says it is good for a boy who hasn't got no sister, to be in love with a girl, and so I kind of tumbled to myself and she don't go nowhere without I go with her. I take her to dancing school, and everywhere, and she loves me like a house afire. Say, was you ever in love? Makes a fellow feel queer, don't it? Well sir, the first time I went home with her I put my arm around her, and honest it scared me. It was just like when you take hold of the handles of an electric battery, and you can't let go till the man turns the knob. Honest, I was just as weak as a cat. I thought she had needles in her belt and was going to take my arm away, but it was just like it was glued on. I asked her if she felt that way too, she said she used to, but it was nothing when you got used to it. That made me mad. But she is older than me and knows more about it. When I was going to leave her at the gate, she kissed me, and that was worse than putting my arm around her. By gosh, I trembled all over, just like I had chills, but I was as warm as toast. She wouldn't let go for as much as a minute, and I was tired as though I had been carrying coal up stairs. I didn't want to go home at all, but she said it would be the best way for me to go home, and come again the next day, and the next morning I went to her house before any of them were up, and her Pa came out to let the cat in, and I asked him what time his girl got up, and he laffed at me and said that I had got it bad and that I better go home and not be picked till I got ripe. Say, how much does it cost to get married?"

"Well, I should say you had got it bad," said the grocery man, as he set out a basket of beets. "Your getting in love will be a great thing for your Pa. You won't have any time to play any more jokes on him."

"O, I guess we can find time to keep Pa from being lonesome. Have you seen him this morning? You ought to have seen him last night. You see, my chum's Pa has got a setter dog stuffed. It is one that died two years ago and he thought a great deal of it, and he had it stuffed for an ornament. Well, my chum and me took the dog and put it on our front steps, and took some cotton and fastened it to the dog's mouth so it looked just like froth, and we got behind the door and waited for Pa to come home from the theater. When Pa started to come up the steps I growled and Pa looked at the dog and said, 'Mad dog, by crimis,' and he started down the sidewalk, and my chum barked just like a dog, and I 'Ki-yi'd' and growled like a dog that gets licked,

PA WANTED HER TO SIT IN HIS LAP.

and you ought to see Pa run. He went around in the alley and was going to get in the basement window, and my chum had a revolver with some blank cartridges, and he went down in the basement and when Pa was trying to open the window my chum began to fire towards Pa. Pa hollered that it was only him, and not a burglar, but after my chum fired four shots Pa run and climbed over the fence, and then we took the dog home and I stayed with my chum all night, and this morning Ma said Pa didn't get home till four o'clock and then a policeman came with him, and Pa talked about mad dogs and being taken for a burglar and nearly killed, and she said she was afraid Pa had took to drinking again, and she asked me if I heard any firing of guns, and I said no, and then she put a wet towel on Pa's head."

"You ought to be ashamed," said the grocery man. "How does your Pa like your being in love with the girl? Does he seem to encourage you in it?"

"Oh Yes, she was up to our house to borrow some tea, and Pa patted her on the cheek and hugged her and said she was a dear little daisy, and wanted her to sit in his lap, but when I wanted him to let me have fifty cents to buy her some ice cream he said that was all nonsense. He said: 'Look ot your Ma. Eating ice cream when she was a girl was what injured her health for life." I asked Ma about it, and she said Pa never laid out ten cents for ice cream or any luxury for her in all the five years he was sparking her. She says he took her to a circus once but he got free tickets for carrying water for the elephant. She says Pa was tighter than the bark to a tree. I tell you it's going to be different with me. If there is anything that girl wants she is going to have it if I have to sell Ma's copper boiler to get the money. What is the use of having wealth if you hoard it up and don't enjoy it? This family will be run on different principles after this, you bet. Say, how much are those yellow wooden pocket combs in the show case? I've a good notion to buy them for her. How would one of them round mirrors, with a zinc cover, do for a present for a girl? There's nothing too good for her."

CHAPTER XVII

HIS PA FIGHTS HORNETS

The Old Man looks bad—The woods of Wauwatosa—The Old Man takes a nap—"Helen damnation"—"Hell is out for noon"—The liver medicine—Its wonderful effects—The bad boy is drunk! Give me a lemon!—A sight of the comet!—The hired girl's religion.

"Go away from here now," said the grocery man to the bad boy, as he came into the store and was going to draw some cider out of a barrel into a pint measure that had flies in it. "Get right out of this place, and don't let me see you around here until the health officer says your Pa has got over the small-pox. I saw him this morning and his face is all covered with postules, and they will have him in the pest house before night. You git," and he picked up a butter tryer and went for the boy, who took refuge behind a barrel of onions, and held up his hands as though Jesse James had drawn a bead on him.

"O, you go and chase yourself. That is not small-pox Pa has got. He had a fight with a nest of hornets," said the boy.

"Hornets! Well, I'll be cussed," remarked the grocery man, as he put up the butter tryer, and handed the boy a slice of rotten muskmelon. "How in the world did he get into a nest of hornets? I hope you did not have anything to do with it."

The boy buried his face in the melon, until he looked as though a yellow gash had been cut from his mouth to his ears, and after swallowing the melon, he said, "Well, Pa says I was responsible, and he says that settles it, and I can go my way and he will go his. He said he was willing to overlook everything I had done to make his life unbearable, but steering him into a nest of hornets, and then getting drunk, was too much, and I can go."

"What, you haven't been drunk," says the grocery man. "Great heavens, that will kill your poor old father."

"O, I guess it won't kill him very much. He has been getting drunk for twenty years, and he says he is healthier to-day than he ever was, since his liver got to working again. You see, Monday was a regular Indian summer day, and Pa said he would take me and my chum out in the woods to gather hickory nuts, if we would be good. I said I would and my chum said he would, and we got a couple of bags and went away out to Wauwatosa, in the woods. We clubbed the trees and got more nuts than anybody, and had a lunch, and Pa was just enjoying his religion first rate. While Pa was taking a nap under a tree, my chum and me looked around and found a hornets' nest on the lower limb of the tree we were sitting under, and my chum said it would be a good joke to get a pole and run it into the hornet's nest and then run. Honest, I didn't think about Pa being under the tree, and I went into the field and got a hop pole, and put the small end of it into the nest, and gouged the nest a couple of times, and when the boss hornet came out of the hole, and looked sassy, and then looked back in the hole and whistled to the other hornets to come out and have a circus and they began to come out, my chum and me run and climbed over a fence, and got behind a pile of hop poles that was stacked up. I guess the hornets saw my Pa just as quick as they got out of the nest, cause pretty soon we heard Pa call to 'Helen Damnation,' or some woman we didn't know, and then he took his coat, that he had been using for a pillow, and whipped around, and he slapped hisself on the shoulders, and then he picked up the lunch basket and pounded around like he was crazy, and bime-by he started on a run toward town, holding his pants up, cause his suspenders was hanging down on his hips, and I never see a man run so, and fan himself with a basket. We could hear him yell, 'Come on boys. Hell is out for noon' and he went over a hill, and we didn't see him any more. We waited till near dark because we was afraid to go after the bags of nuts till the hornets had gone to bed, and then we came home. The bags were awful heavy, and I think it was real mean in Pa to go off and leave us, and not help carry the bags."

THAT IS NOT THE SMALL POX HE HAS GOT.

"I swan," says the grocery man, "You are too mean to live. But what about your getting drunk?"

"O, I was going to tell you. Pa had a bottle of liver medicine in his coat pocket, and when he was whipping his hornets the bottle dropped out, and I picked it up to carry it home to him. My chum wanted to smell of the liver medicine, so he took out the cork and it smelled just like in front of a liquor store on East Water street, and my chum said his liver was bad, too, and he took a swaller, and he said he should think it was enough to cut a feller's liver up in slices, but it was good, and then I had a peculiar feeling in my liver, and my chum said his liver felt better after he took a swaller, and so I took a swaller, and it was the offulest liver remedy I ever tasted. It scorched my throat just like the diphtheria, but it beats the diphtheria, or sore throat, all to pieces, and my chum and me laughed we was so tickled. Did you ever take liver medicine? You know how it makes you feel as if your liver had got on top of your lights, and like you wanted to jump and holler. Well, sir, honest that liver medicine made me dance a jig on the viaduct bridge, and an old soldier from the soldier's home came along and asked us what was the matter, and we told him about our livers, and the liver medicine, and showed him the bottle, and he said he sposed he had the worst liver in the world, and said the doctors at the home couldn't cure him. It's a mean boy that won't help an old veteran cure his liver, so I told him to try Pa's liver remedy and he took a regular cow swaller, and said, 'Here's to your livers, boys.' He must have a liver bigger nor a cow's, and I guess it is better now."

"Then my liver begun to feel curious again, and my chum said his liver, was getting torpid some more, and we both of us took another dose, and started home and we got generous, and gave our nuts all away to some boys. Say, does liver medicine make a feller give away all he has got? We kept taking medicine every five blocks, and we locked arms and went down a back street and sung 'O it is a glorious thing to be a pirut king,' and when we got home my head felt bigger nor a washtub and I thought p'raps my liver had gone to my head, and Pa came to the door with his face tied up in towels, and some yellow stuff on the towels that smelled like anarchy, and I slapped him on the shoulder and shouted, 'Hello, Gov., how's your liver?' and gave him the bottle, and it was empty, and he asked me if we had been drinking that medicine and he said he was ruined, and I told him he could get some more down to the saloon, and he took hold of my collar and I lammed him in the ear, and he bounced me up stairs, and then I turned pale, and had cramps, and I didn't remember any more till I woke up and the doctor was with me, and Pa and Ma looked scared, and the doc. had a tin thing like you

HERE'S TO YOUR LIVER. BOYS.

draw water out of a country cistern, only smaller, and Ma said if it hadn't been for the stomach pump she wouldn't have had any little boy, and I looked at the knobs on Pa's face and I laffed and asked Pa if he got into the hornets, too. Then the doc. laffed, and Ma cried, and Pa swore, and I groaned, and got sick again, and then they let me go to sleep again, and this morning I had the offulest headache, and Pa's face looks like he had fallen on a picket fence. When I got out I went to my chum's house to see if they had got him pumped out, and his Ma drove me out with a broom, and she says I will ruin every boy in the neighborhood. Pa says I was drunk and kicked him in the groin when he fired me up stairs, and I asked him how I could be drunk just taking medicine for my liver, and he said 'Go to the devil,' and I came over here. Say, give me a lemon to settle my stomach."

"But, look-a-here," says the grocery man, as he gave the boy a little dried up lemon, about as big as a prune, and told him he was a terror, "what is the matter with your eye winkers and your hair? They seem to be burned off."

"O, thunder, didn't Pa tell you about the comet exploding and burning us all? That was the worst thing since the flood, when Noar run the excursion boat from Kalamazoo to Mount Ararat. You see we had been reading about the comet, which is visible at four o'clock in the morning, and I heard Pa tell the hired girl to wake him and Ma up when she got up to set the pancakes and go to early mass so they could see the comet. The hired girl is a Cathlick, and she don't make no fuss about it, but she has got more good, square religion than a dozen like Pa. It makes a good deal of difference how religion affects different people, don't it? Now Pa's religion makes him wild, and he wants to kick my pants and pull my hair, but the hired girl's religion makes her want to hug me, if I am abused; and she puts anarchy on my bruises, and gives me pie. Pa wouldn't get up at four o'clock in the morning to go to early mass, unless he could take a fish pole along and some angle worms. The hired girl prays when nobody sees her but God, but Pa wants to get a church full of sisterin', and pray loud, as though he was an auctioneer selling tin razors. Say, it beats all what a difference liver medicine has on two people, too. Now that hickory nut day, when me and my chum got full of Pa's liver medicine, I felt so good natured I gave my hickory nuts away to the children, and wanted to give my coat and pants to a poor tramp, but my chum, who ain't no bigger'n me, got on his ear and wanted to kick the socks off a little girl who was going home from school. It's queer, ain't it? Well, about the comet. When I heard Pa tell the hired girl to wake him and Ma up, I told her to wake me up about half an hour before she waked Pa up, and then I got my chum to stay with me, and we made a comet to play on Pa. You see my room is right over Pa's room, and

I got two lengths of stove pipe and covered them all over with phosphorus, so they looked just as bright as a comet. Then we got two Roman candles and a big sky rocket, and we were going to touch off the Roman candles and the sky rocket just as Pa and Ma got to looking at the comet. I didn't know that a sky rocket would kick back, did you?

Well, you'd a dide to see that comet. We tied a piece of white rubber garden hose to the stove pipe for a tail and went to bed, and when the girl woke us up we laid for Pa and Ma. Pretty soon we heard Pa's window open, and I looked out, and Pa and Ma had their heads and half their bodies out of the window. They had their night shirts on and looked just like the picture of Millerites waiting for the world to come to an end. Pa looked up and seed the stove pipe and he said:

" 'Hanner, for God's sake look up there. That is the damest comet I ever see. It is as bright as day. See the tail of it. Now that is worth getting up to see.'

"Just then my chum lit the two Roman candles and I touched off the rocket, and that's where my eye winkers went. The rocket busted and the joints of the stove pipe and they fell down on Pa, but Ma got her head inside before the comet struck, and wasn't hurt, but one length of the stove pipe struck Pa endways on the neck and almost cut a biscuit out of him, and the fire and sparks just poured down in his hair, and burned his night shirt. Pa was scart. He thought the world was coming to an end, and the window came down on his back and he began to sing, 'Earth's but a desert drear, Heaven is my home.' I see he was caught in the window, and I went down stairs to put out the fire on his night shirt and put up the window to let him in, and he said: 'My boy, your Ma and I are going to Heaven, but I fear you will go to the bad place.' and I told him I would take my chances, and he better put on his pants if he was going anywhere where there would be liable to be ladies present and when he got his head in Ma told him the world was not coming to an end, but somebody had been setting off fireworks, and she said she guessed it was their dear little boy, and when I saw Pa feeling under the bed for a bed slat I got upstairs pretty previous now, and don't you forget it, and Ma put cold cream on where the sparks burn't Pa's shirt, and Pa said another day wouldn't pass over his head before he had me in the Reform School.

Well, if I go to the Reform School somebody's got to pay attention, you can bet your liver. A boy can't have any fun these days without everybody thinks he is an heathen. What hurt did it do to play comet? It's a mean father that won't stand a little scorching in the interest of science."

The boy went out, scratching the place where his eye winkers were, and then the grocery man knew what it was that caused the fire engines to be out around at four o'clock in the morning looking for a fire.

CHAPTER XVIII

HIS PA GOES HUNTING

Mutilated jaw—The old man has taken to swearing again—Out west duck shooting—His coat-tail shot off—Shoots at a wild goose—The gun kicks!—Throws a chair at his son—The astonished old Deacon.

"WHAT has your Pa got his jaw tied up for, and what makes his right eye so black and blue?" asked the grocery man of the bad boy, as the boy came to bring some butter back that was strong enough to work on the street. "You haven't hurt your poor old Pa, have you?"

"O, his jaw is all right now. You ought to have seen him when the gun was engaged in kicking him," says the boy as he set the butter plate on the cheese box.

"Well, tell us about it. What had the gun against your Pa? I guess it was the son-of-a-gun that kicked him," said the grocery man, as he winked at a servant girl who came in with her apron over her head, after two cents worth of yeast.

"I'll tell you, if you will keep watch down street for Pa. He says he is damned if he will stand this foolishness any longer."

"What, does your father swear, while he is on probation?"

"Swear! Well, I should cackle. You ought to have heard him when he come to, and spit out the loose teeth. You see, since Pa quit drinking he is a little nervous, and the doctor said he ought to go out somewhere and get bizness off his mind, and hunt ducks, and row a boat, and get strength, and Pa said shooting ducks was just in his hand, and for me to go and borrow a gun, and I could go along and carry game. So I got a gun at the gun store, and some cartridges, and we went away out west on the cars, more than fifty miles, and stayed two days. You ought to seen Pa. He was just like a boy that was sick, and couldn't go to school. When we got out by the lake he jumped up and cracked his heels together, and yelled. I thought he was crazy, but he was only cunning. First I scared him nearly to death by firing off the gun behind him, as we were going along the bank, and blowing off a piece of his coat-tail. I

THE GUN FLEW OUT OF HIS HANDS.

knew it wouldn't hurt him, but he turned pale and told me to lay down that gun, and he picked it up and carried it the rest of the way, and I was offul glad cause it was a heavy gun. His coat-tail smelled like when you burn a rag to make the air in the room stop smelling so, all the forenoon. You know Pa is a little near sighted but he don't believe it, so I got some of the wooden decoy ducks that the hunters use, and put them in the lake, and you ought to see Pa get down on his belly and crawl through the grass, to get up close to them. He shot twenty times at the wooden ducks, and wanted me to go in and fetch them out, but I told him I was no retriever dog. Then Pa was mad, and said all he brought me along for was to carry game, and I had come near shooting his hind leg off, and now I wouldn't carry ducks. While he was coaxing me to go in the cold water without my pants on, I heard some wild geese squawking, and then Pa heard them, and he was excited. He said 'You lay down behind the muskrat house, and I will get a goose.' I told him he couldn't kill a goose with that fine shot, and I gave him a large cartridge the gun store man loaded for me, with a handful of powder in, and I told Pa it was a goose cartridge, and Pa put it in the gun. The geese came along, about a mile high, squawking, and Pa aimed at a dark cloud and fired. Well, I was offul scared, I thought I had killed him. The gun just rared up and come down on his jaw, shoulder and everywhere, and he went over a log and struck on his shoulder, the gun flew out of his hands, and Pa he laid there on his neck, with his feet over the log, and that was the first time he didn't scold me since he got religion. I felt offul sorry, and got some dirty water in my hat and poured it down his neck, and laid him out, and pretty soon he opened his eyes and asked if any of the passengers got ashore alive. Then his eye swelled out so it looked like a blue door-knob, and Pa felt of his jaw, and asked if the engineer and fireman jumped off, or if they went down with the engine. He seemed dazed, and then he saw the gun, and he said 'Take the dam thing away, it is going to kick me again.' Then he got his senses and wanted to know if he killed a goose, and I told him no, but he nearly broke one's jaw, and then he said the gun kicked him when it went off, and he laid down and the gun kept kicking him more than twenty times, when he was trying to sleep. He went back to the tavern where we were stopping and wouldn't touch the gun, but made me lug it. He told the tavern keeper that he fell over a wire fence, but I think he began to suspect, after he spit the loose teeth out, that the gun was loaded for bear. I suppose he will kill me some day. Don't you think he will?"

"Any coroner's jury would let him off and call it justifiable, if he should kill you. You must be a lunatic. Has your Pa talked much about it since you got back?" asked the grocery man.

"Not much. You see he can't talk much without breaking his jaw. But he was able to throw a chair at me. You see I thought I would joke him a little, cause when anybody feels bad a joke kind of livens em up, so we were talking about Pa's liver and Ma said he seemed to be better since his liver had become more active, and I said, 'Pa, when you was a rolling over with the gun chasing you, and kicking you every round, your liver was active enough, cause it was on top half the time.' Then Pa throwed the chair at me. He says he believes I knew that cartridge was loaded. But you ought to seen the fun when an old she deacon of Pa's church called to collect some money to send to the heathens. Ma wasn't in, so Pa went to the parlor to stand her off, and when she see that Pa's face was tied up, and his eye was black, and his jaw cracked, she held up both hands and said, 'O, my dear brother you have been drunk again. You have backslid. You will have to go back and commence your probation all over again,' and Pa said, 'Damfido,' and the old she deacon screamed and went off without getting enough money to buy a deck of round cornered cards for the heathen. Say, what does 'damfido,' mean? Pa has some of the queerest expressions since he joined the church."

CHAPTER XIX

HIS PA IS "NISHIATED"

Are you a Mason?—No Harm to Play at Lodge—Why Goats are Kept in Stables—The bad boy Gets the Goat up Stairs—The Grand Bumper Degree—Kyan Pepper on the Goat's Beard—"Bring Forth the Royal Bumper"—The Goat on the Rampage.

"SAY, are you a Mason, or a nodfellow, or anything?" asked the bad boy of the grocery man, as he went to the cinnamon bag on the shelf and took out a long stick of cinnamon bark to chew.

"Why, yes, of course I am, but what set you to thinking of that?" asked the grocery man, as he went to the desk and charged the boy's father with half a pound of cinnamon.

"Well, do the goats bunt when you nishiate a fresh candidate?"

"No, of course not. The goats are cheap ones, that have no life, and we muzzle them, and put pillows over their heads, so they can't hurt anybody," says the grocery man, as he winked at a brother Odd Fellow who was seated on a sugar barrel, looking mysterious, "But why do you ask?"

"O, nothin, onlv I wish me and my chum had muzzled our goat with a pillow. Pa would have enjoyed his becoming a member of our lodge better. You see, Pa had been telling us how much good the Masons and Odd Fellows did, and said we ought to try and grow up good so we could jine the lodges when we got big, and I asked Pa if it would do any hurt for us to have a play lodge in my room, and purtend to nishiate, and Pa said it wouldn't do any hurt. He said it would improve our minds and learn us to be men. So my chum and me borried a goat that lives in a livery stable. Say, did you know they keep a goat in a livery stable so the horses won't get sick? They get used to the smell of the goat, and after that nothing can make them sick but a glue factory. I wish my girl boarded in a livery stable, then she would get used to the smell. I went home with her from church Sunday night, and the smell of the goat on my clothes made her sick to her stummick, and she acted just like an excursion on the lake, and said if I didn't go and

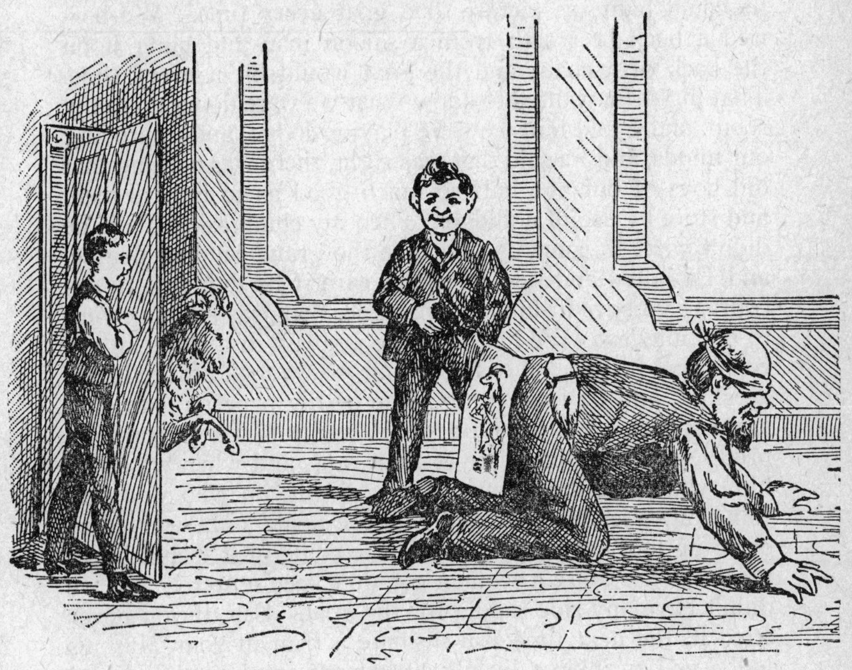

bury myself and take the smell out of me she wouldn't never go with me again. She was just as pale as a ghost, and the prespiration on her lip was just zif she had been hit by a street sprinkler. You see my chum and me had to carry the goat up to my room when Pa and Ma was out riding, and he blatted so we had to tie a handkerchief around his nose, and his feet made such a noise on the floor that we put some baby's socks on his feet. Gosh, how frowy a goat smells, don't it? I should think you Masons must have strong stummicks. Why don't you have a skunk or a mule for a trade mark? Take a mule, and annoint it with limburg cheese and you could nishiate and make a candidate smell just as bad as with a gosh darn mildewed goat.

"Well, my chum and me practiced with that goat until he could bunt the picture of a goat every time. We borried a buck beer sign from a saloon man and hung it on the back of a chair, and the goat would hit it every time. That night Pa wanted to know what we were doing up in my room, and I told him we were playing lodge, and improving our minds, and Pa said that was right, there was nothing that did boys of our age half so much good as to imitate men, and store by useful nollidge. Then my chum asked Pa if he didn't want to come up and take the grand bumper degree, and Pa laffed and said he didn't care if he did, just to encourage us boys in innocent pastime, that was so improving to our intellex. We had shut the goat up in a closet in my room, and he had got over blatting, so we took off the handkerchief, and he was eating some of my paper collars, and skate straps. We went up stairs, and told Pa to come up pretty soon and give three distinct raps, and when we asked him who come there must say 'A pilgrim who wants to join your ancient order and ride the goat.' Ma wanted to come up too, but we told her if she come in it would break up the lodge cause a woman couldn't keep a secret, and we didn't have any side saddle for the goat. Say, if you never tried it, the next time you nishiate a man in your Mason's lodge you sprinkle a little kyan pepper on the goat's beard just afore you turn him loose. You can get three times as much fun to the square inch of goat. You wouldn't think it was the same goat. Well, we got all fixed up and Pa rapped, and we let him in and told him he must be blindfolded, and he got on his knees a laffing and I tied a towel around his eyes, and then I turned him around and made him get down on his hands also, and then his back was right toward the closet door, and I put the buck beer sign right against Pa's clothes. He was laffing all the time, and said we boys were as full of fun as they made 'em and we told him it was a solemn occasion, and we wouldn't permit no levity, and if he didn't stop laffing we couldn't give him the grand bumper degree. Then everything was ready, and my chum had his hand on the closet door, and some kyan pepper in his other hand and I asked Pa in low bass tones if he felt as though he wanted to turn back, or if he had nerve enough to go ahead and take the degree. I warned him that it was full of dangers, as the goat was loaded for bear, and told him he yet had time to retrace his steps if he wanted to. He said he

THE GOAT WOULD HIT IT EVERY TIME.

wanted the whole buzness, and we could go ahead with the menagerie. Then I said to Pa that if he had decided to go ahead, and not blame us for the conquences, to repeat after me the following: 'Bring forth the Royal Bumper and let him Bump.'

"Pa repeated the words and my chum sprinkled the kyan pepper on the goat's mustache, and he sneezed once and looked sassy, and then he see the lager beer goat raring up, and he started for it, just like a cow catcher, and blatted. Pa is real fat, but he knew he got hit, and he grunted, and he said, 'Hell's-fire, what you boys doin'?' and then the goat gave him another degree, and Pa pulled off the towel and got up and started for the stairs, and so did the goat, and Ma was at the bottom of the stairs listening, and when I looked over the banisters Pa and Ma and the goat were all in a heap, and Pa was yelling murder, and Ma was screaming fire, and the goat was blatting, and sneezing, and bunting, and the hired girl came into the hall and the goat took after her and she crossed herself just as the goat struck her and said, 'Howly mother protect me!' and went down stairs the way we boys slide down hill, with both hands on herself, and the goat rared up and blatted, and Pa and Ma went into their room and shut the door, and then my chum and me opened the front door and drove the goat out. The minister, who comes to see Ma every three times a week, was just ringing the bell, and the goat thought he wanted to be nishiated too, and gave him one, for luck, and then went down the sidewalk blatting, and sneezing, and the minister came into the parlor and said he was stabbed, and then Pa came out of his room with his suspenders hanging down, and he didn't know the minister was there, and he said cuss words, and Ma cried and told Pa he would go to hell sure, and Pa said he didn't care, he would kill that kussid goat afore he went, and I told Pa the minister was in the parlor, and he and Ma went down and said the weather was propitious for a revival, and it seemed as though an outpouring of the Spirit was about to be vouchsafed to His people, and none of them sot down but Ma, cause the goat didn't hit her, and while they were talking religion, with their mouths, and kussin the goat inwardly, my chum and me adjourned the lodge, and I went and stayed with him all night, and I haven't been home since. But I don't believe Pa will lick me, cause he said he would not hold us responsible for the consequences. He ordered the goat hisself, and we filled the order, don't you see? Well, I guess I will go and sneak in the back way, and find out from the hired girl how the land lays. She won't go back on me, cause the goat was not loaded for hired girls. She just happened to get in at the wrong time. Good-bye, sir, Remember and give your goat kyan pepper in your lodge."

As the boy went away, and skipped over the back fence, the grocery man said to his brother Odd Fellow, "If that boy don't beat the devil then I never saw one that did. The old man ought to have him sent to a lunatic asylum."

CHAPTER XX

HIS GIRL GOES BACK ON HIM

The grocery man is afraid—But the bad boy is a wreck!—"My girl has shook me!"—The bad boy's heart is broken—Still he enjoys a bit of fun—Cod-liver oil on the pan-cakes—The hired girls made victims—The bad boy vows vengeance on his girl and the telegraph messenger.

"Now you git right away from here," said the grocery man to the bad boy, as he came in with a hungry look on his face, and a wild light in his eye. "I am afraid of you. I wouldn't be surprised to see you go off half cocked and blow us all up. I think you are a devil. You may have a billy goat, or a shot gun or a bottle of poison concealed about you. Condemn you, the police ought to muzzle you. You will kill somebody yet. Here, take a handful of prunes and go off somewhere and enjoy yourself, and keep away from here;" and the grocery man went on sorting potatoes, and watching the haggard face of the boy. "What ails you anyway?" he added, as the boy refused the prunes, and seemed to be sick to the stomach.

"Oh, I am a wreck," said the boy, as he grated his teeth. and looked wicked. "You see before you a shadow. I have drank of the sweets of life, and now only the dregs remain. I look back at the happiness of the past two weeks, during which I have been permitted to gaze into the fond blue eyes of my loved one, and carry her rubbers to school for her to wear home when it rained, to hear the sweet words that fell from her lips as she lovingly told me I was a terror, and as I think it is all over, and that I shall never again place my arm around her waist, I feel as if the world had been kicked off its base and was whirling through space, liable to be knocked into a cocked hat, and I don't care a darn. My girl has shook me."

"Sho! You don't say so," said the grocery man as he threw a rotten potato into a basket of good ones that were going to the orphan asylum. "Well, she showed sense. You would have blown her up, or broken her neck, or something. But don't feel bad. You will soon find another girl that will discount her, and you will forget this one."

"Never!" said the boy, as he nibbled at a piece of codfish that he had picked off. "I shall never allow my affections to become entwined about another piece of calico. It unmans me, sir. Henceforth I am a hater of the whole girl race. From this out I shall harbor revenge in my heart, and no girl can cross my path and live. I want to grow up to become a he school ma'am, or a he milliner, or something, where I can grind girls into the dust under the heel of a terrible despotism, and make them sue for mercy. To think that girl, on whom I have lavished my heart's best love and over thirty cents, in the past two weeks, could let the smell of a goat on my clothes come between us, and break off an acquaintance that seemed to be the forerunner of a happy future, and say, 'ta-ta' to me, and go off to dancing school with a telegraph messenger boy who wears a sleeping-car porter uniform, is too much, and my heart is broken. I will lay for that messenger some night, when he is delivering a message in our ward, and I will make him think lightning has struck the wire and run in on his bench. O, you don't know anything about the woe there is in this world. You never loved many people, did you?"

The grocery man admitted he never loved very hard, but he knew a little something about it from an aunt of his, who got mashed on a Chicago drummer. "But your father must be having a rest while your whole mind is occupied with your love affair," said he.

"Yes," said the boy, with a vacant look, "I take no interest in the pleasure of the chase any more, though I did have a little quiet fun this morning at the breakfast table. You see

I WILL LAY FOR THE MESSENGER BOY.

Pa is the contrariest man ever was. If I complain that anything at the table don't taste good, Pa says it is all right. This morning I took the syrup pitcher and emptied out the white syrup and put in some cod-liver oil that Ma is taking for her cough. I put some on my pancakes and pretended to taste it, and I told Pa the syrup was sour and not fit to eat. Pa was mad in a second, and he poured out some on his pancakes, and said I was getting too confounded particular. He said the syrup was good enough for him and he sopped his pancakes in it and fired some down his neck. He is a gaul durned hypocrite, that's what he is. I could by his face that the cod-liver oil was nearly killing him, but he said that syrup was all right, and if I didn't eat mine he would break my back, and by gosh, I had to eat it, and Pa said he guessed he hadn't got much appetite, and he would just drink a cup of coffee and eat a donut.

"I like to dide, and that is one thing, I think, that makes this disappointment in love harder to bear. But I felt sorry for Ma. Ma ain't got a very strong stummick, and when she got some of that cod-liver oil in her mouth she went right up stairs, sicker'n a horse, and Pa had to help her, and she had nooralgia all the morning. I eat pickles to take the taste out of my mouth, and then I laid for the hired girls. They eat too much syrup, anyway, and when they got on to that cod-liver oil, and swallowed a lot of it, one of them, a Irish girl, she got up from the table and put her hand on her corset, and said, 'Howly Jaysus,' and went out in the kitchen, as pale as Ma is when she has powder on her face, and the other girl who is Dutch, she swallowed a pancake and said, 'Mine Gott, vas de matter from me,' and she went out and leaned on the coal bin, then they talked Irish and Dutch, and got clubs, and started to look for me, and I

thought I would come over here. The whole family is sick, but it not from love, like my illness, and they will get over it, while I shall fill an early grave, but not till I have made that girl and the telegraph messenger wish they were dead. Pa and I are going to Chicago next week, and I'll bet we'll have some fun. Pa says I need a change of air, and I think he is going to try and lose me. It's a cold day when I get left anywhere that I can't find my way back. Well, good-bye, old rotten potatoes."

CHAPTER XXI

HE AND HIS PA IN CHICAGO

Nothing like traveling to give tone—Laughing in the wrong place—A diabolical plot—His Pa arrested as a kidnapper—The numbers on the doors changed—The wrong room—"Nothin' the mazzer with me, pet!"—The tell-tale hat.

"What is this I hear about your Pa's being arrested in Chicago?" said the grocery man to the bad boy, as he came in with a can for kerosene and a jug for vinegar.

"Well, it was true, but the police let him go after they hit him a few licks and took him to the station," said the boy, as he got the vinegar into the kerosene can, and the kerosene in the jug. "You see, Pa and me went down there to stay over night, and have fun. Ma said she druther we would be away than not when they were cleaning house, and Pa thought it would do me good to travel, and sort of get tone, and he thought maybe I'd be better, and not play jokes, but I guess it is born in me. Do you know I actually think of mean things to do when I am in the most solemn places. They took me to a funeral once, and I got to thinking what a stampede there would be if the corpse would come to life and sit up in the coffin, and I snickered right out, and Pa took me out doors and kicked my pants. I don't think he orter kicked me for it, cause I didn't think of it a purpose. Such things have occurred, and I have read about them, and a poor boy ought to be allowed to think, hadn't he?"

"Yes, but what about his being arrested? Never mind the funeral," said the grocery man, as he took his knife and picked some of the lead out of the weights on the scales.

"We went down on the cars, and Pa had a headache, because he had been out all night electioneering for the prohibition ticket, and he was cross, and scolded me, and once he pulled my ear 'cause I asked him if he knew the girl he was winking at in a seat across the aisle. I didn't enjoy myself much, and some men were talking about kidnapping children, and it gave me an ijee, and just before I got to Chicago I went after a drink of water at the other end of the car, and I saw a man who looked as though he wouldn't stand any fooling, and I whispered to him that the bald-headed man I was sitting with was taking me away from my home in Milwaukee, and I mistrusted he was going to make a thief or a pickpocket of me. I said 's-h-h-h,' and told him not to say anything or the man would maul me. Then I went back to the seat and asked Pa to buy me a gold watch, and he looked mad and cuffed me on the ear. The man that I whispered to got talking with some other men, and when we got off the cars at Chicago a policeman came up to Pa and took him by the neck and said, 'Mr. Kidnapper, I guess we will run you in.' Pa was mad and tried to jerk away, and the cop choked him, and another cop came along and helped, and the passengers crowded around and wanted to lynch Pa, and Pa wanted to know what they meant, and they asked him where he stole the kid, and he said I was his kid, and asked me if I wasn't, and I looked scared, as though I was afraid to say no, and I said 'Y-e-s S-e-r, I guess so.' Then the police said the poor boy was scart, and they would take us both to the station, and they made Pa walk spry, and when he held back they jerked him along. He was offul mad and said he would make somebody smart for this, and I hoped it wouldn't be me. At the station they charged Pa with kidnapping a boy from Milwaukee, and he said it was a lie, and I was his boy, and I said of course I was, and the boss asked who told the cops Pa was a kidnapper, and they said 'damfino,' and then the boss told Pa he could go, but not to let it occur again, and Pa and me went away. I looked so sorry for Pa that he never tumbled to me, that I was to blame. We walked around town all day, and went to the stores, and at night Pa was offul tired, and he put me to bed in the tavern and he went out to walk around and get rested. I was not tired, and I walked all around the hotel. I thought Pa had gone to a theater, and that made me mad, and I thought I would play a joke on him. Our room was 210 and the next was 212, and an old maid with a Scotch terrier occupied 212. I saw her twice and she called me names, cause she thought I wanted to steal her dog. That made me mad at her, and so I took my jack **knife** and drew the tacks

WHEN PA HELD BACK, THEY JERKED HIM ALONG.

out of the tin thing that the numbers were painted on, and put the old maid's number on our door and our number on her door, and then I went to bed. I tried to keep awake so as to help Pa if he had any difficulty, but I guess I got asleep, but woke up when the dog barked. If the dog had not woke me up, the woman's scream would, and if that hadn't, Pa would. You see, Pa came home from the theatre about 'leven, and he had been drinking. He says everybody drinks when they go to Chicago, even the minister. Pa looked at the numbers on the doors all along the hall till he found 210 and walked right in and pulled off his coat and threw it on the lounge where the dog was. The old maid was asleep, but the dog barked, and Pa said, 'That cussed boy has bought a dog,' and he kicked the dog, and then the old maid said, 'What is the matter, pet?'

"Pa laffed and said, 'Nothin' the mazzer with *me*, pet,' and then you ought to have heard the yelling. The old maid covered her head and kicked and yelled, and the dog snarled and bit Pa on the pants, and Pa had his vest off and his suspenders unbuttoned, and he got scared and took his coat and vest and went out in the hall, and I opened our door and told Pa he was in the wrong room, and he said he guessed he knowed it, and he came in our room and I locked the door, and then the bell boy, and the porter, and the clerk came up to see what ailed the old maid, and she said a burglar got in the room, and they found Pa's hat on the lounge, and they took it and told her to be quiet and they would find the burglar. Pa was so scared that he sweat like everything, and the bed was offul warm, and he pretended to go to sleep, but he was wondering how he could get his hat back. In the morning I told him it would be hard work to explain it to Ma how he happened to get into the wrong room, and he said it wasn't necessary to say anything about it to Ma.

"Then he gave me five dollars to go out and buy him a new hat, and he said I might keep the change if I would not mention it when I got home, and I got him one for ten shillings, and we took the eight o'clock train in the morning and came home, and I 'spose the Chicago detectives are trying to fit Pa's hat onto a burglar. Pa seemed offully relieved when we got across the state line into Wisconsin. But you'd a dide to see him come out of that old lady's room with his coat and vest on his arm, and his suspenders hanging down, looking scart. He dassent lick me any more or I'll tell Ma where Pa left his hat."

CHAPTER XXII

HIS PA IS DISCOURAGED

"I ain't no Joner!"—The story of the Ancient Prophet—The Sunday School Folks go back on the bad boy—Caged Cats—A Committee Meeting—A remarkable Cat-astrophe!—"That boy beats Hell!"—Basting the bad boy—The Hot-water-in-the-sponge trick.

"SAY, you leave here mighty quick," said the grocery man to the bad boy, as he came in, with his arm in a sling, and backed up against the stove to get warm. "Everything has gone wrong since you got to coming here, and I think you are a regular Jonah. I find sand in my sugar, kerosene in the butter, the codfish is all picked off, and there is something wrong every time you come here. Now you leave."

"I ain't no Joner," said the boy as he wiped his nose on his coat sleeve, and reached into a barrel for a snow apple. "I never swallered no whale. Say, do you believe that story about Joner being in the whale's belly all night? I don't. The minister was telling about it at Sunday school last Sunday, and asked me what I thought Joner was doing while he was in there, and I told him I interpreted the story this way, that the whale was fixed up inside with upper and lower berths, like a sleeping car, and Joner had a lower berth and the porter made up the berth as soon as Joner came in with his satchel, and Joner pulled off his boots and gave them to the porter to black, and put his watch under his pillow and turned in. The boys in Sunday school all laffed, and the minister said I was a bigger fool than Pa was, and that was useless. If you go back on me now, I won't have a friend, except my chum and a dog and I swear, by my halidom that I never put no sand in your sugar, or kerosene in your butter. I admit the picking off of the codfish, but you can charge it to Pa, the same as you did the eggs that I pushed my chum over into last summer, though I thought you did wrong in charging Christmas prices for dog days' eggs. When my chum's Ma scraped his pants she said there was not an egg represented on there that was less than two years old. The Sunday school folks have gone back on me, since I put kyan pepper on the stove, when they were singing 'Little Drops of Water,' and they all had to go out doors and air themselves. But I didn't mean to let the pepper drop on the stove. I was just holding it over the stove to warm it, when my chum hit the funny bone of my elbow. Pa says I am a terror to cats. Every time Pa says anything, it gives me a new idea. I tell you Pa has got a great brain, but sometimes he don't have it with him. When he said I was a terror to cats I thought what fun there is in cats, and me and my chum went to stealing cats right off, and before night we had eleven cats caged. We had one in a canary bird cage, three in Pa's old hat boxes, three in Ma's band box, four in valises, two in a trunk, and the rest in a closet up stairs.

"That night Pa said he wanted me to stay home because the committee that is going to get up a noyster supper in the church was going to meet at our house, and they might want to send me on errands. I asked him if my chum couldn't stay too, cause he is the healthiest infant to run after errands that ever was, and Pa said he could stay, but we must remember that there musn't be no monkey business going on. I told him there shouldn't be no monkey business but I didn't promise nothing about cats. Well, sir, you'd a dide. The committee was in the library by the back stairs, and me and my chum got the cat boxes all together, at the top of the stairs, and we took them all out and put them in a clothes basket, and just as the minister was speaking, and telling what a great good was done by these oyster sociables, in bringing the young people together, and taking their minds from the wickedness of the world, and turning their thoughts into different channels, one of the old tom cats in the basket gave a 'purmeow' that sounded like the wail of a lost soul or a challenge to battle. I told my chum that we couldn't hold the bread-board over the clothes basket much longer, when two or three cats began to yowl. and the minister stopped talking, and Pa told Ma to open

A YELLOW CAT WITHOUT ANY TAIL WAS WALKING OVER THE MINISTER.

the stair door and tell the hired girl to see what was the matter up there. She thought our cat had got shut up in the storm door, and she opened the stair door to yell to the girl, and then I pushed the clothes basket, cats and all down the back stairs. Well, sir, I suppose no committee for a noyster supper was ever more astonished. I heard Ma fall over a willow rocking chair, and say, 'Scat,' and I heard Pa say, 'Well, I'm dam'd,' and a girl that sings in the choir say, 'Heavens, I am stabbed,' then my chum and me run to the front of the house and come down the front stairs looking as innocent as could be, and we went into the library, and I was just going to tell Pa if there was any errands he wanted run, my chum and me was just aching to run them, when a yellow cat without any tail was walking over the minister, and Pa was throwing a hassock at two cats that were clawing each other under the piano, and Ma was trying to get her frizzes back on her head, and the choir girl was standing on the lounge with her dress pulled up, trying to scare cats with her striped stockings, and the minister was holding his hands up, and I guess he was asking a blessing on the cats, and my chum opened the front door and all the cats went out. Pa and Ma looked at me, and I said it wasn't me, and the minister wanted to know how so much cat hair got on my coat and vest, and I said a cat met me in the hall and kicked me, and Ma cried, and Pa said, 'That boy beats hell,' and the minister said I would be all right if he had been properly brought up, and then Ma was mad, and the committee broke up. Well, to tell the honest truth, Pa basted me, and yanked me around until I had to have my arm in a sling, but what's the use of making such a fuss about a few cats? Ma said she never wanted to have any company again, cause I spoiled everything. But I got even with Pa for basting me, this morning, and I dassant go home. You see, Ma has got a great big bath sponge as big as a chair cushion, and this morning I took the sponge and filled it with warm water, and took the feather cushion out of the chair Pa sits in at the table, and put the sponge in its place, and covered it over with the cushion cover, and when we all got set down to the table Pa came in and set down on it to ask a blessing. He started in by closing his eyes and placing his hands up in front of him like a letter V, and then he began to ask that the food we were about to partake of be blessed, and then he was going on to ask that all of us be made to see the error of our ways, when he began to hitch around, and he opened one eye and looked at me and I looked as pious as a boy can look when he knows the pancakes are getting cold, and Pa he kind of sighed and said, 'Amen' sort of snappish, and he got up and told Ma he didn't feel well, and she would have to take his place and pass around the sassidge and potatoes, and he looked kind of scart and went out with his

PA OPENED ONE EYE AND LOOKED AT ME.

hands on his pistol pocket, as though he would like to shoot, and Ma she got up and went around and sat in Pa's chair. The sponge didn't hold more than half a pail full of water, and I didn't want to play no joke on Ma, cause the cats nearly broke her up, but she sat down and was just going to help me, when she rung the bell and called the hired girl, and said she felt as though her nooralgia was coming on, and she would go to her room, and told the girl to sit down and help Hennery. The girl sat down and poured me out some coffee, and then she said, 'Howly Saint Patrick, but I blave those pancakes are burning,' and she went out in the kitchen. I drank my coffee, and then took the big sponge out of the chair and put the cushion in the place of it, and then I put the sponge in the bath room, and I went up to Pa and Ma's room, and asked them if I should go after the doctor, and Pa had changed his clothes and got on his Sunday pants, and he said, 'Never mind the doctor, I guess we will pull through,' and for me to get out and go to the devil, and I came over here. Say, there is no harm in a little warm water, is there? Well, I'd like to know what Pa and Ma and the hired girl thought. I am the only real healthy one there is in our family."

CHAPTER XXIII

HE BECOMES A DRUGGIST

"I have gone into business!"—A new rose geranium perfume—The bad boy in a druggist's store—Practicing on his Pa—An explosion—The seidletz powder—His Pa's frequent pains—Pounding India-Rubber—Curing a wart.

"WHEW! What is that smells so about this store? It seems as though everything had turned frowy," said the grocery man to his clerk, in the presence of the bad boy, who was standing with his back to the stove, his coat tails parted with his hands, and a cigarette in his mouth.

"May be it is me that smells frowy," said the boy as he put his thumbs in the armholes of his vest, and spit at the keyhole in the door. "I have gone into business."

"By thunder, I believe it is you," said the grocery man, as he went up to the boy, snuffed a couple of times, and then held his hands to his nose. "The board of health will kerosene you, if they ever smell that smell, and send you to the glue factory. What business you gone into to make you smell so rank?"

"Well, you see Pa began to think it was time I learned a trade, or a perfession, and he saw a sign in a drug store window, 'Boy wanted,' and as he had a boy he didn't want, he went to the druggist and got a job for me. This smell on me will go off in a few weeks. You know I wanted to try all the perfumery in the store, and after I had got about forty different extracts on my clothes, another boy that worked there he fixed up a bottle of benzine and assafety and brimstone, and a whole lot of other horrid stuff, and labeled it 'rose geranium,' and I guess I just wallered in it. It *is* awful, aint it? It kerflummixed Ma when I went into the dining-room the first night that I got home from the store, and broke Pa all up. He said I reminded him of the time when they had a litter of skunks under the barn. The air seemed fixed around where I am, and everybody seems to know who fixed it. A girl came in the store yesterday to buy a satchet, and there wasn't anybody there but me, and I didn't know what it was, and I took down everything in the store pretty near before I found it, and then I wouldn't have found it only the proprietor came in. The girl asked the proprietor if there wasn't a good deal of sewer-gas in the store, and he told me to go out and shake myself. I think the girl was mad at me because I got a nursing bottle out of the show case, with a rubber nozzle, and asked her if that was what she wanted. Well, she told me a satchet was something for the stummick, and I thought a nursing bottle was the nearest thing to it."

"I should think you would drive all the customers away from the store," said the grocery man, as he opened the door to let the fresh air in.

"I don't know but I will, but I am hired for a month on trial, and I shall stay. You see, I shan't practice on anybody but Pa for a spell. I made up my mind to that when I gave a woman some salts instead of powdered borax, and she came back mad. Pa seems to want to encourage me, and is willing to take anything that I ask him to. He had a sore throat and wanted something for it, and the boss drugger told me to put some tannin and chlorate of potash in a mortar, and grind it, and I let Pa pound it with the mortar, and while he was pounding I dropped in a couple of drops of sulphuric acid, and it exploded and blowed Pa's hat clear across the store, and Pa was whiter than a sheet. He said he guessed his throat was all right, and he wouldn't come near me again that day. The next day, Pa came in and I was laying for him. I took a white seidletz powder and a blue one, and dissolved them in separate glasses, and when Pa came in I asked him if he didn't want some lemonade, and he said he did, and I gave him the sour one and he drank it. He said it was too sour, and then I gave him the other glass, that looked like water, to take the taste out of his mouth, and he drank it. Well, sir, when those two powders got together in Pa's stummick, and began to siz and steam, and foam, Pa

I ASKED HER IF THAT WAS WHAT SHE WANTED.

pretty near choked to death, and the suds came out of his nostrils, and his eyes stuck out, and as soon as he could get his breath he yelled 'Fire,' and said he was poisoned, and called for a doctor, but I thought as long as we had a doctor right in the family there was no use of hiring one, so I got a stomach pump, and I would have had him baled out in no time, only the proprietor came in and told me to go and wash some bottles, and he gave Pa a drink of brandy, and Pa said he felt better. Pa has learned where we keep the liquor, and he comes in two or three times a day with a pain in his stomach. They play awful mean tricks on a boy in a drug store. The first day they put a chunk of something sort of blue into a mortar, and told me to pulverize it, and then make it up into two grain pills. Well, sir, I pounded that chunk all the forenoon, and it never pulverized at all, and the boss told me to hurry up, as the woman was waiting for the pills, and I mauled it till I was nearly dead, and when it was time to go to supper the boss came and looked in mortar, and took out the chunk, and said, 'You darn fool, you have been pounding all day on a chunk of India-rubber instead of blue mass!' Well, how did I know? But I will get even with them if I stay there long enough, and don't you forget it. If you have a prescription you want filled you can come down to the store and I will put it up for you myself, and then you will be sure you get what you pay for."

"Yes," said the grocery man, as he cut off a piece of limberg cheese and put it on the stove, to purify the air in the room. "I should laugh to see myself taking any medicine you put up. You will kill some one yet by giving them poison instead of quinine. But what has your Pa got his nose tied up for? He looks as though he had had a fight."

"O, that was from my treatment. He had a wart on his nose. You know that wart. You remember how the minister told him if other people's business had a button-hole in it, Pa could button the wart in the button-hole, as he always had his nose there. Well, I told Pa I could cure that wart with caustic, and he said he would give five dollars if I could cure it, so I took a stick of caustic and burned the wart off, but I guess I burned down into the nose a little, for it swelled up as big as a lobster. Pa says he would rather have a whole nest of warts than such a nose, but it will be all right in a year or two."

CHAPTER XXIV

HE QUITS THE DRUG BUSINESS

He has dissolved with the drugger—The old lady and the gin—The bad boy ignominiously fired—How he dosed his Pa's brandy—The bad boy as "hawty as a dook"—He gets even with his girl—The bad boy wants a quiet place—The old man threatens the parson.

"What are you loafing around here for?" says the grocery man to the bad boy one day this week. "It is after nine o'clock, and I should think you would want to be down to the drug store. How do you know but there may be somebody dying for a dose of pills?"

"O, darn the drug store. I have got sick of that business, and I have dissolved with the drugger. I have resigned. The policy of the store did not meet with my approval, and I have stepped out and am waiting for them to come and tender me a better position at an increased salary," said the boy, as he threw a cigar stub into a barrel of prunes and lit a fresh one.

"Resigned, eh?" said the grocery man as he fished out the cigar stub and charged the boy's father with two pounds of prunes, "didn't you and the boss agree?"

"Not exactly; I gave an old lady some gin when she asked for camphor and water, and she made a show of herself. I thought I would fool her, but she knew mighty well what it was, and she drank about half a pint of gin, and got to tipping over bottles and kegs of paint, and when the drug man came in with his wife, the old lady threw her arms around his neck and called him her darling, and when he pushed her away, and told her she was drunk, she picked up a bottle of citrate of magnesia and pointed it at him, and the cork came out like a pistol, and he thought he was shot, and his wife fainted away, and the police came and took the old gin refrigerator away, and the drug man told me to face the door, and when I wasn't looking he kicked me four times, and I landed in the street, and he said if I ever came in sight of the store again he would kill me dead. That is the way I resigned. I tell you, they will send for me again. They never can run that store without me."

"I guess they will worry along without you," said the grocery man. "How does your Pa take your being fired out? I should think it would break him all up."

"O, I think Pa rather likes it. At first he thought he had a soft snap with me in the drug store, cause he has got to drinking again like a fish, and he has gone back on the church entirely; but after I had put a few things in his brandy he concluded it was cheaper to buy it, and he is now patronizing a barrel house down by the river.

"One day I put some castile soap in a drink of brandy, and Pa leaned over the back fence more than an hour, with his finger down his throat. The man that collects the ashes from the alley asked Pa if he had lost anything, and Pa said he was only 'sugaring off.' I don't know what that is. When Pa felt better he came in and wanted a little whiskey, to take the taste out of his mouth, and I gave him some with about a teaspoonful of pulverized alum in it. Well, sir, you'd a dide. Pa's mouth and throat was so puckered up, that he couldn't talk. I don't think the drug man will make any thing by firing me out, because I shall turn all the trade that I control to another store. Why sir, sometimes there were eight and nine girls in the store all at wonct, on account of my being there. They came to have me put extracts on their handkerchiefs and to eat gum-drops; he will lose all that trade now. My girl that went back on me for the telegraph messenger boy, she came with the rest of the girls, but she found that I could be as 'hawty as a dook.' I got even with her, though. I pretended I wasn't mad, and when she wanted me to put some perfumery on her handkerchief I said, 'All right,' and I put on a little geranium and white rose, and then I got some tincture of assafet and sprinkled it on her dress and cloak when she went out. That is about the worst smelling stuff that ever was, and I was glad when she went out and met the telegraph boy on the corner. They went off together, but he came back pretty soon, about the homesickest boy you ever saw, and he told my chum he would

THEN THE DRUG MAN TOLD ME TO FACE THE DOOR.

never go with that girl again because she smelled like spoiled oysters or sewer gas. Her folks noticed it, and made her go and wash her feet and soak herself, and her brother told my chum it didn't do any good, she smelled just like a glue factory, and my chum—the darn fool—told her brother that it was me who perfumed her, and he hit me in the eye with a frozen fish, down by the fish store, and that's what made my eye black; but I know how to cure a black eye. I have not been in the drug store eight days, and not know how to cure a black eye, and I guess I learned that girl not to go back on a boy cause he smelled like a goat."

"Well, what was it about your leaving the wrong medicine at houses? The policeman in this ward told me you come pretty near killing several people by leaving the wrong medicine."

"The way of it was this. There was about a dozen different kinds of medicine to leave at different places, and I was in a hurry to go to the roller skating rink, so I got my chum to help me, and we just took the numbers of the houses, and when we rung the bell we would hand out the first package we come to, and I understand there was a good deal of complaint. One old maid who ordered powder for her face, her ticket drew some worm lozengers, and she kicked awfully, and a widow who was going to be married, she ordered a celluloid comb and brush, and she got a nursing bottle with a rubber nozzle, and a toothing ring, and she made quite a fuss; but the woman who was weaning her baby and wanted the nursing bottle, she got the comb and brush and some blue pills, and she never made any fuss at all. It makes a good deal of difference I notice, whether a person gets a better thing than they ordered or not. But the drug business is too lively for me. I have got to have a quiet place, and I guess I will be a cash boy in a store. Pa says he thinks I was cut out for a bunko steerer, and I may look for that kind of a job. Pa he is a terror since he got to drinking again. He came home the other day, when the minister was calling on Ma, and just cause the minister was sitting on the sofa with Ma, and had his hand on her shoulder, where she said the pain was when the rheumatiz came on, Pa was mad and told the minister he would kick his liver clear around on the other side if he caught him there again, and Ma felt awful about it. After the minister had gone away, Ma told Pa he had got no feeling at all, and Pa said he had got enough feeling for one family, and he didn't want no sky-sharp to help him. He said he could cure all the rheumatiz there was around his house, and then he went down town and didn't get home till most breakfast time. Ma says she thinks I am responsible for Pa's falling into bad ways again, and now I am

PA WAS MAD JUST BECAUSE THE MINISTER HAD HIS HAND ON HER SHOULDERS.

going to cure him. You watch me, and see if I don't have Pa in the church in less than a week, praying and singing, and going home with the choir singers, just as pious as ever. I am going to get a boy that writes a woman's hand, to write to Pa, and—but I must not give it away. But you just watch Pa, that's all. Well, I must go and saw some wood. It is coming down a good deal, from a drug clerk to sawing wood, but I will get on top yet, and don't you forget it."

CHAPTER XXV

HIS PA KILLS HIM

A genius at whistling—A fur-lined cloak a sure cure for consumption—Another letter sent to the old man—He resolves on immediate punishment—The bladder-buffer—The explosion—A tragic scene—His Pa vows to reform.

"For heaven's sake dry up that whistling," said the grocery man to the bad boy, as he sat on a bag of peanuts, whistling and filling his pockets. "There is no sense in such whistling. What do you whistle for, anyway?"

"I am practicing my profession," said the boy, as he got up and stretched himself, and cut off a slice of cheese, and took a few crackers. "I have always been a good whistler, and I have decided to turn my talent to account. I am going to hire an office and put out a sign, 'Boy furnished to whistle for lost dogs.' You see there are dogs lost every day, and any man would give half a dollar to a boy to find his dog. I can hire out to whistle for dogs, and can go around whistling and enjoying myself, and make money. Don't you think it a good scheme?" asked the boy of the grocery man.

"Naw," said the grocery man, as he charged the cheese to the boy's father, and picked up his cigar stub, which he had left on the counter, and which the boy had rubbed on the kerosene barrel. "No, sir, the whistle would scare any dog that heard it. Say, what was your Pa running after the doctor in his shirt sleeves for last Sunday morning? He looked scared. Was your Ma sick again?"

"O, no, Ma is healthy enough, now she has got a new fur-lined cloak. She played consumption on Pa and coughed so she like to raise her lights and liver, and made Pa believe that she couldn't live, and got the doctor to prescribe a fur-lined circular, and Pa went and got one, and Ma has improved awfully. Her cough is all gone and she can walk ten miles. I was the one that was sick. You see, I wanted to get Pa into the church again, and get him to stop drinking, so I got a boy to write a letter to him in

PA SAID, "NOW HENNERY."

a female hand, and sign the name of a choir singer Pa was mashed on, and tell him she was yearning for him to come back to the church, and that the church seemed blank without his smiling face, and benevolent heart, and to please come back for her sake. Pa got the letter Saturday night and he seemed tickled, but I guess he dreamed about it all night, and Sunday morning he was mad, and he took me by the ear and said I couldn't come no 'Daisy' business on him the second time. He said he knew I wrote the letter, and for me to go up to the store room and prepare for the almightiest licking a boy ever had, and he went down stairs and broke up an apple barrel and got a stave to whip me with. Well I had to think mighty quick, but I was enough for him. I got a dried bladder in my room, one that me and my chum got to the slaughter house, and blowed it partly up, so it would be sort of flat-like, and I put it down inside of the back part of my pants, right about where Pa hits when he punishes me. I knowed when the barrel stave hit the bladder it would explode. Well, Pa he came up and found me crying. I can cry just as easy as you can turn on water at the faucet, and Pa took off his coat and looked sorry. I was afraid he would give up whipping me when he see me cry and I wanted the bladder experiment to go on, so I looked kind of hard, as if I was defying him to do his worst, and then he took me by the neck and laid me across a trunk. I didn't dare struggle much for fear the bladder would loose itself, and Pa said, 'Now Hennery, I am going to break you of this dam foolishness, or I will break your back,' and he spit on his hands and brought the barrel stave down on my best pants. Well, you'd a dide if you had heard the explosion. It almost knocked me off the trunk. It sounded like firing a fire-cracker away down cellar in a barrel, and Pa looked scared, I rolled off the trunk, on the floor, and put some flour on my face, to make me look pale, and then I kind of kicked my legs like a fellow who is dying on the stage after being stabbed with a piece of lath, and groaned and said, 'Pa you have killed me, but I forgive you,' and then rolled around, and frothed at the mouth, cause I had a piece of soap in my mouth to make foam. Well, Pa was broken up. He said, 'Great God, what have I done? I have broken his spinal column. O, my poor boy do not die!' I kept chewing the soap and foaming at the mouth, and I drew up my legs and kicked and clutched my chair, and rolled my eyes, and then kicked Pa in the stummick as he bent over me, and knocked the breath out of him, and then my limbs began to get rigid, and I said, 'Too late, Pa, I die at the hand of an assassin. Go for a doctor.' Pa throwed his coat over me, and started down stairs on a run, 'I have murdered my brave boy,' and he told Ma to go upstairs and stay with me, cause I had fallen off a trunk and ruptured a blood vessel, and he went after a doctor. When he went out the front door, I sat up and lit a cigarette, and Ma came up and I told her all about how I fooled Pa, and if she would take on and cry, when Pa got back, I would get him to go to church again, and swear off drinking and she said she would.

"So when Pa and the doc. came back, Ma was sitting on a velocipede I used to ride, which was in the store-room, and she had her apron over her face, and she just more than bellowed. Pa he was pale and he told the doc. he was just playing with me with a little piece of board and he heard something crack, and he guessed my spine got broke falling off the trunk. The doctor wanted to feel where my spine was broke, but I opened my eyes and had a vacant kind of stare, like a woman who leads a dog by a string, and looked as though my mind was wandering, and I told the doctor there was no use setting my spine as it was broke in several places and I wouldn't let him feel of the dried bladder. I told Pa I was going to die and I wanted him to promise me two things on my dying bed. He cried and said he would, and I told him to promise me he would quit drinking, and attend church regular, and he said he would never drink another drop, and would go to church every Sunday. I made him get down on his knees beside me and swear it, and the doc. witnessed it, and Ma said she was so glad, and Ma called the doctor out in the hall and told him the joke, and the doc. came in and told Pa he was afraid Pa's presence would excite the patient, and for him to put on his coat and go out and walk around the block, or go to church, and Ma and he would remove me to another room, and do all that was possible to make my last hours pleasant. Pa he cried and said he would put on his plug hat and go to church, and he kissed me and got flour on his nose, and I came near laughing right out, to see the white flour on his red nose, when I thought how the people in church would laugh at Pa. But he went out feeling mighty bad, and then I got up and pulled the bladder out of my pants, and Ma and the doc. laughed awful. When Pa got back from church and asked for me, Ma said that I had gone down town. She said the doctor found my spine was only uncoupled and he coupled it together, and I was all right. Pa said it was 'Almighty strange, cause I heard the spine break, when I struck him with the barrel stave.' Pa was nervous all the afternoon, and Ma thinks he suspects that we played it on him. Say, you don't think there is any harm in playing it on an old man a little for a good cause, do you?"

The grocery man said he supposed, in the interest of reform, it was all right, but if it was his boy that played such tricks he would take an ax to him, and the boy went out, apparently encouraged, saying he hadn't seen the old man since the day before, and he was almost afraid to meet him.

CHAPTER XXVI

HIS PA MORTIFIED

Searching for sewer gas—The powerful odor of limberger cheese at church—The after meeting—Fumigating the house—The bad boy resolves to board at an hotel.

"WHAT was the health officer doing over to your house this morning?" said the grocery man to the bad boy, as the youth was firing frozen potatoes at the man who collects garbage in the alley.

"O, they are searching for sewer gas and such things and they have got plumbers and other society experts till you can't rest, and I came away for fear they would find the sewer gas and warm my jacket. Say, do you think it is right, when anything smells awfully to always lay it to a boy?"

"Well, in nine cases out of ten they would hit it right, but what do you think is the trouble over to your house, honest?"

"Sh-h! Now don't breathe a word of it to a living soul or I am a dead boy. You see I was over to the dairy fair at the exposition building Saturday night, and when they were breaking up, me and my chum helped to carry boxes of cheese and firkins of butter, and a cheese-man gave each of us a piece of limberger cheese, wrapped up in tin foil. Sunday morning I opened my piece, and it made me tired. O, it was the offulest smell I ever heard of, except the smell when they found a tramp who hung himself in the woods on the Whitefish Bay road, and had been dead three weeks. It was just like a old back number funeral. Pa and Ma were just getting ready to go to church, and I cut off a piece of cheese and put it in the inside pocket of Pa's vest, and I put another in the lining of Ma's muff, and they went to church. I went down to church, too, and sat on a back seat with my chum, looking just as pious as though I was taking up a collection. The church was pretty warm, and by the time they got up to sing the first hymn Pa's cheese began to smell a match against Ma's cheese. Pa held one side of the hymn book and Ma held the other, and Pa he always sings for all that is out, and when he braced himself and sang 'Just as I am,' Ma thought Pa's voice was tinctured a little with billiousness and she looked at him, and hunched him and told him to stop singing and breathe through his nose, cause his breath was enough to stop a clock. Pa stopped singing and turned around kind of cross towards Ma, and then he smelled Ma's cheese, and he turned his head the other way and said, 'Whew,' and they didn't sing any more, but they looked at each other as though they smelled frowy. When they sat down they sat as far apart as they could get, and Pa sat next to a woman who used to be a nurse in a hospital, and when she smelled Pa's cheese she looked at him as though she thought he hed the small-pox, and she held her handkerchief to her nose. The man in the other end of the pew, that Ma sat near, he was a stranger from Racine, who belongs to our church, and he looked at Ma sort of queer, and after the minister prayed, and they got up to sing again, the man took his hat and went out, and when he came by me he said something in a whisper about a female glue factory.

"Well, sir, before the sermon was over everybody in that part of the church had their handkerchiefs to their noses, and they looked at Pa and Ma scandalous, and the two ushers they come around in the pews looking for a dog, and when the minister got over his sermon, and wiped the perspiration off his face, he said he would like to have the trustees of the church stay after meeting, as there was some business of importance to transact. He said the question of proper ventilation and sewerage for the church would be brought up, and that he presumed the congregation had noticed this morning that the church was unusually full of sewer gas. He said he had spoken of the matter before, and he expected it would be attended to before this. He said he was a meek and humble follower of the lamb, and was

HE SAID HE WAS A WEAK AND HUMBLE FOLLOWER OF THE LAMB.

willing to cast his lot wherever the Master decided, but he would be blessed if he would preach any longer in a church that smelled like a bone boiling establishment. He said religion was a good thing, but no person could enjoy religion as well in a fat rending establishment as he could in a flower garden, and as far as he was concerned he had got enough. Everybody looked at everybody else, and Pa looked at Ma as though he knew where the sewer gas came from, and Ma looked at Pa real mad, and me and my chum lit out, and went home and distributed my cheese all around. I put a slice in Ma's bureau drawer, down under her underclothes, and a piece in the spare room, under the bed, and a piece in the bath-room in the soap-dish, and a slice in the album on the parlor table, and a piece in the library in a book, and I went to the dining-room and put some under the table, and dropped a piece under the range in the kitchen. I tell you the house was loaded for bear. Ma came home from church first, and when I asked where Pa was, she said she hoped he had gone to walk around a block to air hisself. Pa came home to dinner, and when he got a smell of the house he opened all the doors, and Ma put a comfortable around her shoulders and told Pa he was a disgrace to civilization. She tried to get Pa to drink some carbolic acid. Pa finally convinced Ma it was not him, and then they decided it was the house that smelled so, as well as the church, and all Sunday afternoon they went visiting, and this morning Pa went down to the health office and got the inspector of nuisances to come up to the house, and when he smelled around a spell he said there was dead rats in the main sewer pipe, and they sent for plumbers, and Ma went out to a neighbors to borry some fresh air, and when the plumbers began to dig up the floor in the basement I came over here. If they find any of that limberg cheese it will go hard with me. The hired girls have both quit, and Ma says she is going to break up keeping house and board. That is just into my hand. I want to board at a hotel, where you can have bill-of-fare and tooth picks, and billiards, and everything. Well I guess I will go over to the house and stand in the back door and listen to the mocking bird. If you see me come flying out of the alley with my coat tail full of boots you can bet they have discovered the sewer gas."

CHAPTER XXVII

HIS PA BROKE UP

The bad boy don't think the grocer fit for heaven—He is very severe on his old friend—The need of a new revised edition—The bad boy turns reviser—His Pa reaches for the poker—A special providence—The sled slewed!—His Pa under the mules.

"WELL, I guess I will go to hell. I will see you later," said the bad boy to the grocery man, as he held a cracker under the faucet of the syrup keg, and then sat down on a soap box by the stove and proceeded to make a lunch, while the grocery man charged the boy's father with a gallon of syrup and a pound of crackers.

"What do you mean, you profane wretch, talking about meeting me later in Hades?" said the indignant grocery man. "I expect to pass by the hot place where you are sizzling, and go to the realms of bliss, where there is one continued round of happiness, and angels playing on golden harps and singing hymns of praise."

"Why, Pa says I will surely go to hell, and I thought you would probably be there, as it costs something to get to heaven, and you can get to the other place for nothing. Say, you would be a healthy delegate to go to heaven, with a lot of girl angels, wouldn't you, smelling of frowy butter, as you always do, and kerosene, and herring, and bar soap, and cheese, and rotten potatoes. Say, an angel wouldn't stay on the same golden street with you, without holding her handkerchief to her nose, and you couldn't get in there, anyway, cause you would want to pay your entrance fee out of the store."

"Say, you get out of here, condemn you. You are getting sassy. There is no one that is more free hearted than I am," said the grocery man.

"O, give us a *siesta*. I am on to you bigger than an elevator. When they had the oyster sociable at the church you gave four pounds of musty crackers with worms in, and they tasted of kerosene, and when the minister prayed for those who had generously contributed to the sociable, you raised up your head as though you wanted them all to know he meant you. If a man can get to heaven on four pounds of musty crackers, done up in a paper that has been around mackerel, then what's the use of a man being good, and giving sixteen ounces to the pound? But, there, don't blush and cry. I will use my influence to get your feet onto the golden streets of the New Jerusalem, but you have got to quit sending those small potatoes to our house, with a few big ones on top of the basket. I'll tell you how it was that Pa told me I would go to hell. You see Pa has been reading out of an old back number bible, and Ma and me argued with him about getting a new revised edition. We told him that the old one was all out of style, and that all the neighbors had the newest cut in bibles, with dolman sleeves, and gathered in the back, and they put on style over us, and we could not hold up our heads in society when it was known that we were wearing the old last year's bible. Pa kicked against it, but finally got one. I thought I had as much right to change things in the revised bible, as the other fellows had to change the old one, so I pasted some mottoes and patent-medicine advertisements in it, after the verses. Pa never reads a whole chapter, but reads a verse or two and skips around. Before breakfast, the other morning, Pa got the new bible and started to read the ten commandments and some other things. The first thing Pa struck was, 'Verily I say unto you, try St. Jacob's oil for rheumatism.' Pa looked over his specs at Ma, and then looked at me, but I had my face covered with my hands, sort of pious. Pa said he didn't think it was just the thing to put advertisements in the bible, but Ma said she didn't know as it was any worse than to have a patent medicine notice next to Beecher's sermon in the religious paper. Pa sighed and turned over a few leaves, and read, 'Thou shalt not covet thy neighbor's wife, nor his ox, if you love me as I love you no knife can cut our love in two.' That last part was a motto that I got out of a paper of candy. Pa said that the sentiment was good, but he didn't think the revisers had improved the old commandment very much. Then Pa turned over and read, 'Take a little wine for the stomach's sake, and keep a bottle of Reed's Gilt Edged tonic on your side-board, and you can defy malaria, and chills and fever.'

PA FOLLOWED ME AS FAR AS THE SIDEWALK.

Pa was hot. He looked at it again, and noticed that the tonic commandment was on yellow paper, and the corner curled up and Pa took hold of it, and the paste that I stuck it on with was not good, and it come off, and when I saw Pa lay down the bible, and put his spectacles in the case, and reach for the fire poker, I knew he was not going to pray, and I looked out the window and yelled dog fight, and I lit out, and Pa followed me as far as the sidewalk, and it was that morning when it was so slippery, and Pa's feet slipped out from under him, and he stood on his neck, and slid around on his ear, and the special providence of sleet on the sidewalk saved me. Say, do you believe in special providence? What was the use of that sleet on the sidewalk, if it was not to save sinners?"

"O, I don't know anything about special providence," said the grocery man, "but I know you have got two of your pockets filled with them boneless raisins since you have been talking, and my opinion is you will steal. But, say, what is your Pa on crutches for? I see him hobbling down town this morning. Has he sprained his ankle?"

"Well, I guess his ankle got sprained with all the rest. You see, my chum and me went bobbing, and Pa said he supposed he used to be the greatest bobber, when he was a boy, that ever was. He said he used to slide down a hill that was steeper than a church steeple. We asked him to go with us, and we went to that street that goes down by the depot, and we had two sleds hitched together, and there were more'n a hundred boys, and Pa wanted to steer, and he got on the front sled, and when we got about half way down the sled slewed, and my chum and me got off all right, but Pa got shut up between the two sleds, and the other boys behind they all run over Pa and one sled runner caught him in the trousers' leg, and dragged him over the slippery ice clear to the bottom, and the whole lay-out run into the street car, and the mules got wild and kicked, and Pa's suspenders broke, and when my chum and me got down there was Pa under the car, and a boy's boots was in Pa's shirt bosom, and another boy was straddle of Pa's neck, and the crowd rushed up from the depot, and got Pa out, and began to yell 'fire,' and 'police,' and he kicked at a boy that was trying to get his sled out of the small of Pa's back, and a policeman came along and pushed Pa and said, 'Go away from here, ye owld divil, and let the b'ys enjoy themselves;' and he was going to arrest Pa, when me and my chum told him we would take Pa home. Pa said the hill was not steep enough for him or he wouldn't have fell off. He is offul stiff to-day, but he says he will go skating with us next week, and show us how to skate. Pa means well, but he don't realize that he is getting stiff and can't be as kitteny as he used to be. He is very kind to me. If I had some fathers I would have been a broken-backed disfigured angel long ago. Don't you think so?"

The grocery man said he was sure of it, and the boy got out with his boneless raisins, and pocket full of lump sugar.

CHAPTER XXVIII

HIS PA GOES SKATING

The bad boy carves a turkey—His Pa's fame as a skater—The old man essays to skate on rollers—His wild capers—He spreads himself—Holidays a condemned nuisance—The bad boy's Christmas presents.

"WHAT is that stuff on your shirt bosom, that looks like soap grease?" said the grocery man to the bad boy, as he came into the grocery the morning after Christmas.

The boy looked at his shirt front, put his fingers on the stuff and smelled of his fingers, and then said, "O, that is nothing but a little of the turkey dressing and gravy. You see after Pa and I got back from the roller skating rink yesterday, Pa was all broke up, and he couldn't carve the turkey, and I had to do it, and Pa sat in a stuffed chair with his head tied up and a pillow amongst his legs, and he kept complaining that I didn't do it right. Gol darn a turkey any way. I should think they would make a turkey flat on the back, so he would lay on a greasy platter without skating all around the table. It looks easy to see Pa carve a turkey, but when I speared into the bosom of that turkey, and began to saw on it, the turkey rolled around as though it was on castors, and it was all that I could do to keep it out of Ma's lap. But I rassled with it till I got off enough white meat for Pa and Ma, and dark meat enough for me, and I dug out the dressing, but most of it flew into my shirt bosom, cause the string that tied up the place where the dressing was concealed about the person of the turkey, broke prematurely, and one oyster hit Pa in the eye, and he said I was as awkward as a cross-eyed girl trying to kiss a man with a hair lip. If I ever get to be the head of a family I shall carve turkeys with a corn sheller."

"But what broke your Pa up at the roller skating rink?" asked the grocery man.

"O, everything broke him up. He is split up so Ma buttons the top of his pants to his collar button, like a bicycle rider. Well, he had no business to have told me and my

EVERYBODY GOT OUT OF THE WAY EXCEPT A GIRL.

chum that he used to be the best skater in North America, when he was a boy. He said he skated once from Albany to New York in an hour and eighty minutes. Me and my chum thought that if Pa was such a terror on skates we could get him to put on a pair of roller skates, and enter him as the 'great unknown,' and clean out the whole gang.

We told Pa that he must remember that roller skates were different from ice skates, and that maybe he couldn't skate on them, but he said it didn't make any difference what they were as long as they were skates, and he would just paralyze the whole crowd. So we got a pair of big roller skates for him, and while we were strapping them on, Pa he looked at the skaters glide around on the smooth wax floor just as though they were greased. Pa looked at the skates on his feet, after they were fastened, sort of forlorn like, the way a horse they were greased. Pa looked at the skates on his feet, after they were fastened, sort of forlorn like, the way a horse thief does when they put shackles on his legs, and I told him if he was afraid he couldn't skate with them, we would take them off, but he said he would beat anybody there was there, or bust a suspender. Then we straightened Pa up, and pointed him toward the middle of the room, and he said 'leggo,' and we just give him a little push to start him, and he began to go. Well, by gosh, you'd a dide to have seen Pa try to stop. You see, you can't stick in your heel and stop, like you can on ice skates, and Pa soon found that out, and he began to turn sideways, and then he threw his arms and walked on his heels, and he lost his hat, and his eyes began to stick out, cause he was going right toward an iron post. One arm caught the post, and he circled around it a few times, and then he let go and began to fall, and sir, he kept falling all across the room, and everybody got out of the way, except a girl, and Pa grabbed her by the polonaise, like a drowning man grabs at straws, though there wasn't any straws in her polonaise as I know of, but Pa just pulled her along as though she was done up in shawl-strap, and his feet went out from under him and he struck on his shoulders and kept a going, with the girl dragging along like a bundle of clothes. If Pa had had another pair of roller skates on his shoulders, and castors on his ears, he couldn't have slid along any better. Pa is a short, big man, and as he was rolling along on his back, he looked like a sofa with castors on, being pushed across the room by a girl. Finally Pa came to the wall and had to stop, and the girl fell right across him with her roller skates in his neck, and she called him an old brute, and told him if he didn't let go of her polonaise she would murder him. Just then my chum and me got there, and we amputated Pa from the girl, and lifted him up and told him for heaven's sake to let

I GUESS IT KNOCKED THE BREATH OUT OF HIM.

us take off the skates, 'cause he couldn't skate any more than a cow, and Pa was mad and said for us to let him alone, and he could skate all right, and we let go, and he struck out again. Well, sir, I was ashamed. An old man like Pa ought to know better than to try to be a boy. This last time Pa said he was going to spread himself, and if I am any judge of a big spread, he did spread himself. Somehow the skates had got turned around sideways on his feet; and his feet got to going in different directions, and Pa's feet were getting so far apart that I was afraid I would have two Pa's half the size, with one leg apiece.

"I tried to get him to take up a collection of his legs, and get them both in the same ward but his arms flew around and one hit me on the nose, and I thought if he wanted to strike the best friend he had, he could run his old legs hisself. When he began to separate I could hear the bones crack, but maybe it was his pants, but anyway he came down on the floor like one of those fellows in a circus who spreads hisself, and he kept going and finally he surrounded an iron post with his legs, and stopped, and looked pale, and the proprietor of the rink told Pa if he wanted to give a flying trapeze performance he would have to go to the gymnasium, and he couldn't skate on his shoulders any more, cause other skaters were afraid of him. Then Pa said he would kick the liver out of the proprietor of the rink, and he got up and steadied himself, and he tried to kick the man, but both heels went up to onct, and Pa turned a back somersault and struck right on his vest in front. I guess it knocked the breath out of him, for he didn't speak for a few minutes, and then he wanted to go home, and we put him in a street car, and he laid down on the hay and rode home. O, the work we had to get Pa's clothes off. He had cricks in his back, and everywhere, and Ma was away to one of the neighbors, to look at the presents, and I had to put liniment on Pa, and I made a mistake and got a bottle of furniture polish, and put it on Pa and rubbed it in, and when Ma came home, Pa smelled like a coffin at a charity funeral, and Ma said there was no way of getting that varnish off of Pa till it wore off. Pa says holidays are a condemned nuisance anyway. He will have to stay in the house all this week."

"You are pretty rough on the old man," said the grocery man, "after he has been so kind to you and given you nice presents."

"Nice presents nothing. All I got was a 'Come to Jesus' Christmas card, with brindle fringe, from Ma, and Pa gave me a pair of his old suspenders, and a calender with mottoes for every month, some quotations from scripture, such as 'Honor thy father and thy mother,' and 'Evil communications corrupt two in a bush,' and 'A bird in the hand beats two pair.' Such things don't help a boy to be good. What a boy wants is club skates, and seven shot revolvers, and such things. Well, I must go and help Pa roll over in bed, and put on a new porous plaster. Good-bye."

CHAPTER XXIX

HIS PA GOES CALLING

His Pa starts forth—A picture of the old man "full"—Politeness at a winter picnic—Assaulted by sandbaggers—Resolved to drink no more coffee—A girl full of "aig-nogg."

SAY, you are getting too all-fired smart," said the grocery man to the bad boy as he pushed him into a corner by the molasses barrel, and took him by the neck and chocked him so his eyes stuck out. "You have driven away several of my best customers, and now, confound you, I am going to have your life," and he took up a cheese knife and began to sharpen it on his boot.

"What's the—gurgle—matter?" asked the choking boy, as the grocery man's fingers let up on his throat a little, so he could speak. "I hain't done nothin."

"Didn't you hang up that dead gray Tom cat by the heels, in front of my store, with the rabbits I had for sale? I didn't notice it until the minister called me out in front of the store, and pointing to the rabbits, asked what good fat cats were selling for. By crimus, this thing has got to stop. You have got to move out of this ward or I will."

The boy got his breath and said it wasn't him that put the cat up there. He said it was the policeman, and he and his chum saw him do it and he just come in to tell the grocery man about it, and before he could speak he had his neck nearly pulled off. The boy began to cry and the grocery man said he was only joking, and gave him a box of sardines, and they made up. Then he asked the boy how his Pa put in his New Years, and the boy sighed and said:

"We had a sad time at our house New Years. Pa in-

HE SAID IT WAS A FRIEND OF HIS.

sisted on making calls, and Ma and me tried to prevent it, but he said he was of age and guessed he could make calls if he wanted to, so he looked at the morning paper and got the names of all the places where they were going to receive, and he turned his paper collar, and changed ends with his cuffs, and put some arnica on his handkerchief, and started out. Ma told him not to drink anything, and he said he wouldn't, but he did. He was full the third place he went to. O, *so* full. Some men can get full and not show it, but when Pa gets full, he gets so full his back teeth float, and the liquor crowds his eyes out, and his mouth gets loose and wiggles all over his face, and he laughs all the time, and the perspiration just oozes out of him, and his face gets red, and he walks *so* wide. O, he disgraced us all. At one place he wished the hired girl a happy New Year more than twenty times, and hung his hat on her elbow, and tried to put on a rubber hall mat for his overshoes. At another place he walked up a lady's train, and carried away a card basket full of bananas and oranges. Ma wanted my chum and me to follow Pa and bring him home, and about dark we found him in the door yard of a house where they have statues in front of the house, and he grabbed me by the arm, and mistook me for another caller, and insisted on introducing me to a marble statue without any clothes on. He said it was a friend of his, and it was a winter picnic. He hung his hat on an evergreen, and put his overcoat on the iron fence, and I was so mortified I almost cried. My chum said if his Pa made such a circus of himself he would sand-bag him. That gave me an idea, and when we got Pa most home I went and got a paper box covered with red paper, so it looked just like a brick, and a bottle of tomato ketchup, and when we got Pa up on the steps at home I hit him with the paper brick, and my chum squirted the ketchup on his head, and demanded his money, and then he yelled murder, and we lit out, and Ma and the minister, who was making a call on her, all the afternoon, they came to the door and pulled Pa in. He said he had been attacked by a band of robbers, and they knocked his brains out, but he whipped them, and then Ma saw the ketchup brains oozing out of his head, and she screamed, and the minister said, 'Good heavens he is murdered,' and just then I came in the back door and they sent me after the doctor, and they put Pa on the lounge and tied up his head with a towel to keep the brains in, and Pa began to snore, and when the doctor came in it took them half an hour to wake him, and then he was awful sick to his stummick, and then Ma asked the doctor if he would live, and the doc. analyzed the ketchup and smelled of it and told Ma he would be all right if he had a little Worcester sauce to put on with the ketchup, and when he said Pa would pull through, Ma looked awful sad. Then Pa opened his eyes and saw the minister and said that was one of the robbers that jumped on him, and he wanted to whip the minister, but the doc. held Pa's arms, and Ma sat on his legs, and the minister said he had got some other calls to make, and he wished Ma a happy new year in the hall, much as fifteen minutes. His happy new year to Ma is most as long as his prayers. Well, we got Pa to bed, and when we undressed him we found nine napkins in the bosom of his vest, that he had picked up at the places where he called He is all right this morning, but he says it is the last time he will drink coffee when he makes New Year's calls."

"Well, then you didn't have much fun yourself on New Years. That's too bad," said the grocery man, as he looked at the sad-eyed youth. "But you look hard. If you were old enough I should say you had been drunk, your eyes are so red."

"Didn't have any fun eh? Well, I wish I had as many dollars as I had fun. You see, after Pa got to sleep Ma wanted me and my chum to go to the houses that Pa had called at and return the napkins he had kleptomaniaced, so we dressed up and went. The first house we called at the girls were sort of demoralized. I don't know as I ever saw a girl drunk, but those girls acted queer. The callers had stopped coming, and the girls were drinking something out of shaving cups that looked like lather, and they said it was 'aig-nogg.' They laffed and kicked up their heels wuss nor a circus, and their collars got unpinned, and their faces was red, and they put their arms around me and my chum and hugged us and asked us if we didn't want some of the custard. You'd a dide to see me and my chum drink that lather. It looked just like soap suds with nutmaig in it, but by gosh it got in its work sudden. At first I was afraid when the girls hugged me, but after I had drank a couple of shaving cups full of the 'aig-nogg' I wasn't afraid no more, and I hugged a girl so hard she catched her breath and panted, and said, 'O don't.' Then I kissed her, and she is a great big girl, bigger'n me, but she didn't care. Say, did you ever kiss a girl full of aig-nogg? If you did it would break up your grocery business. You would want to waller in bliss instead of selling mackerel. My chum ain't no slouch either. He was sitting in a stuffed chair holding another New Year's girl, and I could hear him kiss her so it sounded like a cutter scraping on bare ground. But the girl's Pa came in and said he guessed it was time to close the place, unless they had a license for an all night house, and me and my chum went out. But *wasn't* we sick when we got out doors. O, it seemed as though the pegs in my boots was the only thing that kept them down, and my chum he liked to dide. He had been to dinner and supper and I had only been skating all day, so he had more to contend with than I did. O, my, but that lets me out on aig-nogg. I don't know how I got home, but I got in bed with Pa, cause Ma was called away to attend a baby matinee in the night. I don't know how it is, but there never is anybody in our part of the town that has a baby but they have it in the night, and they

I WAS NOT AFRAID NO MORE.

send for Ma. I don't know what she has to be sent for every time for. Ma ain't to blame for all the young ones in this town, but she has got up a reputashun, and when we hear the bell ring in the night Ma gets up and begins to put on her clothes, and the next morning she comes in the dining room with a shawl over her head; and says, 'It's a girl and weighs ten pounds,' or a boy, if it's a boy baby. Ma was out on one of her professional engagements, and I got in bed with Pa. I had heard Pa blame Ma about her cold feet, so I got a piece of ice about as big as a raisin box, just zactly like one of Ma's feet, and I laid it right against the small of Pa's back. I couldn't help laffin, but pretty soon Pa began to squirm and he said, 'Why'n 'ell don't you warm them feet before you come to bed?' and then he hauled back his leg and kicked me clear out in the middle of the floor, and said if he married again he would marry a woman who had lost both of her feet in a railroad accident. Then I put the ice back in the bed with Pa and went to my room, and in the morning Pa said he sweat more'n a pail full in the night. Well you must excuse me. I have an engagement to shovel snow off the sidewalk. But before I go, let me advise you not to drink aig-nogg, and don't sell tom cats for rabbits," and he got out the door just in time to miss the rutabaga that the grocery man threw at him.

CHAPTER XXX

HIS PA DISSECTED

The miseries of the mumps—No pickles thank you—One more effort to reform the old man—The bad boy plays medical student—Proceeds to dissect his Pa—"Gentlemen I am not dead!"—Saved from the scalpel!—"No more whisky for you."

"I UNDERSTAND your Pa has got to drinking again like a fish," says the grocery man to the bad boy, as the youth came in the grocery and took a hand full of dried apples. The boy ate a dried apple and then made up a terrible face, and the grocery man asked him what he was trying to do with his face. The boy caught his breath and then said:

"Say, don't you know any better than to keep dried apples where a boy can get hold of them when he has got the mumps? You will kill some boy yet by such dum carelessness. I thought there were sweet dried apples, but they are sour as a boarding-house keeper, and they make me tired. Didn't you ever have the mumps? Gosh, but don't it hurt though? You have got to be darned careful when you have the mumps, and not go out bob-sledding, or skating, or you will have your neck swell up biggern a milk pail. Pa says he had the mumps once when he was a boy and it broke him all up."

"Well, never mind the mumps, how about your Pa spreeing it? Try one of those pickles in the jar there, won't you? I always like to have a boy enjoy himself when he comes to see me," said the grocery man, winking to a man who was filling an old fashioned tin box with tobacco out of the pail, who winked back as much as to say, "If that boy eats a pickle on top of them mumps we will have a circus, sure."

"You can't play no pickle on me, not when I have the mumps. Ma passed the pickles to me this morning, and I took one mouthful, and like to had the lockjaw. But Ma didn't do it on purpose, I guess. She never had the mumps and didn't know how discouraging a pickle is. Darn if I didn't feel as though I had been struck in the butt of the ear with a brick. But about Pa. He has been fuller'n a goose ever since New Year's day. I thing it's wrong for women to tempt feeble minded persons with liquor on New Year's. Now me and my chum, we can take a drink and then let it alone. We have got brains, and know when we have got enough, but Pa, when he gets to going don't ever

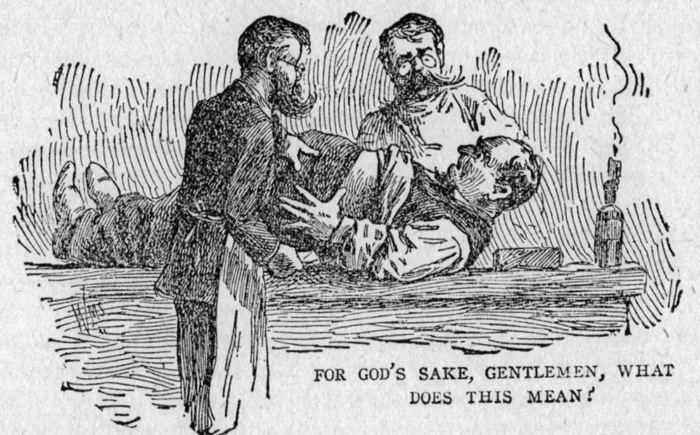

FOR GOD'S SAKE, GENTLEMEN, WHAT DOES THIS MEAN?

stop until he gets so sick that he can't keep his stummick inside of hisself. It is getting so they look to me to brace Pa up every time he gets on a tear, and I guess I fixed him this time so he will never touch liquor again. I scared him so his bald head turned gray in a single night."

"What under the heavens have you done to him now?" says the grocery man, in astonishment. "I hope you haven't done anything you will regret in after years."

"Regret nothing," said the boy, as he turned the lid of the cheese box back and took the knife and sliced off a piece of cheese, and took a few crackers out of a barrel, and sat down on a soap box by the stove, "You see Ma was annoyed to death with Pa. He would come home full, when she had company, and lay down on the sofa and snore, and he would smell like a distillery. It hurt me to see ma cry, and I told her I would break Pa of drinking if she would let me, and she said if I would promise not to hurt Pa to go ahead, and I promised not to. Then I got my chum and another boy, quite a big boy, to help, and Pa is all right. We went down to the place where they sell arms and legs to folks who have served in the army, or a saw mill, or a threshing machine, and lost their limbs, and we borrowed some arms and legs, and fixed up a dissecting room. We fixed a long table in the basement, big enough to lay Pa out on you know, and then we got false whiskers and mustaches, and when Pa came in the house drunk and laid down on the sofa, and got to sleep, we took him and laid him out on the table, and took some trunk straps, and a sircingle and strapped him down to the table. He slept right along all through it, and we had another table with the false arms and legs on, and we rolled up our sleeves, and smoked pipes, just like I read that medical students do when they cut up a man. Well, you'd a dide to see Pa look at us when he woke up. I saw him open his eyes, and then we began to talk about cutting up dead men. We put hickory nuts in our mouths so our voices would sound different, so he wouldn't know us, and I was telling the other boys about what a time we had cutting up the last man we bought. I said he was awful tough, and when we had got his legs off, and had taken out his brain, his friends came to the dissecting room and claimed the body, and we had to give it up, but I saved the legs. I looked at Pa on the table and he began to turn pale, and he squirmed around to get up, but found he was fast. I had pulled his shirt up under his arms, while he was asleep, and as he began to move, and I took an icicle, and in the dim light of the candles, that were sitting on the table in beer bottles, I drew the icicle across Pa's stummick, and I said to my chum, 'Doc, I guess we had better cut open this old duffer and see if he died from inflammation of the stummick, from hard drinking, as the coroner said he did.' Pa shuddered all over when he felt the icicle going over his bare stummick, and he said, 'For God's sake, gentlemen, what does this mean? I am not dead.'

"The other boys looked at Pa with astonishment, and I said, 'Well, we bought you for dead, and the coroner's jury said you were dead, and by the eternal, we ain't going to be fooled out of a corpse when we buy one, are we doc?' My chum said not if he knowed hisself, and the other students said, 'Of course he is dead. He thinks he is alive, but he died day before yesterday, fell dead on the street, and his folks said he had been a nuisance and they wouldn't claim the corpse, and we bought it at the morgue.' Then I drew the icicle across him again, and I said, 'I don't know about this, doctor. I find the blood follows the scalpel as I cut through the cuticle. Hand me the blood sponge please.' Pa

THAT'S A PRETTY NARROW ESCAPE, OLD MAN.

began to wiggle around, and we looked at him, and my chum raised his eye-lid, and looked solemn, and Pa said, 'Hold on, gentlemen. Don't cut into me any more, and I can explain this matter. This is all a mistake. I was only drunk.' We went in a corner and whispered, and Pa kept talking all the time. He said if we would postpone the hog killing he could send and get witnesses to prove that he was not dead, but that he was a respectable citizen, and had a family. After we held a consultaticn I went to Pa and told him that what he said about being alive might possibly be true, though we had our doubts. We had found such cases before in our practice east, where men seemed to be alive, but it was only temporary. Before we had got them cut up they were dead enough for all practical purposes. Then I laid the icicle across Pa's abdomen, and went on to tell him that even if he *was* alive, it would be better for him to play that he was dead, because he was such a nuisance to his family that they did not want him, and I was telling him that I had heard that in his lifetime he was very cruel to his boy, a bright little fellow who was at the head of his class in Sunday school, and a pet wherever he was known, when Pa interrupted me and said, 'Doctor, please take that carving knife off my stummick, for it makes me nervous. As for that boy of mine, he is the condemndest little whelp in town, and he isn't no pet anywhere. Now, you let up on this dissecting business, and I will make it all right with you.' We held another consultation and then I told Pa that we did not feel that it was doing justice to society to give up the body of a notorious drunkard, after we had paid twenty dollars for the corpse. If there was any hopes that he would reform and try and lead a different life, it would be different, and I said to the boys, 'Gentlemen, we must do our duty. Doc, you dismember that leg, and I will attend to the stomach and the upper part of the body. He will be dead before we are done with him. We must remember that society has some claims on us, and not let our better natures be worked upon by the *post mortem* promises of a dead drunkard.'

Then I took my icicle and began fumbling around the abdomen portion of Pa's remains, and my chum took a rough piece of ice and began to saw his leg off, while the other boy took hold of the leg and said he would catch it when it dropped off. Well, Pa kicked like a steer. He said he wanted to make one more appeal to us, and we acted sort of impatient, but we let up to hear what he had to say. He said if we would turn him loose he would give us ten dollars more than we paid for his body, and that he would never drink another drop as long as he lived. Then we whispered some more, and then told him we thought favorably of his last proposition, but he must swear, with his hand on the leg of a corpse we were then dissecting, that he would never drink again, and then he must be blindfolded and be conducted several blocks away from the dissecting room, before we could turn him loose. He said that was all right, and so we blindfolded him, and made him take a bloody oath, with his hand on a piece of ice that we told him was a piece of another corpse, and then we took him out of the house and walked him around the block four times, and left him on a corner, after he had promised to send the money to an address that I gave him. We told him to stand still five minutes after we left him, then remove the blindfold, and go home. We watched him from behind a board fence, and he took off the handkerchief, looked at the name on a street lamp, and found he was not far from home. He started off saying, 'That's a pretty narrow escape, old man. No more whisky for you.' I did not see him again until this morning, and when I asked him where he was last night he shuddered and said, 'None of your darn business. But I never drink any more, you remember that.' Ma was tickled and she told me I was worth my weight in gold. Well, good-day. That cheese is musty." And the boy went and caught on a passing sleigh.

CHAPTER XXXI

HIS PA JOINS A TEMPERANCE SOCIETY

The grocery man sympathizes with the old man—Warns the bad boy that he may have a step-father!—The bad boy scorns the idea—Introduces his Pa to the grand "worthy dude!"—The solemn oath—The brand plucked from the burning.

"DON'T you think my Pa is showing his age a good deal more than usual?" asked the bad boy of the grocery man, as he took a smoked herring out of the box and peeled off the skin with a broken bladed jack-knife, and split it open and ripped off the bone, threw the head at a cat, and took some crackers and began to eat.

"Well, I don't know but he does look as though he was getting old," said the grocery man, as he took a piece of yellow wrapping paper, and charged the boy's poor old father with a dozen herrings and a pound of crackers; "but there is no wonder he is getting old. I wouldn't go through what your father has, the last year, for a million dollars. I tell you, boy, when your father is dead, and you get a step-father, and he makes you walk the chalk mark, you will realize what a bonanza you have fooled yourself out of by killing off your father. The way I figure it, your father will last about six months, and you ought to treat him right, the little time he has to live."

"Well, I am going to," said the boy, as he picked the herring bones out of his teeth with a piece of match that he sharpened with his knife. "But I don't believe in borrowing trouble about a step-father so long before hand. I don't think Ma could get a man to step into Pa's shoes as long as I lived, not if she was inlaid with diamonds, and owned a brewery. There are brave men, I know, that are on the marry, but none of them would want to be brevet father to a cherubim like me, except he got pretty good wages. And then, since Pa was dissected he is going to lead a different life, and I guess I will make a man of him, if he holds out. We got him to join the Good Templars last night."

"No, you don't tell me," said the grocery man, as he thought that his trade in cider for mince pies would be cut off. "So you got him in the Good Templars, eh?"

"Well, he thinks he has joined the Good Templars, so it is all the same. You see my chum and me have been going to a private gymnasium, on the west side, kept by a dutchman, and in a back room he has all the tools for getting up muscle. There, look at my arm," said the boy, as he rolled up his sleeve and showed a muscle about as big as an oyster. "That is the result of training at the gymnasium. Before I took lessons I hadn't any more muscle than you have got. Well, the dutchman was going to a dance on the south side the other night, and he asked my chum to tend the gymnasium, and I told Pa if he would join the Good Templars that night there wouldn't be many at the lodge, and he wouldn't be so embarrassed, as I was one of the officers of the lodge I would put it to him light, and he said he would go, so my chum got five other boys to help us put him through. So we steered him down to the gymnasium, and made him rap on the storm door outside, and I said, 'Who comes there?' and he said it was a pilgrim who wanted to jine our sublime order. I asked him if he had made up his mind to turn from the ways of a hyena, and adopt the customs of the truly good, and he said if he knew his own heart, he had, and then I told him to come in out of the snow and take off his pants. He kicked a little at taking off his pants, because it was cold out there in the storm-door dog house, but I told him they all had to do it. The princes, potentates and paupers all had to come to it. He asked me how it was when we initiated a woman, and I told him women never took that degree. He pulled off his pants, and wanted a check for them, but I told him the

Grand Mogul would hold his clothes, and then I blindfolded him, and with a base ball club I pounded on the floor as I walked around the gymnasium, while the lodge, headed by my chum, sung 'We won't go home till morning.' I stopped in front of the ice-water tank and said, 'Grand Worthy Duke, I bring before you a pilgrim who has drank of the dregs until his stomach won't hold water, and who desires to swear off.' The Grand Mogul asked me if he was worthy and well qualified, and I told him that he had been drunk more or less since the reunion last summer, which ought to qualify him. Then the Grand Mogul made Pa repeat the most blood-curdling oath, in which Pa agreed, if he ever drank another drop, to allow anybody to pull his toe-nails out with tweezers, to have his liver dug out and fed to dogs, his head chopped off, and his eyes removed. Then the Mogul said he would brand the candidate on the bare back with the initial letters of our order, 'G. T.,' that all might read how a brand had been snatched from the burning. You'd a dide to see Pa flinch when I pulled up his shirt, and got ready to brand him.

"My chum got a piece of ice out of the water cooler, and just as he clapped it on Pa's back I burned a piece of horse's hoof in the candle and held it to Pa's nose, and I guess Pa actually thought it was his burning skin that he smelled. He jumped about six feet and said, 'Great heavens, what you dewin!' and then he began to roll over a barrel which I had arranged for him. Pa thought he was going down cellar, and he hung to the barrel, but he was on top half the time. When Pa and the barrel got through fighting I was beside him, and I said, 'Calm yourself, and be prepared for the ordeal that is to follow.' Pa asked how much of this dum fooling there was, and said he was sorry he joined. He said he could let licker alone without having the skin all burned off his back. I told Pa to be brave and not weaken, and all would be well. He wiped the perspiration off his face on the end of his shirt, and we put a belt around his body and hitched it to a tackle, and pulled him up so his feet were just off the floor, and then we talked as though we were away off, and I told my chum to look out that Pa did not hit the gas fixtures, and Pa actually thought he was being hauled clear up to the roof. I could see he was scared by the complexion of his hands and feet, as they clawed the

BIMEBY WE LET HIM DOWN.

air. He actually sweat so the drops fell on the floor. Bimeby we let him down, and he was awfully relieved, thought his feet were not more than two inches from the floor any of the time. We were just going to slip Pa down a board with slivers in to give him a realizing sense of the rough road a reformed man was to travel, and got him straddle of the board, when the dutchman came home from the dance, fullern a goose and he drove us boys out, and we left Pa, and the dutchman said, 'Vot you vas doing here mit dose boys, you old duffer, and vere vas your pants?' and Pa pulled off his handkerchief from his eyes, and the dutchman said if he didn't get out in a holy minute he would kick the stuffing out of him, and Pa got out. He took his pants and put them on in the alley, and then we come up to Pa and told him that was the third time the drunken dutchman had broke up our lodge, but we should keep on doing good until we had reformed every drunkard in Milwaukee, and Pa said that was right, and he would see us through if it cost every dollar he had. Then we took him home, and when Ma asked if she couldn't join the lodge too, Pa said, 'Now you take my advice, and don't you ever join no Good Templars. Your system could not stand the racket. Say, I want you to put some cold cream on my back.' I think Pa will be a different man now, don't you?"

The grocery man said if he was that boy's Pa for fifteen minutes, he would be a different boy, or there would be a funeral, and the boy took a handful of soft-shelled almonds and few layer raisins, and skipped out.

CHAPTER XXXII

HIS PA'S MARVELOUS ESCAPE

The grocery man has no vaseline—The old man provides three fire escapes—One of the escapes tested—His Pa scandalizes the church —"She's a darling!"—Worldly music in the courts of Zion.

"GOT any vaseline?" said the bad boy to the grocery man, as he went into the store one cold morning, leaving the door open, and picked up a cigar stub that had been thrown down near the stove, and began to smoke it.

"Shut the door, dum you. Was you brought up in a saw mill? You'll freeze every potato in the house. No, I haven't got vaseline. What do you want of vaseline?" said the grocery man, as he sat the syrup keg on a chair by the stove where it would thaw out.

"Want to rub it on Pa's legs," said the boy, as he tried to draw smoke through the cigar stub.

"What is the matter with your Pa's legs? Rheumatiz?"

"Wuss nor rheumatiz," said the boy, as he threw away the cigar stub and drew some cider in a broken tea cup. "Pa has got the worst looking hind legs you ever saw. You see, since there has been so many fires Pa has got offul scared, and he has bought three fire escapes, made out of rope with knots in them, and he has been telling us every day how he could rescue the whole family in case of fire. He told us to keep cool, whatever happened, and to rely on him. If the house got on fire we were all to rush to Pa, and he would save us. Well, last night Ma had to go to one of the neighbors where they was going to have twins, and we didn't sleep much, cause Ma had to come home twice in the night to get saffron, and an old flannel petticoat that I broke in when I was a kid, cause the people where Ma went did not know as twins was on the bill of fare, and they only had flannel petticoat for one. Pa was cross at being kept awake, and told Ma he hoped when all the children in Milwaukee were born, and got grown up, she would take in her sign and not go around nights and act as usher to baby matinees. Pa says there ought to be a law that babies should arrive only on the regular day trains, and not wait for the midnight express. Well, Pa he got asleep, and he slept till about eight o'clock in the morning, and the blinds were closed, and it was dark in his room, and I had to wait for my breakfast till I was hungry as a wolf, and the girl told me to wake Pa up, so I went up-stairs, and I don't know what made me think of it, but I had some of this powder they make red fire with in the theater, that me and my chum had the 4th of July, and I put it in a washdish in the bath-room, and I touched it off and hollered fire. I was going to wake Pa up and tell him it was all right and laugh at him. I guess there was too much fire, or I yelled too loud, cause Pa jumped out of bed and grabbed a rope and rushed through the hall toward the back window, that goes out on the shed. I tried to say something, but Pa ran over me and told me to save myself, and I got to the back window to tell him there was no fire just as he let himself out of the window. He had one end of the rope tied to the leg of the washstand, and he was climbing down the back side of the shed by the kitchen, with nothing on but his nightshirt, and he was the horriblest looking object ever was, with his legs flying and trying to stick his toe nails into the rope and side of the house. I don't think a man looks well in society with nothing on but his nightshirt. I didn't blame the hired girls for being scared when they saw Pa and his legs coming down outside the window, and when they yelled I went down to the kitchen, and they said a crazy man with no clothes on but a pillow slip around his neck was trying to kick the window in, and they ran into the parlor, and I opened the door and let Pa in the kitchen. He asked me if anybody else was saved, and then I told him there was no fire, and he must have dreamed that he was in hell, or somewhere. Well, Pa was astonished. and said he must be wrong in the head, and I left him thawing himself by the stove while I went after his pants, and his legs were badly chilled, but I guess nothin' was froze. He lays it all to Ma, and says if she would stay at home and let people run their own baby shows, there would be more comfort in the house. Ma came in with a shawl over her head, and a bowl full of something that smelled frowy, and after she had told us what the result of her visit was, she sent me after vaseline to rub Pa's legs. Pa says he has demonstrated that if a man is cool and collected, in case of fire, and goes deliberately at work to save himself, he will come out all right."

I DIDN'T BLAME THE HIRED GIRLS FOR BEING SCARED.

"Well, you are the meanest boy I ever heard of," said the grocery man. "But what about your Pa's dancing a clog dance in church Sunday? The minister's hired girl was in here after some codfish yesterday morning, and she said the minister said your Pa had scandalized the church the worst way."

"O, he didn't dance in church. He was a little excited, that's all. You see, Pa chews tobacco, and it is pretty hard on him to sit all through a sermon without taking a chew, and he gets nervous. He always reaches around in his pistol pocket, when they stand up to sing the last time, and feels in his tobacco box and gets out a chew, and puts it in his mouth when the minister pronounces the benediction, and then when they get out doors he is all ready to spit. He always does that. Well, my chum had a present, on Christmas, of a music box, just about as big as Pa's tobacco box, and all you have to do is to touch a spring and it plays, 'She's a Daisy, She's a Dumpling.' I borrowed it and put it in Pa's pistol pocket, and when the choir got most through singing, Pa reached his hand in his pocket, and began to fumble around for a chew. He touched the spring, and just as everybody bowed their heads to receive the benediction, and it was so still you could hear a gum drop, the music box began to play, and in the stillness it sounded as loud as a church organ. Well, I thought Ma would sink. The minister heard it, and everybody looked at Pa, too, and Pa turned red, and the music box kept up, 'She's a Daisy,' and the minister looked mad and said 'Amen,' and the people began to put on their coats, and the minister told the deacon to hunt up the source of that worldly music, and they took Pa into the room back of the pulpit and searched him, and Ma says Pa will have to be churched. They kept the music box, and I have got to carry in coal to get money enough to buy my chum a new music box. Well, I shall have to go and get that vaseline or Pa's legs will suffer. Good-day."

CHAPTER XXXIII

HIS PA JOKES WITH HIM

The bad boy caught at last—How to grow a mustache—Tar and cayenne pepper—The grocery man's fate is sealed—Father and son join in a practical joke—Soft soap on the steps—Downfall of ministers and deacons—Ma to the rescue!—The bad boy gets even with his Pa.

"WHAT on earth is that you have got on your upper lip?" said the grocery man to the bad boy, as he came in and began to peel a rutabaga, and his upper lip hung down over his teeth, and was covered with something that looked like shoemaker's wax, 'You look as though you had been digging potatoes with your nose."

"O, that is some of Pa's darn smartness. I asked him if he knew anything that would make a boy's mustache grow. and he told me the best thing he ever tried was tar, and for me to rub it on thick when I went to bed, and wash it off in the morning. I put it on last night, and by gosh I can wash it off. Pa told me all I had to do was to use a scouring brick, and it would come off, and I used the brick, and it took the skin off, and the tar is there yet, and, say, does my lip look very bad?"

The grocery man told him it was the worst looking lip he ever saw, but he could cure it by rubbing a little cayenne pepper in the tar. He said the tar would neutralize the pepper, and the pepper would loosen the tar, and act as a cooling lotion to the lacerated lip. The boy went to a can of pepper behind the counter, and stuck his finger in and rubbed a lot of it on his lip, and then his hair began to raise, and he began to cry, and rushed to the water-pail and ran his face into the water to wash off the pepper. The grocery man laughed, and when the boy had got the pepper washed off, and had resumed his rutabaga, he said:

"That seals your fate. No man ever trifles with the feelings of the bold buccaneer of the Spanish main, without living to rue it. I will lay for you old man, and don't you forget it. Pa thought he was smart when he got me to put tar on my lip, to bring my mustache out, and to-day he lays on a bed of pain, and to-morrow your turn will come. You will regret that you did not get down on your knees and beg my pardon. You will be sorry that you did not prescribe cold cream for my bruised lip, instead of cayenne pepper. Beware, you base twelve ounces to the pound huckster, you gimlet-eyed seller of dog-sausage, you sanded sugar idiot, you small potato three card monte sleight of hand rotten egg fiend, you villain that sells smoked sturgeon and dog-fish for smoked halibut. The avenger is on your track."

"Look here, young man, don't you threaten me, or I will take you by the ear and walk you through green fields, and beside still waters, to the front door, and kick your pistol pocket clear around so you can wear it for a watch pocket in your vest. No boy can frighten me, by crimus! But tell me, how did you get even with your Pa?"

"Well, give me a glass of cider and we will be friends and I will tell you. Thanks! Gosh, but that cider is made out of mouldy dried apples and sewer water," and he took a handful of layer raisins off the top of a box to take the taste out of his mouth, and while the grocer charged a peck of rutabagas, a gallon of cider and two pounds of raisins to the boy's Pa, the boy proceeded: "You see, Pa likes a joke the best of anybody you ever saw, if it is on somebody else, but he kicks like a steer when it is on him. I asked him this morning if it wouldn't be a good joke to put some soft soap on the front step, so the letter carrier would slip up and spill hisself, and Pa said it would be elegant. Pa is a democrat, and he thinks that anything that will make it unpleasant for republican office holders, is legitimate, and he encouraged me to paralyze the letter-carrier. The letter-carrier is as old a man as Pa, and I didn't want to humiliate him, but I just wanted Pa to give his consent, so he couldn't kick if he got caught in his own trap. You see? Well, this morning the minister and two of the deacons called on Pa, to have a talk with him about his actions in church, on two or three occasions, when he pulled out the pack of cards with his handkerchief, and played the music box and they had a pretty hot time in the back parlor, and finally they settled it, and were going to sing a hymn, when Pa handed them a little hymn book, and the minister opened it and turned pale and said, 'What's this?' and they looked at it and it was a book of Hoyle's games instead of a hymn book. Gosh, wasn't the minister mad! He had started to read a hymn and he quit after he read two lines where it said, 'In a game of four handed euchre, never trump your partner's ace, but rely on the ace to take the trick on suit.' Pa was trying to explain how the book came to be there, when the minister and deacons started out, and then I poured the two quart tin pail full of soft soap on the front step. It was this white soap,

THE MINISTER AND TWO DEACONS.

just the color of the step, and when I got it spread I went down in the basement. The visitors came out and Pa was trying to explain to them about Hoyle, when one of the deacons stepped in the soap, and his feet flew up and he struck on his pants and slid down the steps. The minister said, 'Great heavens, deacon, are you hurt? let me assist you,' and he took two quick steps, and you have seen these fellows in a nigger show that kick each other head over heels and fall on their ears, and stand on their heads and turn round like a top. The minister's feet slipped and the next I saw he was standing on his head in his hat, and his legs were sort of wilted and fell limp by his side, and he fell over on his stomach. You talk about spreading the gospel in heathen lands! It is nothing to the way you can spread it with two quarts of soft soap. The minister didn't look pious a bit, when he was trying to catch the railing, he looked as though he wanted to murder every man on earth, but it may be he was tired.

"Well, Pa was paralyzed, and he and the other deacon rushed out to pick up the minister and the first old man, and when they struck the step they went kiting. Pa's feet somehow slipped backward, and he turned a somersault and struck full length on his back, and one heel was across the minister's neck, and he slid down the steps, and the other deacon fell all over the other three, and Pa swore at them, and it was the worst looking lot of pious people I ever saw. I think if the minister had been in the woods somewhere, where nobody could have heard him, he would have used language. They all seemed mad at each other. The hired girl told Ma there was three tramps out on the sidewalk fighting Pa, and Ma she took the broom and started to help Pa, and I tried to stop Ma, 'cause her constitution is not very strong and I didn't want her to do any flying trapeze bizness, but I couldn't stop her, and she went out with the broom and a towel tied around her head. Well, I don't know where Ma did strike, but when she came in she said she had palpitation of the heart, but that was not the place where she put the arnica. O, but she *did* go through the air like a bullet through cheese, and when she went down the steps a bumpity-bump, I felt sorry for Ma. The minister

TALK ABOUT SPREADING THE GOSPEL.

had got so he could sit up on the sidewalk, with his back against the lower step, when Ma came sliding down, and one of the heels of her gaiters hit the minister in the hair, and the other foot went right through between his arm and his side, and the broom like to pushed his teeth down his throat.

But he was not mad at Ma. As soon as he see it was Ma he said, 'Why, sister, the wicked stand in slippery places, don't they?' and Ma she was mad and said for him to let go her stocking, and then Pa was mad and he said, 'Look-a-here, you sky pilot, this thing has gone far enough,' and then a policeman came along, and first he thought they were all drunk, but he found they were respectable, and he got a chip and scraped the soap off of them, and they went home, and Pa and Ma they got in the house some way, and just then the letter-carrier came along, but he didn't have any letters for us, and he didn't come onto the steps, and then I went up stairs and I said, 'Pa, don't you think it is real mean, after you and I fixed the soap on the steps for the letter-carrier, he didn't come on the steps at all?' and Pa was scraping the soap off his pants with a piece of shingle, and the hired girl was putting liniment on Ma, and heating it in for palpitation of the heart, and Pa said, 'You dam idjut, no more of this, or I'll maul the liver out of you,' and I asked him if he didn't think soft soap would help a mustache to grow, and he picked up Ma's work-basket and threw it at my head, as I went down stairs, and I came over here. Don't you think my Pa is unreasonable to get mad at a little joke that he planned himself?"

The grocery man said he didn't know, and the boy went out with a pair of skates over his shoulder, and the grocery man is wondering what joke the boy will play on him to get even for the cayenne pepper.

CHAPTER XXXIV

HIS PA GETS MAD

A boom in court plaster—The bad boy declines being mauled!—The old man gets a hot box—The bad boy borrows a cat!—The battle!—"Helen blazes"—The cat victorious!—The bad boy draws the line at kindling wood!

"I WAS down to the drug store this morning, and saw your Ma buying a lot of court-plaster, enough to make a shirt, I should think. What's she going to do with so much court-plaster?" asked the grocery man of the bad boy, as he came in and pulled off his boots by the stove and emptied

I BORROWED A CAT.

out a lot of snow, that had collected as he walked through a drift, which melted and made a bad smell.

"O, I guess she is going to patch Pa up so he will hold water. Pa's temper got him in the worst muss you ever see, last night. If that museum was here now they would hire Pa and exhibit him as the tattooed man. I tell you I have got too old to be mauled as though I was a kid, and any man who attacks me from this out wants to have his peace made with the insurance companies, and know that his calling and election is sure, because I am a bad man, and don't you forget it." And the boy pulled on his boots and looked so cross and desperate that the grocery man asked him if he wouldn't try a little new cider.

"Good heavens!" said the grocery man, as the boy swallowed the cider, and his face resumed its natural look, and the piratical frown disappeared with the cider. "You have not stabbed your father, have you? I have feared that one thing would bring on another, with you, and that you would yet be hung."

"Naw, I haven't stabbed him. It was another cat that stabbed him. You see, Pa wants me to do all the work around the house. The other day he bought a load of kindling wood, and told me to carry it into the basement. I have not been educated up to kindling wood, and I didn't do it. When supper time came, and Pa found that I had not carried in the kindling wood, he had a hot box, and he told me that if that wood was not in when he came back from the lodge, that he would warm my jacket. Well, I tried to hire some one to carry it in, and got a man to promise to come in the morning and carry it in and take his pay in groceries, and I was going to buy the groceries here and have them charged to Pa. But that wouldn't help me out that night. I knew when Pa came home he would search for me. So I slept in the back hall on a cot. But I didn't want Pa to have all his trouble for nothing, so I borrowed an old tom cat that my chum's old maid aunt owns, and put the cat in my bed. I thought if Pa came in my room after me, and found that by his unkindness I had changed to a tom cat, he would be sorry. That is the biggest cat you ever see, and the worst fighter in our ward. It isn't afraid of anything, and can whip a Newfoundland dog quicker than you can put sand in a barrel of sugar. Well, about eleven o'clock I heard Pa tumble over the kindling wood, and I knew by the remark he made, as the wood slid around under him, that there was going to be a cat fight real quick. He came up to Ma's room, and sounded Ma as to whether Hennery had retired to his virtuous couch. Pa is awful sarcastic when he tries to be. I could hear him take off his clothes, and hear him say, as he picked up a trunk strap, 'I guess I will go up to

PA'S SHIRT WAS NO PROTECTION AT ALL.

his room and watch the smile on his face, as he dreams of the angels. I yearn to press him to my aching bosom.' I thought to myself, 'Maybe you won't yearn so much directly.' He come up stairs, and I could hear him breathing hard. I looked around the corner and could see he just had on his shirt and pants, and his suspenders were hanging down, and his bald head shone like a calcium light just before it explodes. Pa went in my room, and up to the bed, and I could hear him say, 'Come out here and bring in that kindling wood, or I will start a fire on your base-burner with this strap.' And then there was a yowling such as I never heard before, and Pa said, 'Helen Blazes,' and the furniture in my room began to fall around and break. O, *my!* I think Pa took the tom cat right by the neck, the way he does me, and that left all the cat's feet free to get in their work. By the way the cat squalled as though it was being choked, I know Pa had him by the neck. I suppose the cat thought Pa was a whole flock of Newfoundland dogs, and the cat had a record on dogs, and it kicked awful. Pa's shirt was no protection at all in a cat fight, and the cat just walked all around Pa's stomach, and Pa yelled 'Police,' and Fire,' and 'Turn on the hose,' and he called Ma, and the cat yowled. If pa had had the presence of mind enough to have dropped the cat, or rolled it up in the mattress, it would have been all right, but a man always gets rattled in time of danger, and he held onto the cat and started down stairs yelling murder, and he met Ma coming up.

"I guess Ma's night cap, or something frightened the cat some more, cause he stabbed Ma on the night-shirt with one hind foot, and Ma said, 'Mercy on us,' and she went back, and Pa stumbled on a hand-sled that was on the stairs, and they all fell down, and the cat got away and went down in the coal bin and yowled all night. Pa and Ma went into their room, and I guess they anointed themselves with vaseline, and Pond's extract, and I went and got into my bed, cause it was cold out in the hall, and the cat had warmed my bed as well as it had warmed Pa. It was all I could do to go to sleep, with Pa and Ma talking all night, and this morning I came down the back stairs, and haven't been to breakfast, cause I don't want to see Pa when he is vexed. You let the man that carries in the kindling wood have six shillings worth of groceries and charge them to Pa. I have passed the kindling wood period in a boy's life, and have arrived at the coal period. I will carry in coal, but I draw the line at kindling wood."

"Well, you are a cruel, bad boy," said the grocery man, as he went to the book and charged the six shillings.

"O, I don't know. I think Pa is cruel. A man who will take a poor kitty by the neck, that hasn't done any harm, and tries to chastise the poor thing with a trunk strap, ought to be looked after by the humane society. And if it is cruel to take a cat by the neck, how much more cruel is it to take a boy by the neck, that had diphtheria only a few years ago, and whose throat is tender. Say, I guess I will accept your invitation to take breakfast with you," and the boy cut off a piece of bologna and helped himself to the crackers, and while the grocery man was out shoveling off the snow from the sidewalk, the boy filled his pockets with raisins and loaf sugar, and then went out to watch the man carry in his kindling wood.

CHAPTER XXXV

HIS PA AN INVENTOR

The bad boy a martyr—The dog collar in the sausage—A patent stove—The patent tested!—His Pa a burnt offering—Early breakfast!

"HA! Ha! Now I have got you," said the grocery man to the bad boy, the other morning, as he came in, jumped upon the counter and tied the end of a ball of twine to the tail of a dog, and "sicked" the dog on another dog that was following a passing sleigh, causing the twine to pay out until the whole ball was scattered along the block. "Condemn you, I've a notion to choke the liver out of you. Who tied that twine to the dog's tail?"

The boy choked up with emotion, and the tears came into his eyes and he said he didn't know anything about the twine or the dog. He said he noticed the dog come in, and wag his tail around the twine, but he supposed the dog was a friend of the family and did not disturb him. "Everybody lays everything that is done to me," said the boy, as he put his handkerchief to his nose, "and they will be sorry for it when I die. I have a good notion to poison myself by eating some of your glucose sugar."

"Yes, and you do about everything that is mean. The other day a lady came in and told me to send up to her house some of my country sausage, done up in muslin bags, and while she was examining it she noticed something hard inside the bags, and asked me what it was, and I opened it, and I hope to die if there wasn't a little brass padlock and a piece of red morrocco dog collar imbedded in the sausage.

"Now, how do you suppose that got in there?" and the grocery man looked savage.

The boy looked interested and put on an expression as though in deep thought, and finally said: "I suppose the

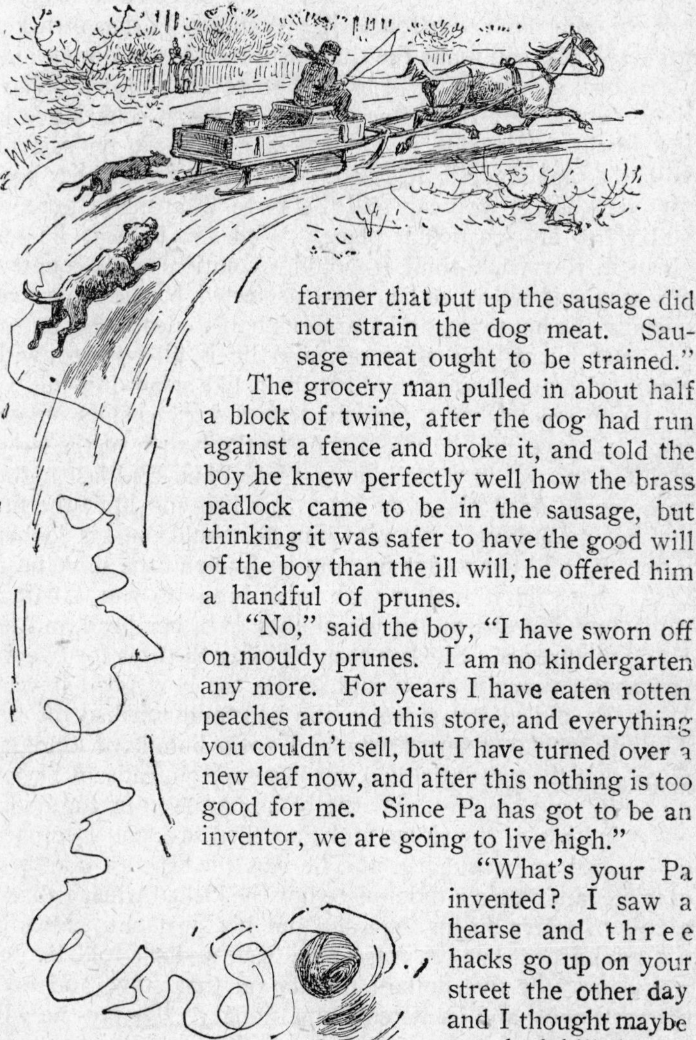

farmer that put up the sausage did not strain the dog meat. Sausage meat ought to be strained."

The grocery man pulled in about half a block of twine, after the dog had run against a fence and broke it, and told the boy he knew perfectly well how the brass padlock came to be in the sausage, but thinking it was safer to have the good will of the boy than the ill will, he offered him a handful of prunes.

"No," said the boy, "I have sworn off on mouldy prunes. I am no kindergarten any more. For years I have eaten rotten peaches around this store, and everything you couldn't sell, but I have turned over a new leaf now, and after this nothing is too good for me. Since Pa has got to be an inventor, we are going to live high."

"What's your Pa invented? I saw a hearse and three hacks go up on your street the other day and I thought maybe you had killed your Pa."

"Not much, there will be more than three hacks when I kill Pa, and don't you forget it. Well sir, Pa has struck a fortune, if he can make the thing work. He has got an idea about coal stoves that will bring him several million dollars if he gets a royalty of five dollars on every cook stove in the world. His idea is to have a coal stove on casters, with the pipe made to telescope out and in, and rubber hose for one joint, so you can pull the stove all around the room and warm any particular place. Well, sir, to hear Pa tell about it, you would think it would revolutionize the country, and maybe it will when he gets it perfected, but he came near burning the house up, and scared us half to death this morning, and burned his shirt off, and he is all covered with cotton with sweet oil on, and he smells like salad dressing.

"You see Pa had a pipe made and some castors put on our coal stove, and he tied a rope to the hearth of the stove and had me put in some kindling wood and coal last night, so he could draw the stove up to the bed and light the fire without getting up. Ma told him he would put his foot in it, and he told her to dry up, and let him run the stove business. He said it took a man with brain to run a patent right, and Ma she pulled the clothes over her head and let Pa do the fire act. She has been building the fires for twenty years, and thought she would let Pa see how good it was. Well, Pa pulled the stove to the bed, and touched off the kindling wood. I guess may-be I got a bundle of kindling wood that the hired girl had put kerosene on, cause it blazed up awful and smoked, and the blaze bursted out the doors and windows of the stove, and Pa yelled fire, and I jumped out of bed and rushed in and he was the scartest man you ever see and you'd a dide to see how he kicked when I threw a pail of water on his legs and put his shirt out. Ma did not get burned, but she was pretty wet, and she told Pa she would pay the five dollars royalty on that stove and take the castors off and let it remain stationary. Pa says he will make it work if he burns the house down. I think it was real mean in Pa to get mad at me because I threw cold water on him instead of warm water, to put his shirt out. If I had waited till I could heat water to the right temperature I would have been an orphan, and Pa would have been a burnt offering. But some men always kick at everything. Pa has given up business entirely and says he shall devote the remainder of his life curing himself of the different troubles

PA SAID IT MADE A MAN FEEL GOOD TO GET UP EARLY.

that I get him into. He has retained a doctor by the year, and he buys liniment by the gallon."

"What was it about your folks getting up in the middle of the night to eat? The hired girl was over here after some soap the other morning, and she said she was going to leave your house."

"Well, that was a picnic. Pa said he wanted breakfast

earlier than we were in the habit of having it, and he said I might see to it that the house was awake early enough. The other night I awoke with the awfulest pain you ever heard of. It was that night that you gave me and my chum the bottle of pickled oysters that had begun to work. Well, I couldn't sleep, and I thought I would call the hired girls, and they got up and got breakfast to going, and then I rapped on Pa and Ma's door and told them the breakfast was getting cold, and they got up and came down. We eat breakfast by gas light, and Pa yawned and said that it made a man feel good to get up and get ready for work before daylight, the way he used to on the farm, and Ma she yawned and agreed with Pa, 'cause she has to, or have a row. After breakfast we sat around for an hour, and Pa said it was a long time getting daylight, and bimeby Pa looked at his watch. When he began to pull out his watch I lit out and hid in the storeroom, and pretty soon I heard Pa and Ma come up stairs and go to bed, and then the hired girls, they went to bed, and when it was all still, and the pain had stopped inside my clothes, I went to bed, and I looked to see what time it was and it was two o'clock in the morning. We got dinner at eight o'clock in the morning and Pa said he guessed he would call up the house after this, so I have lost another job and it was all on account of that bottle of pickled oysters you gave me. My chum says he had the colic too, but he didn't call up his folks. It was all he could do to get up hisself. Why don't you sometimes give away something that is not spoiled?"

The grocery man said he guessed he knew what to give away, and the boy went out and hung up a sign in front of the grocery, that he had made on wrapping paper with red chalk, which read, "Rotten eggs, good enough for custard pies, for 18 cents a dozen."

CHAPTER XXXVI

HIS PA GETS BOXED

A parrot for sale—The old man is down on the grocer—"A contrite heart beats a bob-tail flush!"—Polly's responses—Can a parrot go to hell?—The old man gets another black eye—Duffy hits for keeps—Nothing like an oyster for a black eye.

"You don't want to buy a good parrot, do you?" said the bad boy to the grocery man, as he put his wet mittens on the top of the stove to dry and kept his back to the stove so he could watch the grocery man, and be prepared for a kick, if the man should remember the rotten-egg sign that the boy put up in front of the grocery, last week.

"Naw, I don't want no parrot. I had rather have a fool boy around than a parrot. But what's the matter with your Ma's parrot? I thought she wouldn't part with him for anything."

"Well, she wouldn't until Wednesday night; but now she says she will not have him around, and I may have half I can get for him. She told me to go to some saloon, or some disreputable place and sell him, and I thought maybe he would about suit you," and the boy broke into a bunch of celery, and took out a few tender stalks and rubbed them on a codfish, to salt them, and began to bite the stalks, while he held the sole of one wet boot up against the stove to dry it, making a smell of burned leather that came near turning the stomach of the cigar sign.

"Look-a-here, boy, don't you call this a disreputable place. Some of the best people in this town come here," said the grocery man, as he held up the cheese-knife and grated his teeth as though he would like to jab it into the youth.

"O, that's all right, they come here 'cause you trust; but

you make up what you lose by charging it to other people, Pa will make it hot for you the last of the week. He has been looking over your bill, and comparing it with the hired girl, and she says we haven't ever had a prune, or a dried apple, or a raisin, or any cinnamon, or crackers and cheese out of your store, and he says you are worse than the James Brothers, and that you used to be a three card monte man; and he will have you arrested for highway robbery, but you can settle that with Pa. I like you, because you are no ordinary sneak thief. You are a high-toned, gentlemanly sort of a bilk, and wouldn't take anything you couldn't lift. O, keep your seat, and don't get excited. It does a man good to hear the truth from one who has got the nerve to tell it.

"But about the parrot. Ma has been away from home for a week, having a high old time in Chicago, going to theaters and things, and while she was gone, I guess the hired girl or somebody learned the parrot some new things to say. A parrot that can only say 'Polly wants a cracker,' don't amount to anything—what we need is new style parrots that can converse on the topics of the day, and say things original. Well, when Ma got back, I guess her conscience hurt her for the way she had been carrying on in Chicago, and so when she heard the basement of the church was being frescoed, she invited the committee to hold the Wednesday evening prayer meeting at our house. First, there were four people came, and Ma asked Pa to stay to make up a quorum and Pa said seeing he had two pair, he guessed he would stay in, and if Ma would deal him a queen he would have a full hand. I don't know what Pa meant; but he plays draw poker sometimes. Anyway, there were eleven people come including the minister, and after they had talked about the neighbors a spell, and Ma had showed the women a new tidy she had worked for the heathen, with a motto on it which Pa had taught her: 'A contrite heart beats a bob-tail flush,'—and Pa had talked to the men about a religious silver mine he was selling stock in, which he advised them as a friend to buy for the glory of the church, they all went in the back parlor, and the minister led in prayer. He got down on his knees right under the parrot's cage, and you'd a dide to see Polly hang on to the wires of the cage with one foot, and drop an apple core on the minister's head. Ma shook her handkerchief at Polly, and looked sassy, and Polly got up

MA SHOOK HER HANDKERCHIEF AT POLLY.

on the perch, and as the minister got warmed up, and began to raise the roof, Polly said, 'O, dry up.' The minister had his eyes shut, but he opened one of them a little and looked at Pa. Pa was tickled at the parrot, but when the minister looked at Pa as though it was him that was making irreverent remarks, Pa was mad.

"The minister got to the 'Amen,' and Polly shook hisself and said, 'What you giving us?' and the minister got up and brushed the bird seed off his knees, and he looked mad. I thought Ma would sink with mortification, and I was sitting on a piano stool, looking as pious as a Sunday School superintendent the Sunday before he skips out with the bank's funds; and Ma looked at me as though she thought it was me that had been tampering with the parrot. Gosh, I never said a word to that parrot, and I can prove it by my chum.

"Well, the minister asked one of the sisters if she wouldn't pray, and she wasn't engaged, so she said, 'With pleasure,' and she kneeled down, but she corked herself, 'cause she got one knee on a cast iron dumb bell that I had been practicing with. She said 'O my,' in a disgusted sort of a way, and then she began to pray for the reformation of the youth of the land, and asked for the spirit to descend on the household, and particularly on the boy that was such a care and anxiety to his parents, and just then Polly said, 'O, pull down your vest.' Well, you'd a dide to see that woman look at me. The parrot cage was partly behind the window curtain, and they couldn't see it, and she thought it was me. She looked at Ma as though she was wondering why she didn't hit me with a poker, but she went on, and Polly said, 'Wipe off your chin,' and then the lady got through and got up, and told Ma it must be a great trial to have an idiotic child, and then Ma she was mad and said it wasn't half so bad as it was to be a kleptomaniac, and then the woman got up and said she wouldn't stay no longer, and Pa said to me to take that parrot out doors, and that seemed to make them all good natured again. Ma said to take the parrot and give it to the poor. I took the cage and pointed my finger at the parrot and it looked at the woman and said 'Old catamaran,' and the woman tried to look pious and resigned, but she couldn't. As I was going out the door the parrot ruffed up his feathers and said, 'Dammit, set 'em up,' and I hurried out with the cage for fear he would say something bad, and the folks all held up their hands and said it was scandalous.

Say, I wonder if a parrot can go to hell with the rest of the community. Well, I put the parrot in the woodshed, and after they all had their innings, except Pa, who acted as umpire, the meeting broke up, and Ma says it's the last time she will have that gang at her house."

"That must have been where your Pa got his black eye," said the grocery man, as he charged the bunch of celery to the boy's Pa. "Did the minister hit him, or was it one of the sisters?"

THEN HE GAVE HIM A SIDE WINDER IN BOTH EYES.

"O, he didn't get his black eye at prayer meeting!" said the boy, as he took his mittens off the stove and rubbed them to take the stiffening out. "It was from boxing. Pa told my chum and me that it was no harm to learn to box; 'cause we could defend ourselves, and he said he used to be a holy terror with the boxing gloves when he was a boy, and he has been giving us lessons. Well, he is no slouch, now I tell you, and handles himself pretty well for a church member. I read in the paper how Zack Chandler played it on Conkling by getting Jem Mace, the prize fighter, to knock him silly, and I asked Pa if he wouldn't let me bring a poor boy who had no father to teach him boxing, to our house to learn to box, and Pa said, 'Certainly, fetch him along.' He said he would be glad to do anything for a poor orphan. So I went down in the Third ward and got an Irish boy by the name of Duffy, who can knock the socks off of any boy in the ward. He fit a prize fight once. It would have made you laugh to see Pa telling him how to hold his hands, and how to guard his face. He told Duffy not to be afraid, but to strike right out and hit for keeps. Duffy said he was afraid Pa would get mad if he hit him, and Pa said, 'Nonsense, boy, knock me down if you can, and I will laugh, "ha! ha!"' Well, Duffy he hauled back and gave Pa one in the nose and another in both eyes, and cuffed him on the ear and punched him in the stomach, and lammed him in the mouth and made his teeth bleed, and then he give him a side-winder in both eyes, and Pa pulled off the boxing gloves and grabbed a chair, and we adjourned and went down-stairs as though there was a panic. I haven't seen Pa since. Was his eye very black?"

"Black, I should say so," said the grocery man. "And his nose seemed to be trying to look into his left ear. He was at the market buying beefsteak to put on it."

"O, beefsteak is no account. I must go and see him and tell him that an oyster is the best thing for a black eye. Well, I must go. A boy has a pretty hard time running a house the way it should be run," and the boy went out and hung up a sign in front of the grocery: *"Frowy Butter a Speshulty!"*

PECK'S BAD BOY

AND HIS PA

VOL. II

FIRST AND ONLY COMPLETE EDITION

BY

GEORGE W. PECK

AUTHOR OF

"PECK'S FUN," "PECK'S SUNSHINE," "PECK'S BOSS BOOK," ETC.

WITH 100 ILLUSTRATIONS BY TRUE WILLIAMS

PECK'S BAD BOY AND HIS PA—VOL II

THE GROCERY MAN

AND

PECK'S BAD BOY

CHAPTER I

VARIEGATED DOGS

The bad boy sleeps on the roof—A man doesn't know anything at forty-eight—The old man wants some Pollynurious water. The dyer's dogs—Procession of the dogs—Pink, blue, green and white—"Well I'm dem'd"—His Pa don't appreciate.

"How do you and your Pa get along now?" asked the grocery man of the bad boy, as he leaned against the counter instead of sitting down on a stool, while he bought a bottle of liniment.

"O, I don't know. He don t seem to appreciate me. What he ought to have is a deaf and dumb boy, with only one leg, and both arms broke—then he could enjoy a quiet life. But I am too gay for Pa, and you needn't be surprised if you never see me again. I talk of going off with a circus. Since I played the variegated dogs on Pa, there seems to have been a coldness in the family, and I sleep on the roof."

"Variegated dogs," said the store keeper, "what kind of a game is that? You have not played another Daisy trich on your Pa, have you?

"Oh, no, it was nothing of that kind. You know Pa

thinks he is smart. He thinks because he is forty-eight years old he knows it all; but it don't seem to me as though a man of his age, that had sense, would let a tailor palm off on him a pair of pants so tight that he would have to use a button-hook to button them; but they can catch him on everything, just as though he was a kid smoking cigarettes. Well, you know Pa drinks some. That night the new club opened he came home pretty fruitful, and next morning his head ached so he said he would buy me a dog if I would go down town and get a bottle of pollynurious water for him. You know that dye house on Grand avenue, where they have got the four white spitz dogs. When I went after the penurious water, I noticed they had been coloring their dogs with the dye stuff, and I put up a job with the dye man's little boy to help me play it on Pa. They had one dog dyed pink, another blue, another red, and another green, and I told the boy I would treat him to ice cream if he would let one out at a time, when I came down with Pa, and call him in and let another out, and when we started to go away, to let them all out. What I wanted to do was to paralyze Pa, and make him think he had got 'em, got dogs the worst way. So, about ten o'clock, when his head got cleared off, and his stomach got settled, he changed ends with his cuffs, and we came down town, and I told him I knew where he could get a splendid white spitz dog for me, for five dollars; and if he would get it, I would never do anything disrespectful again, and would just sit up nights to please him, and help him up stairs and get seltzer for him. So we went by the dye house and just as I told him I didn't want anything but a white dog, the door opened, and the pink dog came out and barked at us, and I said, 'That's him' and the boy called him back. Pa looked as though he had the colic, and his eyes stuck out, and he said 'Hennery, that is a pink dog!' and I said 'No, it is a white dog, Pa,' and just then the green dog came out, and I asked Pa if it wasn't a pretty white dog, and Pa, he turned pale and said, 'Hell, boy, that is a green dog—what's got into the dogs?' I told him he must be color blind, and was feeling in my pocket for a strap to tie the dog, and telling him he must be careful of his health or he would see

TOLD HIM THERE WAS ONLY DOG AND A CAT.

something worse than green dogs, when the green dog went in, and the blue dog came rushing out and barked at Pa. Well, Pa leaned against a tree box, and his eyes stuck out like stops on an organ, and the sweat was all over his face in drops as big as kernels of hominy.

"I think a boy ought to do everything he can to make it pleasant for his Pa, don't *you?* And yet, some parents don't realize what a comfort a boy is. The blue dog was called in, and just as Pa wiped the perspiration off his forehead, and rubbed his eyes, and put on his specs, the red maroon dog came out. Pa acted as if he was tired, and sat down on a horse block. Dogs *do* make some people tired, don't they? He took hold of my hand, and his hand trembled just as though he was putting a gun wad in the collection plate at church, and he said, 'My son, tell me truly, is that a red dog?'

"A fellow has got to lie a little if he is going to have any fun with his Pa, and I told him it was a white dog, and I could get it for five dollars. He straightened up just as the dog went into the house, and said, 'Well, I'm dem'd;' and just then the boy let all the dogs out and sicked them on a cat, which ran up a shade tree right near Pa, and they rushed all around us—the blue dog going between his legs, and the green dog trying to climb the tree, and the pink dog barking, and the red dog standing on his hind feet.

"Pa was weak as a cat,and told me to go right home with him, and he would buy me a bicycle. He asked me how many dogs there were, and what was the color of them. I s'pose I did awful wrong, but I told him there was only one dog, and a cat, and the dog was white.

"Well, sir, Pa acted just as he did the night Hancock was beat, and he had to have the doctor to give him something to quiet him (the time he wanted me to go right down town and buy a hundred rat traps, but the doctor said never mind, I needn't go). I took him home, and Ma soaked his feet, and give him some ginger tea, and while I was gone after the doctor he asked Ma if she ever saw a green dog.

"That was what made all the trouble. If Ma had kept her mouth shut I would have been all right, but she up and told him that they had a green dog, and a blue dog, and all colors of spitz dogs down at the dyers. They dyed them just for an advertisement, and for him to be quiet, and he would feel better when he got over it. Pa was all right when I got back and told him the doctor had gone to Wauwatosa, and I had left an order on his slate. Pa said he would leave an order on my slate. He took a harness tug and used it for breeching on me. I don't think a boy's Pa ought to wear a harness on his son, do you? He said he would learn me to play rainbow dogs on him. He said I was a liar, and he expected to see me wind up in Congress. Say, is Congress anything like Waupun or Sing Sing? No, I can't stay, thank you, I must go down to the office and tell Pa I have reformed, and freeze him out of a circus ticket. He is a good enough man, only he don't appreciate a boy that has got all the modern improvements. Pa and Ma are going to enter me in the Sunday school. I guess I'll take first money, don't you?"

And the bad boy went out with a visible limp, and a look of genius cramped for want of opportunity.

CHAPTER II

HIS PA PLAYS JOKES

A man shouldn't get mad at a joke—The magic bouquet—The grocery man takes a turn—His Pa tries the bouquet at church—One for the old maid—A fight ensues—The bad boy threatens the grocery man—A compromise.

"Say, do you think a little practical joke does any hurt?" asked the bad boy of the grocery man, as he came in with his Sunday suit on, and a bouquet in his button-hole, and pried off a couple of figs from a new box that had been just opened.

"No sir," said the grocery man, as he licked off the syrup that dripped from a quart measure, from which he had been filling a jug. "I hold that a man who gets mad at a practical joke, that is, one that does not injure him, is a fool, and he ought to be shunned by all decent people. That's a nice bouquet you have in your coat. What is it, pansies? Let me smell of it," and the grocery man bent over in front of the boy to take a whiff at the bouquet. As he did so a stream of water shot out of the innocent looking bouquet and struck him full in the face, and run down over his shirt, and the grocery man yelled murder, and fell over a barrel of axe helves and scythe snaths, and then groped around for a towel to wipe his face.

"You condemn skunk," said the grocery man to the boy, as he took up an axe helve and started for him, "What kind of a golblasted squirt gun have you got there? I will maul you, by thunder," and he rolled up his shirt sleeves.

"There, keep your temper. I took a test vote of you on the subject of practical jokes, before the machine began to play upon the conflagration that was raging on your whiskey nose, and you said that a man who would get mad at a joke was a fool, and now I know it. Here let me show it to you. There is a rubberhose runs from the bouquet, inside my coat to my pants pocket, and there is a bulb of rubber, that holds about half a pint, and when a feller smells of the posey. I squeeze the bulb, you you see the result. It's fun, where you don't squirt it on a person that gets mad."

IT STRUCK HER RIGHT ON THE NOSE.

The grocery man said he would give the boy half a pound of figs if he would lend the bouquet to him for half an hour, to play it on a customer, and the boy fixed it on the grocery man, and turned the nozzle so it would squirt right back into the grocery man's face. He tried it on the first customer that came in, and got it right in his own face, and then the bulb in his pants pocket got to leaking, and the rest of the water ran down the grocery man's trousers' leg, and he gave it up in disgust, and handed it back to the boy.

"How was it your Pa had to be carried home from the sociable in a hack the other night?" asked the grocery man, as he stood close to the stove so his pants leg would dry. "He has not got to drinking again, has he?"

"O, no," said the boy, as he filled the bulb with vinegar, to practice on his chum. "It was this bouquet that got Pa into the trouble. You see I got Pa to smell of it, and I just filled him chuck full of water. He got mad and called me all kinds of names, and said I was no good on earth, and I would fetch up in state's prison, and then he wanted to borrow it to wear to the sociable. He said he would have more fun than you could shake a stick at, and I asked him if he didn't think he would fetch up in state's prison, and he said it was different with a man. He said when a man played a joke there was a certain dignity about it that was lacking in a boy. So I lent it to him, and we all went to the sociable in the basement of the church. I never see Pa more kitteny than he was that night. He filled the bulb with ice water, and the first one he got to smell of his button-hole bouquet was an old maid who thinks Pa is a heathen, but she likes to be made something of by anybody that wears pants, and when Pa sidled up to her and began talking about what a great work the christian wimmen of the land were doing in educating the heathen, she felt real good, and then she noticed Pa's posey in his button-hole and she touched it, and then she reached over her beak to smell of it. Pa he squeezed the bulb, and about half a teacupful of water struck her right in the nose, and some went into her strangle place, and *O, my,* didn't she yell. The sisters gathered around her and they said her face was all covered with perspiration, and the paint was coming off, and they took her in the kitchen, and she told them Pa had slapped her with a dish of ice cream, and the wimmen told the minister and the deacons, and they went to Pa for an explanation, and Pa told them it was not so, and the minister got interested and got near Pa, and Pa let the water go at him, and hit him in the eye, and then a deacon got a dose, and Pa laughed; and then the minister, who used to go to college, and be a hazer, and box, he got mad and squared off and hit Pa three times right by the eye, and one of the deacons kicked Pa, and Pa got mad and said he could clean out the whole shebang, and began to pull off his coat, when they bundled him out doors, and Ma got mad to see Pa abused, and she

IF I WAS A PROVISION PIRATE.

left the sociable, and I had to stay and eat ice cream and things for the whole family. Pa says that settles it with him. He says they haven't got any more christian charity in that church than they have in a tannery. His eyes are just getting over being black from the sparring lessons, and now he has got to go through oysters and beefsteak cure again. He says it is all owing to me."

"Well, what has all this got to do with your putting up signs in front of my store, 'Rotten Eggs,' and 'Frowy Butter a specialty?'" said the grocery man as he took the boy by the ear and pulled him around. "You have got an idea you are smart, and I want you to keep away from here. The next time I catch you in here I shall call the police and have you pulled. Now git!"

The boy pulled his ear back on the side of his head where it belonged, took out a cigarette and lit it, and after puffing smoke in the face of the grocery cat that was sleeping on the cover to the sugar barrel he said:

"If I was a provision pirate that never sold anything but what was spoiled so it couldn't be sold in a first-class store, who cheated in weights and measures, who bought only wormy figs and decayed cod-fish, who got his butter from a fat rendering establishment, his cider from a vinegar factory, and his sugar from a glucose factory, I would not insult the son of one of the finest families. Why, sir, I could go out on the corner, and when I saw customers coming here, I could tell a story that would turn their stomachs, and send them to the grocery on the next corner. Suppose I should tell them that the cat sleeps in the dried apple barrel, that the mice made nests in the prune box, and rats run riot through the raisins, and that you never wash your hands except on Decoration day and Christmas, that you wipe your nose on your shirt sleeves, and that you have the itch, do you think your business would be improved? Suppose I should tell customers that you buy sour kraut of a wooden-shoed Polacker, who makes it of pieces of cabbage that he gets by gathering swill and sells that stuff to respectable people, could you pay your rent? If I should tell that you put lozengers in the collection plate at church, and charge the minister forty cents a pound for oleomargarine, you would have to close up. Old man, I am onto you, and now you apologize for pulling my ear."

The grocery man turned pale during the recital, and finally said the bad boy was one of the best little fellows in this town, and the boy went out and hung up a sign in front: "Girl wanted to cook."

CHAPTER III

HIS PA STABBED

The grocery man sets a trap in vain—A boom in liniment—His Pa goes to the Langtry show—The bad boy turns burglar—The old man stabbed—His account of the fray—A good single handed liar.

"I HEAR you had burglars over to your house last night," said the grocery man to the bad boy, as he came in and sat on the counter right over a little gimlet hole, where the grocery man had fixed a darning needle so that by pulling a string the needle would fly up through the hole and run into the boy about an inch. The grocery man had been laying for the boy about two days, and now that he had got him right over the hole the first time, it made him laugh to think how he would make him jump and yell, and as he edged off and got hold of the string the boy looked unconscious of impending danger. The grocery man pulled, and the boy sat still. He pulled again, and again, and finally the boy said:

"Yes, it is reported that we had burglars over there. O, you needn't pull that string any more. I heard you was setting a trap for me, and I put a piece of board inside my pants, and thought I would let you exercise yourself. Go ahead, if it amuses you. It don't hurt me."

The grocery man looked sad, and then smiled a sickly sort of a smile, at the failure of his plan to puncture the boy, and then he said, "Well, how was it? The policeman didn't seem to know much about the particulars. He said there was so much deviltry going on at your house that nobody could tell when anything was serious, and he was inclined to think it was a put up job."

"Now let's have an understanding," says the boy. "Whatever I say you are not to give me away. It's a go, is it? I have always been afraid of you, because you have a sort of decayed egg look about you. You are like a peck of potatoes with the big ones on top, a sort of strawberry box with the bottom raised up, so I have thought you would go back on a fellow. But if you won't give this away, here goes. You see, I heard Ma tell Pa to bring up another bottle of liniment last night. When Ma corks herself, or has a pain

"I HAVE RECEIVED MY DEATH WOUND."

anywhere, she just uses liniment for all that is out, and a pint bottle don't last more than a week. Well, I told my chum, and we laid for Pa. This liniment Ma uses is offul hot, and almost blisters. Pa went to the Langtry show, and did not get home till eleven o'clock, and me and my chum decided to teach Pa a lesson. I don't think it is right for a man to go to the theaters and not take his wife or his little boy.

"So we concluded to burgle Pa. We agreed to lay on the stairs, and when he came up my chum was to hit him on the head with a dried bladder, and I was to stab him on his breast pocket with a stick, and break the liniment bottle, and make him think he was killed.

"It couldn't have worked better if we had rehearsed it. We had talked about burglars at supper time, and got Pa nervous, so when he came up stairs and was hit on the head with the bladder, the first thing he said was 'Burglars, by mighty,' and he started to go back, and I hit him on the breast pocket, where the bottle was, and then we rushed by him, down stairs, and I said in a stage whisper, 'I guess he's a dead man,' and we went down cellar and up the back stairs to my room and undressed. Pa hollered to Ma that he was murdered, and Ma called me, and I came down in my night-shirt, and the hired girl she came down, and Pa was on the lounge, and he said his life-blood was fast ebbing away. He held his hand on the wound, and said he could feel the warm blood trickling clear down to his boots. I told Pa to stuff some tar into the wound, such as he told me to put on my lip to make my mustache grow, and Pa said, 'My boy, this is no time for trifling. Your Pa is on his last legs. When I came up stairs I met six burglars, and I attacked them, and forced four of them down, and was going to hold them and send for the police, when two more, that I did not know about, jumped on me ,and I was getting the best of them when one of them struck me over the head with a crowbar, and the other stabbed me in the heart with a butcher knife. I have received my death wound, my boy and my hot southern blood, that I offered up so freely for my country in her time of need, is passing from my body, and soon your Pa will be only a piece of poor clay. Get some ice and put on my stomach, and all the way down, for I am burning up.' I went to the water pitcher and got a chunk of ice and put inside Pa's shirt, and while Ma was tearing up an old skirt to stop the flow of blood, I asked Pa if he felt better, and if he could describe the villains who had murdered him. Pa gasped and moved his legs to get them cool from the clotted blood, he said, and he went on, 'One of them was about six feet high, and had a sandy

THE DEACON GOT OFF THE COUNTER WITH HIS HAND CLASPED.

mustache. I got him down and hit him on the nose, and if the police find him, his nose will be broke. The second one was thick set, and weighed about two hundred. I had him down and my boot was on his neck, and I was knocking two more down when I was hit. The thick set one will have the mark of boot heels on his throat. Tell the police when I'm gone, about the boot heel marks.'

"By this time Ma had got the skirt tore up and she stuffed it under Pa's shirt, right where she said he was hit, and Pa was telling us what to do to settle his estate, when Ma began to smell the liniment, and she found the broken bottle in his pocket, and searched Pa for the place where he was stabbed, and then she began to laugh, and Pa got mad and said he didn't see as a death-bed scene was such an almighty funny affair; and then she told him he was not hurt, but that he had fallen on the stairs and broke his bottle, and that there was no blood on him, and he said, 'Do you mean to tell me my body and legs are not bathed in human gore?' and then Pa got up and found it was only the liniment. He got mad and asked Ma why she didn't fly around and get something to take that liniment off his legs, as it was eating them right through to the bone; and then he saw my chum put his head in the door, with one gallus hanging down, and Pa looked at me, and then he said, 'Look-a-here, if I find out it was you boys that put up this job on me, I'll make it so hot for you that you will think liniment is ice cream in comparison. I told Pa it didn't look reasonable that me and my chum could be six burglars, six feet high, with our noses broke, and boot-heel marks on our neck, and Pa he said for us to go to bed all-fired quick, and give him a chance to rinse off that liniment, and we retired. Say, how does my Pa strike you as a good single-handed liar?" and the boy went up to the counter, while the grocery man went after a scuttle of coal.

In the meantime one of the grocery man's best customers—a deacon in the church—had come in and sat down on the counter over the darning needle, and as the grocery man came in with the coal, the boy pulled the string, and went out the door and tipped over a basket of rutabages, while the deacon got down on the counter with his hands clasped, and anger in every feature, and told the grocery man he could whip him in two minutes. The grocery man asked what was the matter, and the deacon hunted up the source from whence the darning needle came through the counter, and as the boy went across the street, the deacon and the grocery man were rolling on the floor, the grocery man trying to hold the deacon's fists while he explained about the darning needle and that it was intended for the boy. How it came out the boy did not wait to see.

CHAPTER IV

HIS PA BUSTED

The craze for mining stock—What's a bilk?—The pious bilk—The old man invests—The deacons and even the hired girls invest—Hot maple syrup for one—Getting a man's mind off his troubles.

"SAY, can't I sell you some stock in a silver mine?" asked the bad boy of the grocery man, as he came in the store and pulled from his breast pocket a document printed on parchment paper, and representing several thousand dollars stock in a silver mine.

"Look-a-here," said the grocery man, as he turned pale, and thought of telephoning to the police station for a detective, "you haven't been stealing your father's mining stock, have you? Great heavens, it has come at last! I have known all the time that you would turn out to be a burglar, or a defaulter or robber of some kind. Your father has the reputation of having a bonanza in a silver mine, but if you go lugging his silver stock around he will soon be ruined. Now you go right back home and put that stock in your Pa's safe, like a good boy."

"Put it in the safe! O, no, we keep it in a box stall now, in the barn. I will trade you this thousand dollars in stock for two heads of lettuce, and get Pa to sign it over to you, if you say so. Pa told me I could have the whole trunk full if I wanted it, and the hired girls are using the silver stock to clean the windows, and kindle fires, and Pa has quit the church, and says he won't belong to any concern that harbors bilks. What's a bilk?" said the boy, as he opened a candy jar and took out four sticks of hoarhound candy.

"A bilk," said the grocery man, as he watched the boy, "is a fellow that plays a man for candy, or money, or anything, and don't intend to return an equivalent. You are a small sized bilk. But what's the matter with your Pa and the church, and what has the silver mine stock got to do with it?"

"Well, you remember that exhorter that was here last fall, that used to board around with the church people all the week and talk about Zion and laying up treasures where the moths wouldn't gnaw them, and they wouldn't get rusty, and where thieves wouldn't pry off the hinges. He was the one that used to go home with Ma from prayer meetings,

AND PA USED TO SIT UP NIGHTS TO LOOK AT IT.

when Pa was down town, and who wanted to pay off the church debt in solid silver bricks. He's the bilk. I guess if Pa should get him by the neck he would jerk nine kinds of revealed religion out of him. O, Pa is hotter than he was when the hornets took the lunch off of him. When you strike a pious man on the pocket-book it hurts him. That fellow prayed and sang like an angel, and boarded around like a tramp. He stopped at our house over a week, and he had specimens of rock that were chuck full of silver and gold, and he and Pa used to sit up nights and look at it. You could pick pieces of silver out of the rock as big as buck shot, and he had some silver bricks that were beautiful. He had been out in Colorado and found a hill full of silver rock, and he wanted to form a stock company and dig out millions of dollars. He didn't want anybody but pious men that belonged to the church, in the company, and I think that was one thing that caused Pa to unite with the church so suddenly. I know he was as wicked as could be a few days before he joined the church; but this revivalist, with his words about the beautiful beyond where all shall dwell together in peace and sing praises; and his description of that Colorado mountain where the silver stuck out so you could hang your hat on it, converted Pa. That man's scheme was to let all the church people who were in good standing, and who had plenty of money, into the company, and when the mine begun to return dividends by the car load, they could give largely to the church and pay the debts of all the churches, and put down carpets and fresco the ceiling. The man said he felt that he had been steered on to that silver mine by a higher power, and his idea was to work it for the glory of the cause. He said he liked Pa and would make him vice-president of the company. Pa, he bit like a bass, and I guess he invested five thousand dollars in stock, and Ma, she wanted to come in, and she put in a thousand dollars that she had laid up to buy some diamond ear-rings, and the man gave Pa a lot of stock to sell to other members of the church. They all went into it, even the minister. He drew his salary ahead, and all of the deacons they came in, and the man went back to Colorado with about thirty thousand dollars of good, pious money. Yesterday Pa got a paper from Colorado, giving the whole snap away, and the pious man has been spending the money in Denver, and whooping it up. Pa suspected something was wrong two weeks ago, when he heard that the pious man had been on a toot in Chicago, and he wrote to a man in Denver, who used to get full with Pa years ago when they were both on the turf; and Pa's friend said the man that sold the stock was a fraud, and that he didn't own no mine, and that he borrowed the samples of ore and silver bricks from a pawnbroker in Denver. I guess it will break Pa up for a while, though he is well enough fixed with mortgages and things; but it hurts him to be took in. He lays it all to Ma—she says if she hadn't let that exhorter for the silver mine go home with her this would not have occurred, and Ma says she believes Pa was in partnership with the man to beat her out of her thousand dollars that she was going to buy a pair of diamond ear-rings with. O, it is a terror over to the house now. Both of the hired girls put in all money they had, and took stock and they threaten to sue Pa for arson, and they are going to leave to-night, and Ma will have to do the work. Don't you never try to get rich quick," said the boy as he peeled a herring, and took a couple of crackers.

I TOLD PA IF HE WOULD PUT SOME TAR ON HIS LEGS.

"Never you mind me," said the grocery man, "they don't catch me on any of their silver mines; but I hope this will have some influence on you and teach you to respect your Pa's feelings, and not play jokes on him while he is feeling so bad over his being swindled."

"O, I don't know about that, I think when a man is in trouble, if he has a good little boy to take his mind from his troubles, and get him mad at something else, it rests him. Last night we had hot maple syrup and biscuit for supper, and Pa had a saucer full in front of him, just a steaming. I could see he was thinking too much about his mining stock, and I thought if there was anything I could do to take his mind off of it and place it on something else, I would be doing a kindness that would be appreciated. I sat on the right of Pa, and when he wasn't looking I pulled the table cloth so the saucer of red hot maple syrup dropped off in his lap. Well, you'd a dide to see how quick his thoughts turned from his financial troubles to his physical misfortunes. There was about a pint of hot syrup, and it went all over his lap, and you know how hot melted maple sugar is, and how it sort of clings to anything. Pa jumped up and grabbed hold of his pants' legs to pull them away from hisself, and he danced around and told Ma to turn the hose on him, and then he took a pitcher of ice-water and poured it down his pants, and he said the condemned old table was getting so rickety that a saucer wouldn't stay on it, and I told Pa if he would put some tar on his legs, the same kind that he told me to put on my lip to make my mustache grow, the syrup wouldn't burn so; and then he cuffed me, and I think he felt better. It is a great thing to get a man's mind off his troubles, but where a man hasn't got any mind, like you, for instance—"

At this point the grocery man picked up a fire poker, and the boy went out in a hurry and hung up a sign in front of the grocery:

CASH PAID   *FOR FAT DOGS.*

CHAPTER V

HIS PA AND DYNAMITE

The old man selling silver stock—Fenian scare—"Dynamite" in Milwaukee—The Fenian boom—"Great God, Hanner, we are blowed up!"—His Ma has lots of sand—The old man useless in trouble—The dog and the false teeth.

"I GUESS your Pa's losses in the silver mine have made him crazy, haven't they?" said the grocery man to the bad boy, as he came into the store with his eye-winkers singed off, and powder marks on his face, and began to play on the harmonica, as he sat down on the end of a stick of stove wood, and balanced himself.

"O, I guess not. He has hedged. He got in with a deacon of another church, and sold some of his stock to him, and Pa says if I will keep my condemned mouth shut he will unload the whole of it, if the churches hold out. He goes to a new church every night there is prayer meeting or anything, and makes Ma go with him to give him tone, and after meeting she talks with the sisters about how to piece a bed quilt, while Pa gets in his work selling silver stock. I don't know but he will order some more stock from the factory, if he sells all he has got," and the boy went on playing, "There's a land that is fairer than day."

"But what was he skipping up street for the other night with his hat off, grabbing at his coat tails as though they were on fire? I thought I never saw a pussy man run any faster. And what was the celebration down on your street about that time. I thought the world was coming to an end," and the grocery man kept away from the boy, for fear he would explode.

"O, that was only a Fenian scare. Nothing serious. You see Pa is a sort of half Englishman. He claims to be an American citizen when he wants office, but when they talk about a draft he claims to be a subject of Great Britain, and he says they can't touch him. Pa is a darned smart man, and don't you forget it. They don't any of them get ahead of Pa much. Well, Pa has said a good deal about the wicked Fenians, and that they ought to be pulled, and all that, and when I read the story in the papers about the explosion in the British Parliament, Pa was hot. He said the damnirish was ruining the whole world. He didn't dare to say it at the table, or our hired girl would have knocked him silly with a spoonful of mashed potatoes, 'cause she is a nirish girl, and she can lick any Englishman in this town. Pa said there ought to have been somebody there to have taken that bomb up and throwed it in the sewer before it exploded. He said that if he should ever see a bomb he would grab it right up and throw it away where it wouldn't hurt anybody. Pa has me read the papers to him nights, 'cause his eyes have got splinters in 'em, and after I had read all there was in the paper, I made up a lot more and pretended to read it, about how it was rumored that the Fenians here in Milwaukee were going to place dynamite bombs at every house where an Englishman lived, and at a given signal blow them all up. Pa looked pale around the gills, but he said he wasn't scared.

"Pa and Ma were going to call on a she-deacon that night, that has lots of money in the bank, to see if she didn't want to invest in a dead sure paying silver mine, and me and my chum concluded to give them a send-off. We got my big black injy rubber foot ball, and painted '*Dinymite*' in big white letters on it, and tied a piece of tarred rope to it for a fuse, and got a big fire-cracker, one of those old Fourth of July horse scarers, and a basket full of broken glass. We put the foot ball in front of the step and lit the tarred rope and got under the step with the fire-crackers and the basket, where they go down into the basement. Pa and Ma came out of the front door and down the steps, and Pa saw the foot ball and the burning fuse, and he said 'Great God, Hanner, we are blowed up!' and he started to run, and Ma she stopped to

"GREAT GOD! HANNER, WE ARE BLOWED UP."

look at it. Just as Pa started to run I touched off the fire-cracker, and my chum arranged it to pour out the broken glass on the brick pavement just as the fire-cracker went off.

Well, everything went just as we expected, except Ma. She had examined the foot ball and concluded it was not dangerous, and was just giving it a kick as the fire-cracker went off, and the glass fell, and the fire-cracker was so near her that it scared her, and when Pa looked around Ma was flying across the sidewalk, and Pa heard the noise and he thought the house was blown to atoms. O, you'd a dide to see him go around the corner. You could play crokay on his coat-tail, and his face was as pale as Ma's when she goes to a party. But Ma didn't scare much. As quick as she stopped against the hitching post she knew it was us boys, and she came down there, and maybe she didn't maul me. I cried and tried to gain her sympathy by telling her the fire-cracker went off before it was due, and burned my eyebrows off, but she didn't let up until I promised to go and find Pa.

"I tell you, my Ma ought to be engaged by the British government to hunt out the dynamite fiends. She would corral them in two minutes. If Pa had as much sand as Ma has got, it would be warm weather for me. Well, me and my chum went and headed Pa off or I guess he would be running yet. We got him up by the lake shore, and he wanted to know if the house fell down. He said he would leave it to me if he ever said anything against the Fenians, and I told him that he had always claimed that the Fenians were the nicest men in the world, and it seemed to relieve him very much. When he got home and found the house there he was tickled, and when Ma called him an old bald-headed coward, and said it was only a joke of the boys with a foot ball, he laughed right out, and said he knew it all the time, and he ran to see if Ma would be scared. And, then he wanted to hug me, but it wasn't my night to hug and I went down to the theater. Pa don't amount to much when there is trouble. The time Ma had them cramps, you remember, when you got your cucumbers first last season, Pa came near fainting away, and Ma said ever since they had been married when anything ailed her, Pa has had pains just the same as she has, only he grunted more, and thought he was going to die. Gosh, if I was a man I wouldn't be sick every time one of the neighbors had a back ache, would you?

"Well, you can't tell. When you have been married twenty or thirty years you will know a good deal more than you do now. You think you know it all, now, and you are pretty intelligent for a boy that has been brought up carelessly, but there are things that you will learn after a while that will astonish you. But what ails your Pa's teeth? The hired girl was over here to get some corn meal for gruel, and she said your Pa was gumming it, since he lost his teeth."

HE LOOKED JUST LIKE PA WHEN HE TRIES TO SMILE.

"O, about the teeth. That was too bad. You see my chum has got a dog that is old and his teeth have all come out in front, and this morning I borried Pa's teeth before he got up, to see if we couldn't fix them in the dog's mouth, so he could eat better. Pa says it is an evidence of a kind heart for a boy to be good to dumb animals, but it is a darned mean dog that will go back on a friend. We tied the teeth in the dog's mouth with a string that went around his upper jaw, and another around his under jaw, and you'd a dide to see how funny he looked when he laffed. He looked just like Pa when he tried to smile so as to get me to come up to him so he can lick me. The dog pawed his mouth a spell to get the teeth out, and then we gave him a bone with some meat on, and he began to gnaw the bone, and the teeth came off the plate, and he thought it was pieces of the bone, and he swallowed the teeth. My chum noticed it first, and he said we had got to get in our work pretty quick to save the plates and I thinl we were in luck to save them. I held the dog, and my chum, who was better acquainted with him, untied the strings and got the gold plates out, but there were only two teeth left, and the dog was happy. He woggled his tail for more teeth, but we hadn't any more. I am going to give him Ma's teeth some day. My chum says when a dog gets an appetite for anything you have got to keep giving it it him or he goes back on you. But I think my chum played dirt on me. We sold the gold plates to a jewelry man, and my chum kept the money. I think, as long as I furnished the goods, he ought to have given me something besides the experience, don't you? After this I don't have no more partners, you bet." All this time the boy was marking on a piece of paper, and soon after he went out the grocery man noticed a crowd outside, and on going out he found a sign hanging up which read:

WORMY FIGS

FOR PARTIES.

CHAPTER VI

HIS PA AN ORANGEMAN.

The grocery man shamefully abused—He gets hot—Butter, oleomargarine and axle grease—the old man wears orange on St. Patrick's day—He has to run for his life—the bad boy at Sunday school—Ingersoll and Beecher voted out—"Mary had a little lamb."

"SAY, will you do me a favor?" asked the bad boy of the grocery man, as he sat down on the soap box and put his wet boots on the stove.

"Well, y-e-s," said the grocery man hesitatingly, with a feeling that he was liable to be sold. "If you will help me catch the villain who hangs up those disreputable signs in front of my store, I will. What is it?"

"I want you to lick this stamp and put it on this letter. It is to my girl and I want to fool her," and the boy handed over the letter and stamp, and while the grocery man was licking it and putting it on, the boy filled his pockets with dried peaches out of a box.

"There, that's a small job," said the grocery man, as he pressed the stamp on the letter with his thumb and handed it back. "But how are you going to fool her?"

"That's just the business," said the boy, as he held the letter to his nose and smelled of the stamp. "That will make her tired. You see every time she gets a letter from me she kisses the stamp, because she thinks I licked it. When she kisses this stamp and gets the fumes of plug tobacco, and stale beer, and limberger cheese, and mouldy potatoes, it will knock her down, and then she will ask me what ailed the stamp, and I will tell her I got you to lick it, and then it will make her sick, and her parents will stop trading here. O, it will paralyze her. Do you know, you smell like a glue factory. Gosh, I can smell you all over the store. Don't you smell anything that smells spoiled?"

The grocery man thought he did smell something that was rancid, and he looked around the stove and finally kicked the boy's boot off the stove and said, "It's your boot burning Gracious, open the door! It smells like a hot box on a caboose. Whew! And there comes a couple of my best lady customers." The ladies came in and held their handkerchiefs to their noses, and while they were trading the boy said, as though continuing the conversation:

"Yes, Pa says that last oleomargarine I got here is nothing but axle grease. Why don't you put your axle grease in a different kind of a package? The only way you can tell axle grease from oleomargarine is in spreading it on pancakes. Pa says axle grease will spread, but your alleged butter just rolls right up and acts like lip salve, or ointment, and is only fit to use on a sore—"

At this point the ladies went out of the store in disgust, without buying anything, and the grocery man took a dried codfish by the tail and went up to the boy and took him by the neck. "Golblast you, I have a notion to kill you. You have driven away more custom from this store than your neck is worth. Now you git," and he struck the boy across the back with the codfish.

"That's just the way with you all," says the boy, as he put his sleeve up to his eyes and pretended to cry, "when a fellow is up in the world, there is nothing too good for him, but when he gets down you maul him with a codfish. Since Pa drove me out of the house, and told me to go shirk for my living, I haven't had a kind word from anybody. My chum's dog won't even follow me, and when a fellow gets so low down that a dog goes back on him there is nothing left for him to do but to loaf around a grocery, or sit on a jury, and I am too young to sit on a jury, though I know more than some of the dead beats that lay around the court to get on a jury. I am going to drown myself, and my death will be laid to you. They will find evidences of codfish on my clothing, and you will be arrested for driving me to a suicide's grave. Good-bye. I forgive you," and the boy started for the door.

"Hold on here," says the grocery man, feeling that he had been too harsh. "Come back here, and have some maple sugar. What did your Pa drive you away from home for?"

THE GROCERYMAN TOOK A DRIED CODFISH BY THE TAIL.

"O, it was on account of St. Patrick's Day," said the bad boy as he bit off half a pound of maple sugar, and dried his tears. "You see, Pa never sees Ma buy a new silk handkerchief, but he wants it. T'other day Ma got one of these orange-colored handkerchiefs, and Pa immediately had a sore throat and wanted to wear it, and Ma let him put it on. I thought I would break him of taking everything nice that Ma got, so when he went down town with the orange handkerchief on his neck, I told some of the St. Patrick boys in the Third ward, who had green ribbons on, that the old duffer that was putting on style was an orange-man, and he said he could whip any St. Patrick's Day man in town. The fellers laid for Pa, and when he came along one of them threw a barrel at Pa, and another pulled the yellow handkerchief off his neck, and they all yelled 'Hang him,' and one grabbed a rope that was on the sidewalk where they were moving a building, and Pa got up and dusted. You'd a dide to see Pa run. He met a policeman and said more'n a hundred men had tried to murder him, and they had mauled him, and stolen his yellow handkerchief. The policeman told Pa his life was not safe, and he better go home and lock himself in, and he did, and I was telling Ma about how I got the boys to scare Pa, and he heard it, and he told me that settled it. He said I had caused him to run more foot races than any champion pedestrian, and had made his life unbearable, and now I must go it alone. Now I want you to send a couple of pounds of crackers over to the house, and have your boy tell the hired girl that I have gone down to the river to drown myself, and she will tell Ma, and Ma will tell Pa, and pretty soon you will see a bald-headed pussy man whooping it up toward the river with a rope. They may think at times that I am a little tough, but when it comes to parting forever, they weaken."

"Well, the teacher says you are a hardened infidel," said the grocery man, as he charged the crackers to the boy's Pa. "He says he had to turn you out to keep you from ruining the morals of the other scholars. How was that?"

"It was about speaking a piece. When I asked him what I should speak, he told me to learn some speech of some great man, some lawyer or statesman, so I learned one of Bob Ingersoll's speeches. Well, you'd a dide to see the teacher and the school committee, when I started in on Bob Ingersoll's lecture, the one that was in the paper when Bob was here. You see I thought if a newspaper that all the pious folks takes in their families, could publish Ingersoll's speech, it wouldn't do any hurt for a poor little boy who ain't knee high to a giraffe, to speak it in school, but they made me dry up. The teacher is a republican, and when Ingersoll was speaking around here on politix, the time of the election, the teacher said Bob was the smartest man this

THE POLICEMAN TOLD PA TO GO HOME AND LOCK HIMSELF IN.

country ever produced. I heard him say that in a corcus, when he went bumming around the ward settin' 'em up nights, 'specting to be superintendent of schools. He said Bob Ingersoll just took the cake, and I think it was darned mean in him to go back on Bob and me, too, just 'cause there was no 'lection. The school committee made the teacher stop me, and they asked me if I didn't know any other piece to speak, and I told them I knew one of Beecher's, and they let me go ahead, but it was one of Beecher's new ones where he said he didn't believe in any hell, and afore I got warmed up they said that was enough of that, and I had to wind up on 'Mary had a Little Lamb.' None of them didn't kick on Mary's Lamb and I went through it, and they let me go home. That's about the safest thing a boy can speak in school now-days, either 'Mary had a Little Lamb,' or 'Twinkle, Twinkle Little Star.' That's about up to the average intelleck of the committee. But if a boy tries to branch out as a statesman, they choke him off. Well, I am going down to the river, and I will leave my coat and hat by the wood yard, and get behind the wood, and you steer Pa down there and you will see some tall weeping over them clothes, and maybe Pa will jump in after me, and then I will come out from behind the wood and throw in a board for him to swim ashore on. Good-bye. Give my pocket comb to my chum," and the boy went out and hung up a sign in front of the grocery as follows:

POP CORN THAT THE CAT HAS SLEPT

IN, CHEAP FOR

POP CORN BALLS FOR SOCIABLES.

Bad Boy's Chum.

CHAPTER VII

HIS MA DECEIVES HIM

The bad boy in search of saffron—"Well, it's a girl if you must know"—The bad boy is grieved at his Ma's deception —"S-h-h tootsy go to sleep"—"By low, baby"—That settled it with the cat—A baby! bah! it makes me tired.

"GIVE me ten cents worth of saffron, quick," said the bad boy to the grocery man, as he came in the grocery on a gallop, early one morning, with no collar on and no vest. He looked as though he had been routed out of bed in a hurry and had jumped into his pants and boots, and put on his coat and hat on the run.

"I don't keep saffron," said the grocery man as he picked up a barrel of ax-handles the boy had tipped over in his hurry. "You want to go over to the drug store on the corner, if you want saffron. But what on earth is the mat——"

At this point the boy shot out of the door, tripping over a basket of white beans and disappearing in the drug store. The grocery man got down on his knees on the sidewalk and scooped up the beans, occasionally looking over to the drug store, and just as he got them picked up, the boy came out of the drug store and walked deliberately towards his home as though there was no particular hurry. The grocery man looked after him, took up an ax-handle, spit on his hands, and shouted to the boy to come over pretty soon, as he wanted to talk with him. The boy did not come to the grocery till towards night; but the grocery man had seen him running down town a dozen times during the day and once he rode up to the house with the doctor, and the grocer surmised what was the trouble. Along towards night the boy came in in a dejected sort of a tired way, sat down on a barrel of sugar, and never spoke.

"What is it, a boy or girl?" said the grocery man, winking at an old lady with a shawl over her head, who was trying to hold a paper over a pitcher of yeast with her thumb.

"How in blazes did you know anything about it?" said the boy, as he looked around in astonishment, and with some indignation. "Well, it's a girl, if you must know, and that's enough," and he looked down at the cat playing on the floor with a potato, his face a picture of dejection.

"O, don't feel bad about it," said the grocery man, as he opened the door for the old lady. "Such things are bound to occur; but you take my word for it, that young one is going to have a hard life unless you mend your ways. You will be using it for a cork to a jug, or to wad a gun with, the first thing your Ma knows."

"I wouldn't touch the darn thing with the tongs," said the boy as he rallied enough to eat some crackers and cheese. "Gosh, this cheese tastes good. I hain't had nothing to eat since morning. I have been all over this town trolling for nurses. They think a boy hasn't got any feelings. But I wouldn't care a goldarn, if Ma hadn't been sending me for neuralgia medicine, and hay fever stuff all winter, when she wanted to get rid of me. I have come into the room lots of times when Ma and the sewing girl were at work on some flannel things, and Ma would hide them in a basket and send me off after medicine. I was deceived up to about four o'clock this morning, when Pa come to my room and pulled me out of bed to go over on the West Side after some old woman that knew Ma, and they have kept me whooping ever since. What does a boy want of a sister, unless it is a big sister? I don't want no sister that I have got to hold, and rock, and hold a bottle for. This affair breaks me all up," and the boy picked the cheese out of his teeth with a sliver he cut from the counter.

"Well, how does your Pa take it?" asked the grocery man, as he charged the boy's Pa with cheese, and saffron and a number of such things.

"O, Pa will pull through. He wanted to boss the whole

concern until Ma's chum, an old woman that takes snuff, fired him out into the hall. Pa sat there on my hand-sled, a perfect picture of despair, and I thought it would be a kindness to play it on him. I found the cat asleep in the bathroom, and I rolled the cat up in a shawl and brought it out to Pa and told him the nurse wanted him to hold the baby. It seemed to do Pa good to feel that he was indispensable around the house, and he took the cat on his lap as tenderly as you ever saw a mother hold her infant. Well, I got in the back hall, where he couldn't see me, and pretty soon the cat began to wake up and stretch himself, and Pa said, 'S-h-h-tootsy, go to sleep now, and let its Pa hold it,' and Pa rocked back and forth on the hand-sled and began to sing 'By, low, baby.' That settled it with the cat. Well, some cats can't stand music, anyway, and the more the cat wanted to get out of the shawl the harder Pa sung, and bimeby I heard something rip, and Pa yelled, 'Scat you brute,' and when I looked around the corner of the hall the cat was bracing hisself against Pa's vest with his toe nails, and yowling and Pa fell over the sled and began to talk about the hereafter like the minister does when he gets excited in church, and then Pa picked up the sled, and

SCAT YOU BRUTE.

seemed to be looking for me or the cat, but both of us was offul scarce. Don't you think there are times when boys and cats are kind of few around their accustomed haunts? Pa don't look as though he was very smart, but he can hold a cat about as well as the next man. But I am sorry for Ma. She was just getting ready to go to Florida for her neuralgia, and this will put a stop to it, 'cause she has to stay and take care of that young one. Pa says I will have a nice time this summer pushing the baby wagon. By the great horn spoons, there has got to be a dividing line somewhere between business and pleasure, and I strike the line at wheeling a baby. I had rather catch a string of perch than to wheel all the babies ever was. They needn't procure no baby on my account, if it is to amuse me. I don't see why babies can't be sawed off onto people that need them in their business. Our folks don't need a baby any more than you need a safe, and there are people just suffering for babies. Say, how would it be to take the baby some night and leave it on some old bachelor's door-step? If it had been a bicycle, or a breech-loading shot-gun, I wouldn't have cared, but a baby! Bah! It makes me tired. I'd druther have a prize package. Well, I am sorry Pa allowed me to come home after he drove me away last week. I guess all he wanted me to come back for was to humiliate me, and send me on errands. Well, I must go and see if he and the cat have made up."

And the boy went out and put a paper sign in front of the store:

LEAVE YOUR MEASURE FOR

SAFFRON TEA.

CHAPTER VIII

THE BABY AND THE GOAT

The bad boy thinks his sister will be a fire engine—"Old number two" —Baby requires goat milk—The goat is frisky—Takes to eating Roman candles—The old man, the hired girl and the goat—The bad boy becomes teller in the livery stable.

"WELL, how is the baby?" asked the grocery man of the bad boy, as he came into the grocery smelling very "horsey," and sat down on the chair with the back gone, and looked very tired.

"O, darn the baby. Everybody asks me about the b a b y as though it was mine. I don't pay no attention to the darn thing, except to notice the foolishness going on around the house. Say, I guess that baby will grow up to be a fire engine. The nurse coupled the baby onto a section of rubber hose that runs down into a bottle of milk, and it began to get up steam and pretty soon the milk began to disappear, just like the water does when a fire engine couples onto a hydrant. Pa calls the baby 'Old Number Two.' I am 'Number One,' and if Pa had a hook and ladder truck and a

OLD NUMBER TWO.

hose cart, and a fire gong he would imagine he was chief engineer of the fire department. But the baby kicks on this milk wagon milk, and howls like a dog that's got lost. The doctor told Pa the best thing he could do was to get a goat, but Pa said since we 'nishiated him into the Masons with the goat he wouldn't have a goat around no how. The doc. told Pa the other kind of a goat, I think it was a Samantha goat he said, wouldn't kick with its head, and Pa sent me up into the Polack settlement to see if I couldn't borrow a milk goat for a few weeks. I got a woman to lend us her goat till the baby got big enough to chew beef, for a dollar a week, and paid a dollar in advance, and Pa went up in the evening to help me to get the goat. Well, it was the darndest mistake you ever see. There was two goats so near alike you could not tell which was the goat we leased, and the other goat was the chum of our goat, but it belonged to a nirish woman. We got a bed cord hitched around the Irish goat, and that goat didn't recognize the lease, and when we tried to jerk it along it rared right up, and made things real quick for Pa. I don't know what there is about a goat that makes it get so spunky, but that goat seemed to have a grudge against Pa from the first. If there were any places on Pa's manly form that the goat did not explore, with his head, Pa don't know where the places are. O, it lammed him and when I laffed Pa got mad. I told him every man ought to furnish his own goats, when he had a baby, and I let go the rope and started off, and Pa said he knew how it was, I wanted him to get killed. It wasn't that, but I saw the Irish woman that owned the goat coming around the corner of the house with a cistern pole. Just as Pa was getting the goat out of the gate the goat got crossways of the gate, and Pa yanked, and doubled the goat right up, and I thought he had broke the goat's neck, and the woman thought so too, for she jabbed Pa with the cistern pole just below the belt and she tried to get a hold on Pa's hair, but he had her there. No woman can get the advantage of Pa that way, 'cause Ma has tried it. Well, Pa explained it to the woman and she let Pa off if he would pay her two dollars for damages to her goat, and he paid it, and then we took the nanny goat, and it went right along with us. But I have my opinion of a baby that will drink goat's milk. Gosh, it is like this stuff that comes in a spoiled cocoanut. The baby hasn't done anything but blat since the nurse coupled it onto the goat hydrant. I had to take all my playthings out of the basement to keep the goat from eating them. I guess the milk will taste of powder and singed hair now. The goat got to eating some Roman candles me and my chum had laid away in the coal bin, and chewed them around the furnace, and the powder leaked out and a coal fell out of the furnace on the hearth, and you'd a dide to see Pa and the hired girl and the goat. You see Pa can't milk nothing but a milk wagon, and he got the hired girl to milk the goat, and they were just hunting around the basement for the goat with a tin cup, when the fireworks went off. Well, there was balls of green, and red and blue fire, and spilled powder blazed up, and the goat just looked astonished, and looked on as though it was sorry so much good fodder was spoiled, but when its hair began to burn, the goat gave one snort and went between Pa and the hired girl like it was shot out of a cannon, and it knocked Pa over a wash boiler into the coal bin and the hired girl in amongst the kindling wood, and she crossed herself and repeated the catechism, and the goat jumped up on the brick furnace, and they couldn't get it down. I heard the celebration and went down and took Pa by the pants and pulled him out of the coal bin, and he said he would surrender and plead guilty of being the biggest fool in Milwaukee. I pulled the kindling wood off the hired girl, and then she got mad, and said she would milk the goat or die. O, that girl has got sand. She used to work in a glass factory. Well, sir, it was a sight worth two shillings admission, to see that hired girl get up on a step ladder to milk that goat on top of the furnace, with Pa sitting on a barrel of potatoes, bossing the job. They are going to fix a gang plank to get the goat down off the furnace. The baby kicked on the milk last night. I guess besides tasting of powder and burnt hair, the milk was too warm on account of the furnace. Pa has got to grow a new lot of hair on the goat, or the woman won't take it back. She don't want no bald goat. Well, they can run the baby and goat to suit themselves, 'cause I have resigned. I have gone into business. Don't you smell anything that would lead you to surmise that I had gone into business? No drug store this time," and the boy got up and put his thumbs in the armholes of his vest, and looked proud.

"O, I don't know as I smell anything except the faint odor of a horse blanket. What you gone into, anyway?" and the grocery man put the wrapping paper under the counter, and put the red chalk in his pocket, so the boy couldn't write any sign to hang up outside.

"You hit it the first time. I have accepted a situation of teller in a livery stable," said the boy, as he searched around for the barrel of cut sugar, which had been removed.

"Teller in a livery stable! Well, that is a new one on me. What is a teller in a livery stable?" and the grocery man looked pleased, and pointed the boy to a barrel of seven cent sugar.

"Don't you know what a teller is in a livery stable? It is the same as a teller in a bank. I have to grease the harness, oil the buggies, and curry off the horses, and when a man comes in to hire a horse I have to go down to the saloon and tell the livery man. That's what a teller is. I like the teller part of it; but greasing harness is a little too rich for my blood, but the livery man says that if I stick to it I will be governor some day, 'cause most all the great men have begun life taking care of horses. It all depends on my girl whether I stick or not. If she likes the smell of horses I shall be a statesman, but if she objects to it and sticks up her nose, I shall not yearn to be governor, at the expense of my girl. It beats all, don't it, that wimmin settle every great question? Everybody does everything to please wimmin, and if they kick on anything that settles it. But I must go and umpire that game between Pa and the hired girl and the goat. Say, can't you come over and see the baby? 'Taint bigger than a small satchel," and the boy waited till the grocery man went to draw some vinegar, when he slipped out and put up a sign written on a shingle with white chalk:

YELLOW SAND WANTED
FOR
MAPLE SUGAR.

CHAPTER IX

A FUNERAL PROCESSION

The bad boy on crutches—"You ought to see the minister!"—An eleven dollar funeral—The minister takes the lines—An earthquake—After the earthquake was over—The policeman fans the minister—A minister should have sense.

"WELL, great Julius Cæsar's bald-headed ghost, what's the matter with you?" said the grocery man to the bad boy, as he came into the grocery on crutches, with one arm in a sling, one eye blackened, and a strip of court plaster across his face. "Where was the explosion, or have you been in a fight, or has your Pa been giving you what you deserve, with a club? Here, let me help you; there, sit down on that keg of apple-jack. Well, by the great guns, you look as though you had called somebody a liar. What's the matter?" and the grocery man took the crutches and stood them up against the showcase.

"O, there's not much the matter with me," said the boy in a voice that sounded all broke up, as he took a big apple off a basket, and began peeling it with his upper front teeth. "If you think I'm a wreck, you ought to see the minister; they had to carry him home in installments, the way they buy sewing machines. I am all right, but they have got to stop him up with oakum and tar, before he will hold water again."

"Good gracious, you have not had a fight with the minister, have you? Well, I have said all the time, and I stick to it, that you would commit a crime yet, and go to state's prison. What was the fuss about?" and the grocery man laid the hatchet out of the boy's reach for fear he would get excited and kill him.

"O, it was no fuss, it was in the way of business. You see the livery man that I was working for promoted me. He let me drive a horse to haul sawdust for bedding, first, and when he found I was real careful he let me drive an express wagon to haul trunks. Day before yesterday, I think it was—yes, I was in bed all day yesterday — day before yesterday there was a funeral, and our stable furnished the outfit. It was only a common, eleven dollar funeral so they let me go to drive the horse for the minister — you know, the buggy that goes ahead of the hearse. They gave me an old horse that is thirty years old, that has not been off a walk since nine years ago, and they told me to give him a loose rein, and he would go along all right. It' the same old horse that used to pace so fast on the avenue, years ago, but I didn't know it. Well, I wasn't to blame. I just let him walk along as though he was hauling sawdust, and gave him a loose rein. When we got off the pavement, the fellow that drives the hearse, he was in a hurry, 'cause his folks was going to have ducks for dinner, and he wanted to get back, so he kept driving along side of my buggy, and telling me to hurry up. I wouldn't do it 'cause the livery

MY LITTLE MAN I GUESS YOU'D BETTER DRIVE.

man told me to walk the horse. Then the minister, he got nervous, and said he didn't know as there was any use of going so slow, because he wanted to get back in time to get his lunch and go to a minister's meeting in the afternoon, but I told him we would all get to the cemetery soon enough if we took it cool, and as for me I wasn't in no sweat. Then one of the drivers that was driving the mourners, he came up and said he had to get back in time to run a wedding down to the one o'clock train, and for me to pull out a little. I have seen enough of disobeying orders, and I told him a funeral in the hand was worth two weddings in the bush, and as far as I was concerned, this funeral was going to be conducted in a decorous manner, if we didn't get back till the next day. Well, the minister said, in his regular Sunday school way, 'My little man, let me take hold of the lines,' and like a darned fool I gave them to him. He slapped the old horse on the crupper with the lines and then jerked up, and the old horse stuck up his off ear, and then the hearse driver told the minister to pull hard and saw on the bit a little, and the old horse would wake up. The hearse driver used to drive the old pacer on the track, and he knew what he wanted. The minister took off his black kid gloves and put his umbrella down between us, and pulled his hat down tight on his head, and began to pull and saw on the bit. The old cripple began to move along sort of sideways, like a hog going to war, and the minister pulled some more, and the hearse driver, who was behind, he said, so you could hear him clear to Waukesha, 'Ye-e-up,' and the old horse kept going faster, then the minister thought the procession was getting to quick, and he pulled harder, and yelled 'Who-a,' and that made the old horse worse, and I looked through the little window in the buggy top, behind, and the hearse was about two blocks behind, and the driver was laughing, and the minister he got pale and said, 'My little man I guess you'd better drive,' and I said, 'Not much, Mary Ann, you wouldn't let me run this funeral the way I wanted to, and now you can boss it, if you will let me get out,' but there was a street car ahead, and all of a sudden there was an earthquake, and when I come to there were about six hundred people pouring water down my neck, and the hearse was hitched to the fence, and the hearse driver was asking if my leg was broke, and a policeman was fanning the minister with a plug hat that looked as though it had been struck by a pile driver, and some people were hauling our buggy into the gutter, and some men were trying to take old pacer out of the windows of the street-car, and then I guess I fainted away again. O, it was worse than telescoping a train loaded with cattle."

"Well, I swan," said the grocery man as he put some eggs in a funnel shaped brown paper for a servant girl, "What did the minister say when he come to?"

"Say! What could he say? He just yelled 'Whoa,' and kept sawing with his hands, as though he was driving. I heard that the policeman was going to pull him for fast driving, till he found it was an accident. They told me, when they carried me home in a hack, that it was a wonder everybody was not killed, and when I got home Pa was going to sass me, until the hearse driver told him it was the minister that was to blame. I want to find out if they got the minister's umbrella back. The last I see of it the umbrella was running up his trouser's leg, and the point came out by the small of his back. But I am all right, only my shoulder sprained, and my legs bruised, and my eye black. I will be all right, and shall go to work to-morrow, 'cause the livery man says I was the only one in the crowd that had any sense. I understand the minister is going to take a vacation on account of his liver and nervous prostration. I would if I was him. I never saw a man that had nervous prostration any more than he did when they fished him out of the barbed wire fence, after we struck the street car. But that settles the minister business with me. I don't drive for no more preachers. What I want is a quiet party that wants to go on a walk," and the boy got up and hopped on one foot toward his crutches, filling his pistol pocket with figs as he hobbled along.

"Well, sir," said the grocery man, as he took a chew of tobacco out of a pail, and offered some to the boy, knowing that was the only thing in the store the boy would not take, "Do you know I think some of these ministers have about as little sense on worldly matters, as anybody? Now, the idea of that man jerking on an old pacer. It don't make any difference if the pacer was a hundred years old, he *would* pace if he was jerked on."

"You bet," said the boy, as he put his crutches under his arms and started for the door. "A minister may be sound on the atonement, but he don't want to saw on an old pacer. He may have the subject of infant baptism down finer than a cambric needle, but if he has ever been to college, he ought to have learned enough not to say '*ye-up*' to an old pacer that has been the boss of the road in his time. A minister may be endowed with sublime power to draw sinners to repentance, and make them feel like getting up and dusting for the beautiful beyond, and cause them, by his eloquence, to see angels bright and fair in their dreams, and chariots of fire flying through the pearly gates and down the golden streets of New Jerusalem, but he wants to turn out for a street car all the same, when he is driving a 2:20 pacer. The next time I drive a minister to a funeral, he will walk," and the boy hobbled out and hung out a sign in front of the grocery:

SMOKED DOG FISH AT HALIBUT

PRICES, GOOD ENOUGH

FOR COMPANY.

CHAPTER X

THE OLD MAN MAKES A SPEECH

The grocery man and the bad boy have a fuss—The Bohemian Band—The bad boy organizes a serenade—"Baby mine"—The old man eloquent—The Bohemians create a famine—The Y. M. C. A. announcement.

"THERE, you drop that," said the grocery man to the bad boy, as he came limping into the store and began to fumble around a box of strawberries. "I have never kicked at your eating my codfish, and crackers and cheese, and herring, and apples, but there has got to be a dividing line somewhere, and I make it at strawberries at six shillings a box, and only two layers in a box. I only bought one box, hoping some plumber or gas man would come along and buy it, and by gum, everybody that has been in the store has sampled a strawberry out of that box, shivered as though it was sour and gone off without asking the price," and the grocery man looked mad, took a hatchet and knocked in the head of a barrel of apples, and said: "There, help yourself to dried apples."

"O, I don't want your strawberries or dried apples," said the boy, as he leaned against a show case and looked at a bar of red, transparent soap. "I was only trying to fool you. Say, that bar of soap is old enough to vote. I remember seeing it in your show case when I was about a year old, and Pa came in here with me and held me up to the show case to look at that tin tobacco box, and that round zinc looking-glass, and the yellow wooden pocket comb, and the soap looks just the same, only a little faded. If you would wash yourself once in a while your soap wouldn't dry up on your hands," and the boy sat down on the chair without any back, feeling that he was even with the grocery man.

"You never mind the soap. It is paid for and that is more than your father can say about the soap that has been used in his house the past month," said the grocery man, as he split up a box to kindle the fire. "But we won't quarrel. What was it I heard about a band serenading your father, and his inviting them in to lunch?"

"Don't let that get out or Pa will kill me dead. It was a joke. One of those Bohemian bands that goes about town playing tunes for pennies, was over on the next street, and I told Pa I guessed some of his friends who had heard we had a baby at the house, had hired a band and was coming in a few minutes to serenade him and he better prepare to make a speech. Pa is proud of being a father at his age, and he thought it no more than right for the neighbors to serenade him, and he went to loading himself for a speech, in the library, and me and my chum went out and told the leader of the band there was a family up there that wanted to have some music, and they didn't care for expense, so they quit blowing where they was and came right along. None of them could understand English except the leader, and he only understood enough to go and take a drink when he is invited. My chum steered the band up to our house and got them to play 'Babies on our Block,' and 'Baby Mine,' and I stopped all the men who were going home and told them to wait a minute and they would see some fun; so when the band got through the second tune, and the Prussians were emptying the beer out of the horns, and Pa stepped out on the porch, there was more nor a hundred people in front of the house. You'd a dide to see Pa, when he put his hand in the breast of his coat, and struck an attitude. He looked like a congressman, or a tramp. The band was scared, 'cause they thought he was mad, and some of them were going to run, thinking he was going to throw pieces of brick house at them, but my chum and the leader kept them. Then Pa sailed in. He commenced, 'Fellow Citizens,' and then went away back to Adam and Eve, and worked up to the present day, giving a history of the notable people who had acquired children, and kept the crowd interested. I felt sorry for Pa, 'cause I knew how he would feel when he came to find out how he had been sold. The Bohemians in the band that couldn't understand English, they looked at each other, and wondered what it was all about,

PA STEPPED OUT ON THE PORCH.

and finally Pa wound up by stating that it was every citizen's duty to own children of his own, and then he invited the band and the crowd in to take some refreshments. Well, you ought to have seen that band come in the house. They fell over each other getting in, and the crowd went home, leaving Pa and my chum and me and the band. Eat? Well, I should smile. They just reached for things and talked Bohemian. Drink? O, no. I guess they didn't pour it down. Pa opened a dozen bottles of champagne, and they fairly bathed in it, as though they had a fire inside. Pa tried to talk with them about the baby, but they couldn't understand, and finally they got full and started out, and the leader asked Pa for three dollars, and that broke him. Pa told the leader he supposed the gentlemen who had got up the serenade had paid for the music and the leader pointed to me and said I was the gentleman that got it up. Pa paid him, but he had a wicked look in his eye, and me and my chum lit out, and the Bohemians came down the street bilin' full, with their horns on their arms, and they were talking Bohemian for all that was out. They stopped in front of a vacant house, and began to play; but you couldn't tell what tune it was they were so full, and a policeman came along and drove them home. I guess I will sleep at the livery stable to-night, 'cause Pa is so offul unreasonable when anything costs him three dollars besides the champagne."

"Well, you have made a pretty mess of it," said the grocery man. "It's a wonder your Pa does not kill you. But what is it I hear about the trouble at the church? They lay that foolishness to you."

"It's all a lie. They lay everything to me. It was some of them ducks that sing in the choir. I was just as much surprised as anybody when it occurred. You see our minister is laid up from the effects of the ride to the funeral, when he tried to run over a street car, and an old deacon who had symptoms of being a minister in his youth, was invited to take the minister's place, and talk a little. He is an absent minded old party, who don't keep up with the events of the day, and who ever played it on him knew that he was too pious to even read the daily papers. There was a notice of a choir meeting to be read, and I think the tenor smuggled in the other notice between that and the one about the weekly prayer meeting. Anyway, it wasn't me, but it like to broke up the meeting. After the deacon read the choir notice he took up the other one and read, 'I am requested to announce that the Y. M. C. Association will give a friendly entertainment with soft gloves, on Tuesday evening, to which all are invited. Brother John Sullivan, the eminent Boston revivalist, will lead the exercises, assisted by Brother Slade, the Maori missionary from Australia. There will be no slugging, but a collection will be taken up at the door to defray expenses.' Well, I thought the people in church would sink through the floor. There was not a person in the church except the poor old deacon, but who understood that some wicked wretch had deceived him, and I know by the way the tenor tickled the soprano that he did it. I may be mean, but everything I do is innocent, and I wouldn't be as mean as a choir singer for two dollars. I felt real sorry for the old deacon, but he never knew what he had done, and I think it would be real mean to tell him. He won't be at the slugging match. That remark about taking up a collection settled the deacon. I must go down to the stable, now, and help grease a hack, so you will have to excuse me. If Pa comes here looking for me, tell him you heard I was going to drive a picnic party out to Waukesha, and may not be back in a week. By that time Pa will have got over that Bohemian serenade," and the boy filled his pistol pocket with dried apples, and went out and hung a sign in front of the grocery:

STRAWBERRIES, TWO SHILLINGS

A SMELL,

AND ONE SMELL IS ENOUGH.

CHAPTER XI

GARDENING UNDER DIFFICULTIES

The grocery man is deceived—The bad boy don't like moving—Goes into the coloring business—The old man thoroughly disguised—Uncle Tom and Topsy—The old man arrested—What the grocery man thinks—The bad boy moralizes on his fate—Resolves to be good.

"SEE here, you coon, get out of here," said the grocery man to the bad boy, as he came in the store with his face black and shining, "I don't want any colored boys around here. White boys break me up bad enough."

"O, philopena," said the bad boy as he put his hands on his knees and laughed so the candy jars rattled on the shelves. "You didn't know me. I am the same boy that comes in here and talks your arm off," and the boy opened the cheese box and cut off a piece of cheese so natural that the grocery man had no difficulty in recognizing him.

"What in the name of the seven sleeping sisters have you got on your hands and face?" said the grocery man, as he took the boy by the ear and turned him around. "You would pass in a colored prayer meeting, and no one would think you were galvanized. What you got up in such an outlandish rig for?"

"Well, I'll tell you, if you will keep watch at the door. If you see a bald-headed colored man coming along the street with a club, you whistle, and I will fall down cellar. The bald-headed colored man will be Pa. You see, we moved yesterday. Pa told me to get a vacation from the livery stable, and we would have fun moving. But I don't want any more fun. I know when I have got enough fun. Pa carried all the light things, and when it came to lifting, he had a crick in the back. Gosh, I never was so tired as I was last night, and I hope we have got settled, only some of the goods haven't turned up yet. A drayman took one load over on the West Side, and delivered them to a house that seemed to be expecting a load of household furniture. He thought it was all right, if everybody that was moving got a load of

THE POLICEMAN TOOK PA BY THE NECK.

goods. Well, after we got moved Pa said we must make a garden, and we said we would go out and spade up the ground and sow peas, and radishes and beets. There was some neighbors lived in the next house to our new one, that was all wimmin, and Pa don't like to have them think he had to work, so he said it would be a good joke to disguise ourselves as tramps and the neighbors would think we had hired some tramps to dig in the garden. I told Pa of a boss scheme to fool them. I suggested that we take some of his shoe blacking that is put on with a sponge, and black our faces, and the neighbors would think we had hired an old colored man and his boy to work in the garden. Pa said it was immense, and he told me to go and black up, and if it worked he would black hisself. So I went and put this burnt cork on my face, 'cause it would wash off, and Pa looked at me and said it was wack, and for me to fix him up too. So I got the bottle of shoe blacking and painted Pa so he looked like a colored coal heaver. Actually, when Ma saw him she ordered him off the premises, and when he laffed at her and acted sassy, she was going to throw biling water on Pa. But I told her the scheme and she let up on Pa. O, you'd a dide to see us out in the garden. Pa looked like Uncle Tom, and I looked like Topsy, only I ain't that kind of a colored person. We worked till a boy throwed some tomato cans over the alley fence and hit me, and I piled over the fence after him and left Pa. It was my chum, and when I had caught him we put up a job to get Pa to chase us. We throwed some more cans, and Pa come out and my chum started, and I after him, and Pa after both of us. He chased us two blocks and then we got behind a policeman, and my chum told the policeman it was a crazy old colored man that wanted to kidnap us, and the policeman took Pa by the neck and was going to club him, but Pa said he would go home and behave. He was offul mad, and he went home, and we looked through the alley fence and Pa was trying to wash off the blacking. You see that blacking won't wash off. You have to wear it off. Pa would wash his face with soap suds, and then look in the glass, and he was blacker every time he washed, and when Ma laffed at him he said the offulest words, something like 'Sweet spirit hear my prayer,' then he washed himself again. I am going to leave my burnt cork cork on, 'cause if I washed it off Pa would know there had been some smouging somewhere. I asked the shoe store man how long it would take the blacking to wear off, and he said it ought to wear off in a week. I guess Pa won't go out doors much, unless it is in the night. I am going to get him to let me go off in the country fishing, till mine wears off, and when I get out of town I will wash up. Say, you don't think a little blacking hurts a man's complexion, do you, and you don't think a man ought to get mad because it won't wash off, do you?"

"O, probably it don't hurt the complexion," said the grocery man, as he sprinkled some fresh water on the wilted lettuce, so it would look fresh while the hired girl was buying some, "and yet it is mighty unpleasant, where a man has got an engagement to go to a card party, as I know your Pa has to-night. As to getting mad about it, if I was your Pa I would take a barrel stave and shatter your castle scandalous. What kind of a fate do you think awaits you when you die, anyway?"

"Well, I am mixed on the fate that awaits me when I die. If I should go off sudden, with all my sins on my head, and this burnt cork on my face, I should probably be a neighbor to you down below, and they would give me a job as fireman, and I should feel bad for you every time I chucked in another chunk of brimstone, and thought of you trying to swim dog-fashion in the lake of fire, and straining your eyes to find an iceberg that you could crawl on to cool your parched hind legs. If I don't die slow so I will have time to repent and be saved, I shall be toasted brown. That's what the minister says, and they wouldn't pay him two thousand dollars a year and give him a vacation to tell anything that was not so. I tell you it is painful to think of that place that so many pretty fair average people here are going to when they die. Just think of it, a man that swears just once, if he don't hedge, and take it back will go to the bad place. If a person steals a pin, just a small, no account pin, he is as bad as if he stole all there was in a bank, and he stands the best chance of going to the bad place. You see, if a fellow steals a little thing like a pin, he forgets to repent, 'cause it don't seem to be worth while to make so much fuss about. But if a fellow robs a bank, or steals a whole lot of money from orphans, he knows it is a mighty serious matter, and he gets in his work repenting, too quick, and he is liable to get to the good place, while you, who have only stole a few potatoes out of a bushel that you sold to the orphan asylum, will forget to repent, and you will sizzle. I tell you, the more I read about being good, and going to heaven, the more I think a fellow can't be too careful, and from this out you won't find a better boy than I am. When I come in here after this and take a few dried peaches or crackers and cheese, you charge it right up to Pa, and then I won't have it on my mind and have to answer for it at the great judgment day. I am going to shake my chum, cause he chews tobacco, which is wicked, though I don't see how that can be, when the minister smokes, but I want to be on the safe side. I am going to be good or bust a suspender, and hereafter you can point to me as the boy who has seen the folly of an ill-spent life, and if there is such a thing as a fifteen year old boy, who has been a terror, going to heaven, I am the hairpin. I tell you, when I listen to the minister tell about the angels flying around there, and I see pictures of them purtier than any girl in this town, with chubby arms and dimples in the elbows and shoulders, and long golden hair, and think of myself here cleaning off horses in a livery stable and smelling like an old harness, it makes me tired, and I wouldn't miss going there for ten dollars. Say, you would make a healthy angel, for a back street of the new Jerusalem, but you would give the whole crowd away unless you washed up, and sent that shirt to the Chinese laundry. Yes, sir, hereafter you will find me as good as I know how to be. Now I am going to wash up and go and help the minister move."

As the boy went out the grocery man sat for several minutes thinking of the change that had come over the bad boy, and wondered what had brought it about and then he went to the door to watch him as he wended his way across the street with his head down, as though in deep thought, and the grocery man said to himself, "That boy is not as bad as some people think he is," and then he looked around and saw a sign hanging up in front of the store, written on a piece of box cover, with a blue pencil:

> *SPOILED*
> *CANNED HAM AND TONGUE*
> *GOOD ENOUGH*
> *FOR CHURCH PICNICS.*

and he looked after the boy who was slipping down an alley and said: "The condemn little whelp. Wait till I catch him."

CHAPTER XII

THE OLD MAN SHOOTS THE MINISTER

The bad boy tries to lead a different life—Murder in the air—The old man and his friends give themselves away—Dreadful stories of their wicked youth—The chicken coop invaded—The old man to the rescue—The minister and the deacons salted.

"SAY, I thought you was going to try to lead a different life," said the grocery man to the bad boy, as the youth came in with his pockets full of angle worms, and wanted to borrow a baking powder can to put them into, while he went fishing, and he held a long angle worm up by the tail and let it wiggle so it frightened a girl that had come in after two cents worth of yeast, so she dropped her pitcher and went out of the grocery as though she was chased by an anaconda.

"I am going to lead a different life; but a boy can't change his whole course of life in a minute, can he? Grown persons have to go on probation for six months before they can lead a different life, and half the time they lose their cud before the six months expire, and have to commence again. When it is so all fired hard for a man that is endowed with sense to break off being bad, you shouldn't expect too much from a boy. But I am going to do as well as could be expected—I ain't half as bad as I was! Gosh, why don't you burn a rag? That yeast that the girl spilled on the floor smells like it was sick. I should think that bread that was raised with that yeast would smell like this cooking butter you sell to hired girls."

"Well, never you mind the cooking butter. I know my business. If people want to use poor butter when they have company, and then blow up the grocer before folks, I can stand it if they can. But what is this I hear about your Pa fighting a duel with the minister in your back yard, and wounding him in the leg, and then trying to drown himself in the cistern? One of your new neighbors was in here this morning, and told me there was murder in the air at your house last night, and they are going to have the police pull your place as a disorderly house. I think you were at the bottom of the whole business!"

MA WENT TO THE HEAD OF THE STAIRS AND TOLD PA.

"O, it's all a darned lie and those neighbors will find they better keep still about us, or we will lie about them a little. You see, since Pa got that blacking on his face he don't go out any, and to make it pleasant for him Ma invited in a few friends to spend the evening. Ma has got up around, and the baby is a daisy, only it smells like a goat on account of drinking the goat's milk. Ma invited the minister among the rest, and after supper the men went up into Pa's library to talk. O, you think I am bad, don't you, but of the nine men at our house last night I am an angel compared with what they were when they were boys. I got into the bathroom to untangle my fish line, and it is next to Pa's room, and I could hear everything they said, but I went away 'cause I thought the conversation would hurt my morals. They would all steal, when they were boys, but darned if I ever stole. Pa has stolen over a hundred wagon loads of watermelons, one deacon used to rob orchards, another one shot tame ducks belonging to a farmer, and another tipped over grindstones in front of the village store, at night, and broke them, and run, and another used to steal eggs, and go out in the woods and boil them, and the minister was the worst of the lot, 'cause he took a seine, with some other boys, and went to a stream where a neighbor was raising brook trout, and cleaned the stream out, and to ward off suspicion, he went to the man next day and paid him a dollar to let him fish in the stream, and then kicked because there were no trout, and the owner found the trout were stolen and laid it to some Dutch boys. I wondered, when those men were telling their experience, if they ever thought of it now when they were preaching and praying, and taking up collections. I should think they wouldn't say a boy was going to hell right off 'cause he was a little wild nowadays, when he has such an example. Well, lately, somebody has been burgling our chicken coop, and Pa loaded an old musket with rock salt, and said he would fill the fellow full of salt if he caught him, and while they were talking up stairs Ma heard a rooster squawk, and she went to the stairway and told Pa there was somebody in the hen house. Pa jumped up and told the visitors to follow him, and they would see a man running down the alley full of salt, and he rushed out with the gun, and the crowd followed him. Pa is shorter than the rest, and he passed under the first wire clothes line in the yard all right, and was going for the hen house on a jump, when his neck caught the second wire clothes line just as the minister and two of the deacons caught their necks under the other wire. You know how a wire, hitting a man on the throat, will set him back, head over appetite. Well, sir, I was looking out of the back window, and I wouldn't be positive, but I think they all turned double back somersaults, and struck on their ears. Anyway, Pa did, and the gun must have been cocked, or it struck the hammer on a stone, for it went off, and it was pointed toward the house, and three of the visitors got salted. The minister was hit the worst, one piece of salt taking him in the hind leg, and the other in the back, and he yelled as though it was dynamite. I suppose when you shoot a man with salt, it smarts, like when you get corned beef brine on your chapped hands. They all yelled and Pa seemed to have been knocked silly, some way, for he pranced around and seemed to think he had killed

I THOUGHT OF THE CISTERN.

them. He swore at the wire clothes line, and then I missed Pa and heard a splash like when you throw a cat in the river, and then I thought of the cistern, and I went down and we took Pa by the collar and pulled him out. O, he was awful damp. No, sir, it was no duel at all, but a naxident, and I didn't have anything to do with it. The gun wasn't loaded to kill, and the salt only went through the skin, but those men *did* yell. Maybe it was my chum that stirred up the chickens, but I don't know. He has not commenced to lead a different life yet, and he might think it would make our folks sick if nothing occurred to make them pay attention. I think where a family has been having a good deal of exercise, the way ours has, it hurts them to break off too suddenly. But the visitors went home, real quick, after we got Pa out of the cistern, and the minister told Ma he always felt when he was in our house, as though he was on the verge of a yawning crater, ready to be engulfed any minute, and he guessed he wouldn't come any more. Pa changed his clothes and told Ma to have them wire clothes lines changed for rope ones. I think it is hard to suit Pa, don't you?"

"O, your Pa is all right. What he needs is rest. But why are you not working at the livery stable? You haven't been discharged, have you?" And the grocery man laid a little lump of concentrated lye, that looked like maple sugar on a cake of sugar that had been broken, knowing the boy would nibble it.

"No, sir, I was not discharged, but when a livery man lends me a kicking horse to take my girl out riding, that settles it. I asked the boss if I couldn't have a quiet horse that would drive himself if I wound the lines around the whip, and he let me have one he said would go all day without driving. You know how it is, when a fellow takes a girl out riding he don't want his mind occupied holding lines. Well, I got my girl in, and we went out on the Whitefish Bay road, and it was just before dark, and we rode along under the trees, and I wound the lines around the whip, and put one arm around my girl, and patted her under the chin with my other hand, and her mouth looked so good, and her blue eyes looked up at me and twinkled as much as to dare me to kiss her, and I was all of a tremble, and then my hand wandered around by her ear and I drew her head up to me and gave her a smack. Say, that was no kind of a horse to give to a young fellow to take a girl out riding. Just as I smacked her I felt as though the buggy had been struck by a pile-driver, and when I looked at the horse he was running away and kicking the buggy, and the lines were dragging on the ground. I was scared, I tell you. I wanted to jump out but my girl threw her arms around my neck and screamed, and said we would die together, and just as we were going to die the buggy struck a fence and the horse broke loose and went off, leaving us in the buggy tumbled down by the dash board, but we were not hurt. The old horse stopped and went to chewing grass and looked up at me as though he wanted to say 'philopena.' I tried to catch him, but he wouldn't catch, and then we waited till dark and walked home, and I told the livery man what I thought of such treatment, and he said that if I had attended to my driving, and not kissed the girl, I would have been all right. He said I ought to have told him I wanted a horse that wouldn't shy at kissing, but how did I know I was going to get up courage to kiss her? A livery man ought to take it for granted that when a young fellow goes out with his girl he is going to kiss her, and give him a horse according. But I quit him at once. I won't work for a man that hasn't got sense. Gosh! What kind of maple sugar is that? Jerusalem! Whew, give me some water! O, my, it is taking the skin off my mouth!"

The grocery man got him some water and seemed sorry that the boy had taken the lump of concentrated lye by mistake, and when the boy went out the grocery man pounded his hands on his knees and laughed, and presently he went out in front of the store and found a sign:

FRESH LETIS, BEEN PICKED

MORE'N A WEEK

TUFFER'N TRIPE.

CHAPTER XIII

THE BAD BOY A THOROUGHBRED

The bad boy with a black eye—A poor friendless girl excites his pity—Proves himself a gallant knight—The old man is charmed at his son's courage—The grocery man moralizes—Fifteen Christs in Milwaukee—The tables turned—The old man wears the boy's old clothes.

"Ah, ha, you have got your deserts at last," said the grocery man to the bad boy, as he came in with one eye black, and his nose peeled on one side, and sat down on a board across the coal scuttle, and began whistling as unconcerned as possible. "What's the matter with your eye?"

"Boy tried to gouge it out without my consent," and the bad boy took a dried herring out of the box and began peeling it. "He is in bed now, and his ma is poulticing him, and she says he will be out about the last of next week."

"O, you are going to be a prize fighter, ain't you?" said the grocery man, disgusted. "When a boy leaves a job where he is working, and goes to loafing around, he becomes a fighter the first thing. What your Pa ought to do is bind you out with a farmer, where you would have to work all the time. I wish you would go away from here, because you look like one of these fellows that comes up before the police judge Monday morning, and gets thirty days in the house of correction. Why don't you go out and loaf around a slaughter house, where you would look appropriate?" and the grocery man took a hair-brush and brushed some sugar and tea that was on the counter, into the sugar barrel.

"Well, if you have got through with your sermon, I will toot a little on my horn," and the boy threw the remains of the herring over behind a barrel of potatoes, and wiped his hands on a coffee sack. "If you had this black eye, and got it the way I did, it would be a more priceless gem in the crown of glory you hope to wear, than any gem you can get by putting quarters in the collection plate, with the holes filled with lead, as you did last Sunday, when I was watching you. O, didn't you look pious when you picked that filled quarter out, and held your thumb over the place where the lead was? The way of the black eye was this. I got a job tending a soda water fountain, and last night, just before we closed, there was two or three young loafers in the place, and a girl came in for a glass of soda. Five years ago she was one of the brightest scholars in the ward school, when I was in the intermediate department. She was just as handsome as a peach, and everybody liked her. At recess she used to take my part when the boys knocked me around, and she lived near us. She had a heart as big as that cheese box, and I guess that's what's the matter. Anyway, she left school, and then it was said she was going to get married to a fellow who is now in the dude business, but he went back on her, and after awhile her ma turned her out doors, and for a year or two she was jerking beer in a concert saloon, until the mayor stopped concerts. She tried hard to get sewing to do, but they wouldn't have her, I guess 'cause she cried so much when she was sewing, and the tears wet the cloth she was sewing on. Once I asked Pa why Ma didn't give her some sewing to do, and he said for me to dry up and never speak to her if I met her on the street. It seemed tough to pass her on the street when she had tears in her eyes as big as marbles, and not speak to her when I know her so well, and she had been so kind to me at school just 'cause the dude wouldn't marry her, but I wanted to obey Pa, so I used to walk around a block when I see her coming, 'cause I didn't want to hurt her feelings. Well, last night she came in the store, looking pretty shabby, and wanted a glass of soda, and I gave it to her, and O, how her hand trembled when she raised the glass to her lips, and how wet her eyes were, and how pale her face was. I choked up so I couldn't speak when she handed me the nickel, and when she looked up at me and smiled just like she used to, and said I was getting to be almost a man since we went to school at the old school house, and put her handkerchief to her eyes, by gosh my eyes got so full I couldn't tell whether it was a nickel or a lozenger she gave me. Just then one of those loafers began to laugh at her, and call her names, and say the police ought to take her up for a stray, and he made fun of her until she cried some more, and I got hot, and went around to where he was, and told him if he said another unkind word to that girl I would maul him. He laughed and asked if she was my sister, and I told him that a poor, friendless girl, who was sick and in distress, and who was insulted, ought to be every boy's sister, for a minute, and any boy who had a spark of manhood, should protect her, and then he laughed and said I ought to be one of the Little Sisters of the Poor, and he took hold of her faded shawl and pulled the weak girl against the show case, and said something mean to her, and she looked as though she wanted to die, and I mashed that boy one right on the nose. Well, the air seemed to be full of me for a minute, 'cause he was bigger than me, and he got me down, and got his thumb in my eye. I guess he was going to take my eye out, but I turned him over and got on top, and I mauled him until he begged, but I wouldn't let him up till he asked the girl's pardon, and swore he would whip any boy that insulted her, and then I let him up and the girl thanked me; but I told her I couldn't speak to her, 'cause she was tough, and Pa didn't want me to speak to anybody who was tough; but if anybody ever insulted her so she had to cry, that I would whip him if I had to take a club. I told Pa about it, and I thought he would be mad at me for taking the part of a girl that was tough, but, by gosh, Pa hugged me, and the tears came in his eyes, and he said I had got good blood in me, and I did just right; and if I would show him the father of the boy that I whipped, Pa said he could whip the old man, and Ma said for me to find the poor girl and send her up to the house, and she would give her a job making pillow cases and night shirts. Don't it seem darn queer to you that everybody goes back on a poor girl 'cause she makes a mistake, and the blasted whelp that is to blame, gets a chromo? It makes me tired to think of it," and the boy got up and shook himself, and looked into the

O, HOW HER HAND TREMBLED WHEN SHE RAISED THE GLASS.

cracked mirror hanging upon a post, to see how his eye was getting along.

"Say, young fellow, you are a thoroughbred," said the grocery man, as he sprinkled some water on the asparagus and lettuce, "and you can come in here and get all the herring you want, and never mind the black eye. I wish I had it myself. Yes, it does seem tough to see people never allow a girl to reform. Now, in Bible times, the Saviour forgave

Mary or somebody, I forget now what her name was, and she was a better girl than ever. What we need is more of the spirit of Christ, and the world would be better."

"What we want is about ten thousand Christs. We ought to have ten or fifteen right here in Milwaukee, and they would find plenty of business, too. But this climate seems to be too rough. Say, did I tell you about Pa and Ma having trouble?"

"No, what's the row?"

"Well, you see Ma wants to economize all she can, and Pa has been getting thinner since he quit drinking and reformed, and I have kept on growing until I am bigger than he is. Funny, ain't it, that a boy should be bigger than his Pa? Pa wanted a new suit of clothes, and Ma said she would fix him, and so she took one of my old suits and made it over for Pa; and he wore them a week before he knew it was an old suit made over, but one day he found a handful of dried up angle worms in the pistol pocket that I had forgot when I was fishing, and Pa laid the angle worms to Ma, and Ma had to explain that she made over one of my old suits for Pa. He was mad and took them off and threw them out the back window, and swore he would never humiliate himself by wearing his son's old clothes. Ma tried to reason with him, but he was awfully worked up, and said he was no charity hospital, and he stormed around to find his old suit of clothes, but Ma had sold them to a plaster of Paris image peddler, and Pa hadn't anything to wear, and he wanted Ma to go out in the alley and pick up the suit he threw out the window; but a rag man had picked them up and was going away, and Pa, he grabbed a linen duster and put it on and went out after the rag picker, and he run, and Pa after him; and the rag man told a policeman there was an escaped lunatic from the asylum, and he was chasing people all over the city, and the policeman took Pa by the linen ulster, and pulled it off, and he was a sight when they took him to the police station. Ma and me had to go down and bail him out, and the police lent us a tarpaulin to put over Pa, and we got him home, and he is wearing his summer pants while the tailor makes him a new suit of clothes. I think Pa is too excitable, and too particular. I never kicked on wearing Pa's old clothes, and I think he ought to wear mine now. Well, I must go down to the sweetened wind factory, and jerk soda," and the boy went out and hung up a sign in front of the store:

SPINAGE FOR GREENS, THAT
THE CAT HAS MADE
A NEST IN OVER SUNDAY.

CHAPTER XIV

ENTERTAINING Y. M. C. A. DELEGATES.

The bad boy ministers at the Y. M. C. A. water fountain—The delegates flood themselves with soda—Two delegates dealt to his Ma—The night key—The fall of the flower stand—Delegates in the cellar all night—The bad boy's girl is working his reformation.

"WELL, how's your eye?" said the grocery man to the bad boy, as he blew in with the wind on the day of the cyclone, and left the door open. "Shut that door. You want to blow everything out of the store? Had any more fights, protecting girls from dudes?"

"No, everything is quiet so far. I guess since I have got a record as a fighter, the boys will be careful who they insult when I am around. But I have had the hardest week I ever experienced, jerking soda for the Young Men's Christian Association," said the boy, as he peeled a banana.

"What do you mean, boy? Don't cast any reflections on such a noble Association. They don't drink, do they?"

"Drink! O, no! They don't drink anything intoxicating but when it comes to soda they flood themselves. You know there has been a National Convention of delegates from all the Young Men's Christian Associations of the whole country, about three hundred, here, and our store is right on the street where they pass four times a day, and I never saw such appetites for soda. There has been one continual fizz in our store since Wednesday. The boss wanted me to play it on some of them by putting some brandy in with the perfumery a few times, but I wouldn't do it. I guess a few weeks ago, before I had led a different life, I wouldn't had to be asked twice to play the game on anybody. But a man can buy soda of me and be perfectly safe. Of course, if a man winks, when I ask him what flavor he wants, and says 'Never mind,' I know enough to put in brandy. That is different. But I wouldn't smuggle it into a man for nothing. This Christian Association Convention has caused a coldness between Pa and Ma, though."

"How's that? Your Pa isn't jealous, is he?" and the grocery man came around from behind the counter to get the latest gossip to retail to the hired girls who traded with him.

"Jealous nothin'," said the boy, as he took a few raisins out of a box. "You see, the delegates were shuffled out to all the church members to take care of, and they dealt two to Ma, and she never told Pa anything about it. They came to supper the first night, and Pa didn't get home, so when they went to the Convention in the evening, Ma gave them a night key, and Pa came home from the boxing match about eleven o'clock, and Ma was asleep. Just as Pa got most of his clothes off, he heard somebody fumbling at the front door, and he thought it was burglars. Pa has got nerve enough, when he is on the inside of the house and the burglars are on the outside. He opened a window and looked out and saw two suspicious looking characters trying to pick the lock with a skeleton key, and he picked up a new slop-jar that Ma bought when we moved, cover and all, and dropped it right down between the two delegates. Gosh, if it had hit one of them, there would have been the solemnest funeral you ever saw. Just as it struck, they got the door opened and came into the hall, and the wind was blowing pretty hard and they thought a cyclone had taken the cupola off the house. They were talking about being miraculously saved, and trying to strike a match on their wet pants, when Pa went to the head of the stairs and pushed over a wire stand filled with potted plants, which struck pretty near the delegates, and one of them said the house was coming down sure, and they better go into the cellar, and they went and got behind the furnace. Pa called me up and wanted me to go down cellar and tell the burglars we were onto them, and for them to get out, but I wasn't very well, so Pa locked his door and went to bed. I guess it must have been half-an-hour before Pa's cold feet woke Ma up, and then Pa told her not to move for her life, 'cause there were two of the savagest looking burglars that ever was, rummaging over the house. Ma smelled Pa's breath to see if he had got to drinking again, and then she got up and hid her oraide watch in her shoes, and her Onalaska diamond ear-rings in the Bible, where she said no burglar would ever find them, and Pa and Ma laid awake till daylight, and then Pa said he wasn't afraid, and he and Ma went down cellar. Pa stood on the bottom stair and looked around, and one of the delegates said, 'Mister, is the storm over, and is your family safe?' and Ma recognized the voice and said, 'Why, it's one of the delegates. What are you doing down there?' and Pa said, 'What's a delegate?' and then Ma explained it, and Pa apologized, and the delegate said it was no matter as they had enjoyed themselves real well in the cellar. Ma was mortified most to death, and the delegate told her it was all right. She was mad at Pa, first, but when she saw the broken slop-bowl on the front steps, and the potted plants in the hall, she wanted to kill Pa,, and I guess she would only for the society of the delegates. She couldn't help telling Pa that he was a bald headed old fool, but Pa didn't retaliate—he is too much of a gentleman to talk back in company. All he said was that a woman who is old enough to have delegates sawed off on her, ought to have sense enough to tell her husband, and then they all drifted off into conversation about the convention and the boxing match, and everything was all right on the surface; but after breakfast, when the delegates went to the convention, I noticed Pa went right down town and bought a new slop-jar and some more plants. Pa and Ma didn't speak all the forenoon, and I guess they wouldn't up to this time, only Ma's bonnet came home from the milliner's and she had to have some money to pay for it. Then she called Pa 'Pet,' and that settled it. When Ma calls Pa 'Pet,' that is twenty-five dollars. 'Dear, old darling,' means fifty dollars. But say, those christian young men do a heap of good, don't they? Their presence seems to make people better. Some boys down by the store were going to tie a

I COULD SEE MY GIRL'S BANGS RAISE RIGHT UP.

can on a dog's tail, yesterday, and somebody said, 'Here comes the Christian Association,' and those bad boys let the dog go. They tried to find the dog after the crowd had got by, but the dog knew his business. Well, I must go down and charge the soda fountain for a picnic that is expected from the country."

"Hold on a minute," said the grocery man as he wound a piece of brown paper around a cob and stuck it in a syrup jug he had just filled for a customer, and then licked his fingers. "I want to ask you a question. What has caused you to change so from being bad? You were about as bad as they make 'em, up to a few weeks ago, and now you seem to have a soul, and get in your work doing good about as well as any boy in town. What is it that ails you?"

"O, sugar, I don't want to tell," said the boy, as he blushed and wiggled around on one foot, and looked silly; "but if you won't laugh, I will tell you. It is my girl that has made me good. It may be only temporary. If she goes back on me I may be tough again; but if she continues to hold out faithful I shall be a daisy all the time. Say, did you ever love a girl? It would do you good, if you loved anybody regular old fashioned the way I do, people could send little children here to trade, and you wouldn't palm off any wilted vegetables on to them, or give them short weight—if you was in love, and felt that the one you loved saw every act of yours, and you could see her eyes every minute, you would throw away anything that was spoiled, and not try to sell it, for fear you would offend her. I don't think any man is fit to do business honestly unless he is in love, or has been in love once. Now I couldn't do anything wrong if I tried, because I should hear the still small voice of my girl saying to me, 'Hennery, let up on that.' I slipped up on a banana peel yesterday, and hurt myself, and I was just going to say something offul, and I could see my girl's bangs raise right up, and there was a pained look in her face, and a tear in her eye, and, by gosh, I just smiled and looked tickled till her hair went down and the smile came back again to her lips, though it hurt me like blazes where I struck the sidewalk. I was telling Pa about it, and asked him if he ever felt as though his soul was going right out toward somebody, and he said he did once on a steamboat excursion; but he ate a lemon and got over it. Pa thinks it is my liver, and wants me to take pills, but I tell you, boss, it has struck in me too deep for pills, unless it is one that weighs about a hundred and forty pounds, and wears a hat with a feather on. Say, if my girl should walk right into a burning lake of red-hot lava, and beckon me to follow, I would take a hop, skip and jump, and—"

"O, give us a rest," said the grocery man, as he took a basin of water and sprinkled the floor, preparatory to sweeping out. "You have got the worst case I ever saw, and you better go out and walk around a block," and the boy went out and forgot to hang out any sign.

CHAPTER XV

HE TURNS SUPE

The bad boy quits jerking soda—Enters the dramatic profession—"What's a super"—The privileges of a supe's father—Behind the scenes—The bad boy has played with McCullough—"I was the populace"—Plays it on his Sunday school teacher—"I prithee, au reservior, I go hence!"

"You look pretty sleepy," said the grocery man to the bad boy, as he came in the store yawning, and stretched himself out on the counter with his head on a piece of brown wrapping paper, in reach of a box of raisins, "What's the matter? Been sitting up with your girl all night?"

"Naw! I wish I had. Wakefulness with my girl is sweeter and more restful than sleep. No, this is the result of being a dutiful son, and I am tired. You see Pa and Ma have separated. That is, not for keeps, but Pa has got frightened about burglars, and he gets up into the attic to sleep. He says it is to get fresh air, but he knows better. Ma has got so accustomed to Pa's snoring that she can't go to sleep without it, and the first night Pa left she didn't sleep a wink, and yesterday I was playing on an old accordion that I traded a dog collar for after our dog was poisoned, and when I touched the low notes I noticed Ma dozed off to sleep, it sounded so much like Pa's snore, and last night Ma made me set up and play for her to sleep. She rested splendid, but I am all broke up, and I sold the accordion this morning to the watchman who watches our block. It is queer what a different effect music will have on different people. While Ma was sleeping the sleep of innocence under the influence of my counterfeit of Pa's snore, the night-watchman was broke of his rest by it, and he bought it of me to give to the son of an enemy of his. Well, I have quit jerking soda."

"No, you don't tell me," said the grocery man, as he moved the box of raisins out of reach. "You will never amount to anything unless you stick to one trade or profession. A rolling hen never catches the early angleworm."

"O, but I am all right now. In the soda water business

MA MADE ME PLAY FOR HER TO SLEEP

there is no chance for genius to rise unless the soda fountain explodes. It is all wind, and one gets tired of the constant fizz. He feels that he is a fraud, and when he puts a little syrup in a tumbler, and fires a little sweetened wind and water in it until the soapsuds fills the tumbler, and charges ten cents for that which only costs a cent a sensitive soda jerker, who has reformed, feels that it is worse than three card monte. I couldn't stand the wear on my conscience, so I have got a permanent job as a super, and shall open the 1st of September."

"Say, what's a super? It isn't one of these free lunch places, that the mayor closes at midnight, is it?" and the grocery man looked sorry.

"O, thunder, you want salt on you. A super is an adjunct of the stage. A supe is a fellow that assists the stars and things, carrying chairs and taking up carpets, and sweeping the sand off the stage after a dancer has danced a jig, and he brings beer for the actors, and helps lace up corsets, and anything he can do to add to the effect of the play. Privately, now, I have been acting as a supe for a long time, on the sly, and my folks didn't know anything about it, but since I reformed and decided to be good, I felt it my duty to tell Ma and Pa about it. The news broke Ma all up, at first, but Pa said some of the best actors in this country were supes once, and some of them were now, and he thought suping would be the making of me. Ma thought going on the stage would be my ruination. She said the theater was the hot-bed of sin, and brought more ruin than the church could head off. But when I told her that they always gave a supe two or three extra tickets for his family, she said the theater had some redeeming features, and when I said my entrance upon the stage would give me a splendid opportunity to get the recipe for face powder from the actresses, for Ma, and I could find out how the actresses managed to get number four feet into number one shoes, Ma said she wished I could commence suping right off. Ma says there are some things about the theater that are not so all-fired bad, and she wants me to get seats for the first comic opera that comes along. Pa wants it understood with the manager that a supe's father has the right to go behind the scenes to see that no harm befalls him, but I know what Pa wants. He may seem pious, and all that, but he likes to look at ballet girls better than any meek and lowly follower I ever see, and some day you will hear music in the air. Pa thinks theaters are very bad, when he has to pay a dollar for a reserved seat, but when he can get it for nothing as a relative of one of the 'perfesh,' the theater has many redeeming qualities. Pa and Ma think I am going into the business fresh and green, but I know all about it. When I played with McCullough here once—"

"Oh, what are you giving us?" said the grocery man in disgust, "when you played with McCullough! What did you do?"

"What did I do? Why, you old seed cucumber, the whole play centered around me. Do you remember the scene in the Roman forum, where McCullough addressed the populace of Rome? I was the populace. Don't you remember a small fellow standing in front of the Roman orator taking it in; with a night shirt on, with bare legs and arms? That was me, and everything depended on me. Suppose I had gone off the stage at the critical moment, or laughed when I should have looked fierce at the inspired words of the Roman senator, it would have been a dead give away on McCullough. As the populace of Rome I consider myself a glittering success, and Mc took me by the hand when they carried Cæsar's dead body out, and he said, 'Us three did ourselves proud.' Such praise from McCullough is seldom accorded to a supe. But I don't consider the populace of the imperial city of Rome my master piece. Where I excel is in coming out before the curtain between the acts, and unhooking the carpet. Some supes go out and turn their backs to the audience, showing patches on their pants, and rip up the carpet with no style about them, and the dust flies, and the boys yell 'supe,' and the supe gets nervous and forgets his cue, and goes off tumbling over the carpet, and the orchestra leader is afraid the supe will fall on him. But I go out with a quiet dignity that is only gained by experience and I take hold of the carpet the way Hamlet takes up the skull of Yorick, and the audience is paralyzed. I kneel down on the carpet, to unhook it, in a devotional sort of a way that makes the audience bow their heads as though they were in church, and before they realize that I

18

am only a supe I have the carpet unhooked and march out the way a 'Piscopal minister does when he goes out between the acts at church to change his shirt. They never 'guy' me, 'cause I act well my part. But I kick on holding dogs for actresses. Some supes think they are made if they can hold a dog, but I have an ambition that a pug dog will not fill. I held Mary Anderson's cud of gum once, while she went on the stage, and when she came off and took her gum her fingers touched mine and I had to run my fingers in my hair to warm them. Gosh, but she'd freeze ice cream without salt. I'll be glad when the theatrical season opens, 'cause we actors get tired laying off."

"Well, I'd like to go behind the scenes with you some night," said the grocery man, offering the bad boy an orange to get solid with him, in view of future complimentary tickets. "No danger, is there?"

"No danger if you keep off the grass. But you'd a dide to see my Sunday school teacher one Saturday night last summer. He keeps books in a store, and is pretty soon week days, but he can tell you more about Daniel in the lion's den on Sunday than anybody. He knew I was solid at the theater, and wanted me to get him behind the scenes one night, and another supe wanted to go to the sparring match, and I thought it wouldn't be any harm to work my teacher in, so I got him a job that night to hold the dogs. for Uncle Tom's show. He was in one of the wings holding the chains, and the dogs were just anxious to go on, and it was all my teacher could do to hold them. I told him to wind the chains around his wrists, and he did so, and just then Eliza began to skip across the ice, and we sicked the blood hounds on before my teacher could unwind the chains from his wrists, and the dogs pulled him right out on the stage, on his stomach, and drawed him across, and he jerked one dog and kicked him in the stomach, and the dog turned on my teacher and took a mouthful of his coat tail and shook it, and I guess the dog got some meat, anyway the teacher climbed up a step-ladder, and the dogs treed him, and the step-ladder fell down, and we grabbed the dogs and put some court plaster on my teacher's nose, where the fire extinguisher peeled it, and he said he would go home, b'cause the theater was demoralizing in its tendencies. I s'pose it was not right, but when the teacher stood up to hear our Sunday

JUST THEN ELIZA BEGAN TO SKIP ACROSS THE ICE.

school lesson the next day, 'cause he was tired where the dog bit him, I said 'Sick-em,' in a whisper, when his back was turned, and he jumped clear over to the Bible class, and put his hands around to his coat tail as though he thought the Uncle Tom's Cabin party was giving a matinee in the church. The Sunday school lesson was about the dog's licking the sores of Lazarus, and the teacher said we must not confound the good dogs of Bible time with the savage beasts of the present day, that would shake the daylights out of Lazarus, and make him climb the cedars of Lebanon quicker than you could say Jack Robinson, and go off chewing a cud of bitter reflection on Lazarus' coat tail. I don't think a Sunday school teacher ought to bring up personal reminiscences before a class of children, do you? Well, some time next fall you put on a clean shirt and a pair of sheet iron pants, with stove legs on the inside, and I will take you behind the scenes to see some good moral show. In the meantime, if you have an occasion to talk with Pa, tell him that Booth and Barrett, and Keene commenced on the stage as supes, and Salvini roasted peanuts in the lobby of some theater. I want our folks to feel that I am taking the right course to become a star. I prythee *au reservoir,* I go hence! but to return. Avaunt!" And the boy walked out on his toes *a la* Booth.

CHAPTER XVI

UNCLE EZRA PAYS A VISIT

Uncle Ezra causes the bad boy to backslide—Uncle Ezra and the old man were bad pills—Their record is awful—Keeping Uncle Ezra on the ragged edge—The bed slats fixed—The old man tangled up —This world is not run right—Uncle Ezra makes him tired.

"I HEAR your Uncle Ezra is here on a visit," said the grocery man to the bad boy. "I suppose you have been having a high old time. There is nothing that does a boy more good than to have a nice visit with a good uncle, and hear him tell about old times when he and the boy's father were boys together."

"Well, I don't know about it," said the boy, as he took a stick of mararoni, and began to blow paper wads through it at a wood sawyer, who was filing a saw outside the door. "When a boy who has been tough has got his pins all set to reform, I don't think it does him any good to have a real nice Uncle come to the house visiting. Anyway, that's my experience. I have backslid the worst way, and it is going to take me a month after Uncle Ezra goes away to climb up to the grace that I have fallen from. It is darn discouraging," said the boy as he looked up to the ceiling in an innocent sort of a way, and hid the macaroni under his coat when the wood sawyer, who had been hit in the neck, dropped his saw and got up mad.

"What's the trouble? Your uncle has the reputation where he lives of being one of the pillars of society. But you can't tell about these fellows when they get away from home. Does he drink?"

"No, he don't drink; but as near as I can figure it, he and Pa were about the worst pills in the box, when they were young. I don't want you to repeat it, but when Pa and Ma were married they eloped. Yes, sir—actually ran away and defied their parents—and they had to hide about a week, for fear Ma's father would fill Pa so full of cold lead that he would sink if he fell in the water. Pa has been kicked over the fence and chased down alleys dozens of times by Ma's grandfather, when he was sparking Ma, and Ma was a terror, too, 'cause her mother couldn't do anything with her, though she is awful precise now, and wants everybody to be too good. Why, Ma's mother used to warm her ears, and shake the daylights out of her, but it didn't do any good. She was mashed on Pa, and there was no cure for her except to have Pa prescribed for her as a husband, and they ran away. Uncle Ezra told me all about it. Ma hain't got any patience with girls now days that have minds of their own about fellows, and she thinks their parents ought to have all the say. Well, maybe she thinks she knows all about it. But when people get in love it is the same now as when Pa and Ma was trying to get out of the reach of my grandfather's shot gun. But Pa and Uncle Ezra and Ma are good friends, and they talk over old times and have a big laugh. I guess Uncle Ezra was too much for Pa in joking when they were boys 'cause Pa told me that all rules against joking were suspended while Uncle Ezra was here, and for me to play anything on him I could. I told Pa I was trying to lead a different life, but he said what I wanted to do was to make Uncle Ezra think of old times, and the only way was to kept him on the ragged edge. I thought if there was anything I could do to make it pleasant for my Uncle, it was my duty to do it, so I fixed the bed slats on the spare bed so they would fall down at 2 A. M. the first night, and then I retired. At two o'clock I heard the awfulest noise in the spare room, and a howling and screaming, and I went down to meet Uncle Ezra in the hall, and he asked me what was the matter in there, and I asked him if he didn't sleep in the spare room, and he said no, that Pa and Ma was in there, and he slept in their room. Then he went in the spare room and you'd a dide to see Pa. Ma had jumped out when the slats first fell; and was putting her hair up in curl papers when we got in, but Pa was all tangled up in the springs and things. His head had gone down first, and the mattress and quilts rolled over him, and he was almost smothered

GRANDFATHER'S SHOT GUN.

and we had to take the bedstead down to get him out, the way you have to unharness a horse when he runs away and falls down before you can get him up. Pa was mad, but Uncle Ezra laughed at him, and told him he was only foundered, and all he wanted was a bran mash and some horse liniment, and he would come out all right. Uncle Ezra went out into the hall to get a pail of water to throw on Pa, 'cause he said Pa was afire, when Pa asks me why in blazes I didn't fix the other bed slats, and I told him I didn't know they were going to change beds, and then Pa said 'Don't let it occur again. Pa lays everything to me. He is the most changeable man I ever saw. He told me to do everything Uncle Era wanted me to do, and then, when I helped Uncle Ezra to play a joke on Pa, he was mad. Say, I don't think this world is run right, do you? I haven't got much time to talk to you to-day, 'cause Uncle Ezra and me are going fishing, but don't it strike you that it is queer that parents trounce boys for doing just what they did themselves? Now, I have got a friend whose father is a lawyer. That lawyer would warm his boy if he should tell a lie or associate with anybody that was bad, and yet the lawyer will defend a man he knows is guilty of stealing, and get him clear and take the money he got from the thief, who stole it, to buy the same boy a new coat to wear to church, and he will defend a man who committed murder, and make an argument to the jury that will bring tears to their eyes, and they will clear the murderer. Queer, ain't it? And say, how is it that we send missionaries to Burmah, to convert them from heathenism, and the same vessel that takes the missionaries there carries from Boston a cargo of tin gods to sell to the heathen? Why wouldn't it be better to send the missionaries to Boston? I think the more a boy learns the more he gets mixed."

"Well, how's your theater? Have any of the great actors supported you lately?" said the grocery man, to change the subject.

"No, we are all off on vacations. Booth and Barrett, and lots of the stars, are gone to Europe, and the rest work down to less high-toned places. Some of the theater girls are waiters at summer resorts, and lots are visiting relatives on farms. I tell you, it makes a difference whether the relatives are visiting you or you are visiting them. Actors and actresses feel awfully when an old granger comes to town where they are playing, and wants to see them. They are ashamed of his homespun clothes, and cowhide boots, and they want to meet him in an alley somewhere, or in the

MY UNCLE EZRA IS PRETTY ROUGH.

basement of the theater, so other actors will not laugh at their rough relatives, but when the season is over an actor who can remember a relative out on a farm, is tickled to death, and the granger is all right enough there, and the actor does not think of the rough nutmeg grater hands, and the blistered nose, as long as the granger relative will put up fried pork and things, and 'support' the actor. My Uncle Ezra is pretty rough and it makes me tired sometimes when I am down town with him to have him go into a store where there are girl clerks and ask what things are for, that I know he don't want, and make the girls blush, but he is a good hearted old man, and he and me are going to make a mint of money during vacation. He lives near a summer resort hotel, and has a stream that is full of minnows, and we are going to catch minnows and sell them to the dudes for fish bait. He says some of the fools will pay ten cents apiece for minnows, so if we sell a million minnows, we make a fortune. I am coming back in September and will buy out your grocery. Say, let me have a pound of raisins, and I'll pay you when I sell my uncle's minnows."

CHAPTER XVII

HE DISCUSSES THEOLOGY

Meditations on Noah's ark—The garden of Eden—The ancient dude —Adam with a plug hat on—"I'm a thinker from Thinkersville" —The apostles in a patrol wagon—Elijah and Elisha—The prodigal son—A veal pot pie for dinner.

"WHAT are you sitting there for a half-an-hour for, staring at vacancy?" said the grocery man to the bad boy, as he sat on the stool by the stove one of these foggy mornings, when everybody feels like quarreling, with his fingers clasped around his knee, looking as though he did not know enough to last him to bed. "What you thinking about, anyway?"

"I was wondering where you would have been to-day if Noah had run his ark into such a fog as this, and there had been no fog-horn on Mount Ararat, and he had passed by with his excursion and not made a landing, and had floated around on the freshet until all the animals starved, and the ark had struck a snag and burst a hole in its bottom. I tell you, we can all congratulate ourselves that Noah happened to blunder on that high ground. If that ark had been lost, either by being foundered, or being blowed up by Fenians because Noah was an Englishman, it would have been cold work trying to populate this world. In that case another Adam and Eve would have to be made out of dirt and water, and they might have gone wrong again and failed to raise a family, and where would we have been? I tell you, when I think of the narrow escapes we have had, it is a wonder to me that we have got along as well as we have."

"Well, when did you get out of the asylum?" said the grocery man, who had been standing back with his mouth open looking at the boy as though he was crazy. "What you want is to have your head soaked. You are getting so you reach out too far with that small mind of yours. In about another year you will want to run this world yourself. I don't think you are reforming very much. It is wicked for a boy of your size to argue about such things. Your folks better send you to college."

"What do I want to go to college for, and be a heartless hazer, and a poor baseball player? I can be bad enough at home. The more I read, the more I think. I don't believe I can ever be good enough to go to heaven, anyway, and I guess I will go into the newspaper business, where they don't have to be good, and where they have passes everywhere. Do you know, I think when I was built they left out a cog wheel or something in my head. I can't think like some boys. I get to thinking about Adam and Eve in the garden of Eden, and of the Dude with the cloven hoof that flirted with Eve, and treated her and Adam to the dried apples, and I can't think of them as some boys do, with a fig leaf polonaise, and fig leaf vests. I imagine them dressed up in the latest style. I know it is wrong, but that is what a poor boy has to suffer who has an imagination, and where did I get the imagination? This confounded imagination of mine shows me Adam with a plug hat on, just like our minister wears, and a stand-up collar, and tight pants, and peaked-toed shoes, and Eve is pictured to me with a crushed-angle-worm colored dress and brown striped stockings, and newspapers in her dress to make it stick out, and a hat with dandelions on, and a red parasol, and a lace handkerchief, which she puts to her lips, and winks with her left eye to the masher who is standing by the corner of the house, in an attitude, while the tail with the dart on the end is wound around the rain-water barrel, so Eve won't see it and get scared. Say, don't you think it is better for a boy to think of our first parents with clothes on, than to think of them almost naked, exposed to the inclemency of the weather, with nothing but fig leaves pinned on? I want to do right, as near as I can, but I had rather think of them dressed like our folks are to-day, than to think of them in a cyclone with leaves for wearing apparel. Say, it is wrong to fight, but don't you think if Adam had put on a pair of boxing gloves, when he found the devil was getting too fresh about the place, and knocked

I KNOW IT'S WRONG TO THINK SO, BUT HOW CAN I HELP IT?

him out in a couple of rounds, and pasted him in the nose, and fired him out of the summer garden, that it would have been a big thing for this world? Now, honest?"

"Look-a-here," said the grocery man, who had been looking at the boy in dismay, "you better go right home, and let your Ma fix up some warm drink for you, and put you to bed. You are all wrong in the head, and if you are not attended to you will have brain fever. I tell you, boy, you are in danger. Come, I will go home with you."

"O, danger, nothin'. I am just telling how things look to a boy who has not got the facilities for being too good in his youth. Some boys can take things as they read them, and not think any for themselves, but I am a Thinker from Thinkersville, and my imagination plays the dickens with me. There is nothing I read about old times, but what I compare it with the same line of business at the present day. Now, when I think of the fishermen of Gallilee, drawing their seines, I wonder what they would have done if there had been a law against hauling seines, as there is in Wisconsin to-day, and I can see a constable with a warrant for the arrest of the Gallilee fishermen, snatching the old apostles and taking them to the police station in a patrol wagon. I know it is wrong to think like that, but how can I help it? Say, suppose those fishermen had been out hauling their seines, and our minister should come along with his good clothes on, his jointed rod, his nickel plated reel, and his silk fish line, and his patent fish hook, and put a frog on the hook and cast his line near the Gallilee fisherman and go to trolling for bass? What do you suppose the lone fisherman of the Bible times would have thought about the gall of the jointed-rod fisherman? Do you suppose they would have thrown stones in the water where he was trolling, or would they have told him there was good trolling around a point about half a mile up the shore, where they knew he wouldn't get a bite in a week, the way a fellow at Muskego lake lied to our minister a spell ago? I tell you, boss, it is a sad thing for a boy to have an imagination," and the boy put his other knee in the sling made by the clenched fingers of both hands, and waited for the grocery man to argue with him.

"I wish you would go away from here. I am afraid of you," said the grocery man. "I would give anything if your Pa or the minister would come in and have a talk with you. Your mind is wandering," and the grocery man went to the door and looked up and down the street to see if somebody wouldn't come in and watch the crazy boy, while he went to breakfast.

"O, Pa and the minister can't make a first payment on me. Pa gets mad when I ask questions, and the minister thinks I am past redemption. Pa said yesterday that baldness was caused, in every case, by men's wearing plug hats,

FINALLY HE GOT TO BE A COWBOY, HERDING HOGS.

and when I asked him where the good Elisha (whom the boys called 'Go up old bald head,' and the bears had a free lunch on them), got his plug hat, Pa said school was dismissed and I could go. When the minister was telling me about the good Elijah going up through the clouds in a chariot of fire, and I asked the minister what he thought Elijah would have thought if he had met our Sunday school superintendent coming down through the clouds on a bicycle, he put his hand on my head and said my liver was all wrong. Now, I will leave it to you if there was anything wrong about that. Say, do you know what I think is the most beautiful thing in the Bible?"

"No," said the grocery man, "and if you want to tell it I will listen five minutes, and then I am going to shut up the store and go to breakfast. You make me tired."

"Well, I think the finest thing is that story about the prodigal son, where the boy took all the money he could scrape up and went out West to paint the town red. He spent his money in riotous living, and saw everything that was going on, and got full of benzine, and struck all the gangs of toughs, both male and female, and his stomach went back on him, and he had malaria, and finally he got to be a cowboy, herding hogs, and had to eat husks that the pigs didn't want, and got pretty low down. Then he thought it was a pretty good scheme to be getting around home, where they had three meals a day, and spring mattresses; and he started home, beating his way on trains, and he didn't know whether the old man would receive him with open arms or pointed boots; but the old man came down to the depot to meet him, and right there before the passengers and the conductor and brakemen, he wasn't ashamed of his boy, though he was ragged, and looked as though he had been on the war path; and the old man fell on his neck and wept, and took him home in a hack, and had veal pot pie for dinner. That's what I call sense. A good many men now days would have put the police on the tramp and had him ordered out of town. What, are you going to close up the store? Well, I will see you later. I want to talk with you about something that is weighing on my mind," and the boy got out just in time to save his coat tail from being caught in the door, and when the grocery man came back from breakfast he found a sign in front:

THIS STORE IS CLOSED TILL FURTHER NOTICE.

SHERIFF.

CHAPTER XVIII

THE DEPARTED ROOSTER

The grocery man discourses on death—The dead rooster—A biographical sketch—The tenderness between the rooster and his faithful hen—The hen retires to set—The chickens!—The proud rooster dies—The fickle hen flirting in indecent haste.

"WHY don't you take an ice pick and clean the dirt out from under your finger nails?" said the grocery man to the bad boy, as he came into the store and stroked the cat the wrong way as she lay in the sun on the counter, on a quire of manilla paper.

"Can't remove the dirt for thirty days—it is an emblem of mourning. Had a funeral at our house, yesterday," and the boy took a pickle out of a tub and put it in the cat's mouth, and shut her teeth together on it, and then went to the showcase, while the grocery man, whose back had been turned during the pickle exercise, thought by the way the cat jumped into the dried apple barrel and began to paw and scratch with all four of her feet, and yowl, that she was going to have a fit.

"I haven't heard about it," said the grocery man, as he took the cat by the neck and tossed her out in the back shed into an old oyster box full of sawdust, with a parting injunction that if she was going to have fits she had better go out where there was plenty of fresh air. "Death is always a sad thing to contemplate. One day we are full of health and joy and cold victuals, and the next we are screwed down in a box, a few words are said over our remains, a few tears areshed and there is a race to see ho wshall get back from the cemetery first; and though we may think we are an important factor in the world's progress and sometimes feel as though it would be unable to put up margins and have to stop the deal, the world goes right along, and it must annoy people who die to realize that they don't count for game. The greatest man in the world is only a nine spot when he is dead because somebody else takes the tricks the dead man ought to have taken. But, say, who is dead at your house?"

"Our rooster! Take care, don't you hit me with that canvassed ham!" said the boy as the grocery man looked mad to learn that there was nobody dead but a rooster, when he had preached such a sermon on the subject. "Yes, how soon we are forgotten when we are gone. Now, you would have thought that rooster's hen would have remained faithful to him for a week at least. I have watched them all the spring and I never saw a more perfect picture of devotion than that between the bantam rooster and his hen. They were constantly together and there was nothing too good for her. He would dig up angle worms and call her, and when she came up on a gallop and saw the great big worm on the ground, she would look so proud of her rooster, and he would straighten up and look as though he was saying to her, 'I'm a daisy,' and then she would look at him as if she would like to bite him, and just as she was going to pick up the worm he would snatch it and swallow it himself and chuckle and walk around and be full of business, as though wondering why she didn't take the worm after he had dug it for her, and then the hen would look disappointed at first, and then she would look resigned, as much as to say, 'Worms are too rich for my blood anyway, and the poor dear rooster needs them more than I do, because he has to do all the crowing;' and she would go off and find a grasshopper and eat it on the sly for fear he would see her and complain because she didn't divide. O, I have never seen anything that seemed to me so human as the relations between that rooster and hen. He seemed to try to do everything for her. He would make her stop cackling when she laid an egg, and he would try to cackle, and crow over it as though he had laid it, and she would get off in a corner and cluck in a modest, retiring manner, as though she wished to convey the idea to the servant girls in the kitchen that the rooster had to do all the hard work, and she was only a useless appendage, fit only for society and company for him. But I was disgusted with him when the poor hen was setting. The first week that she sat on the eggs he seemed to be glad to have his hen retire to her boudoir to set, but after he had been shooed out of the gardens and flower beds he seemed to be nervous, and evidently wanted to be petted, and he would go near the hen and she would seem to tell him to go and take a walk around the block, because she hadn't time to leave her business, and if she didn't attend to it they would have a lot of spoiled eggs on their hands, and no fam-

I NEVER SAW A MORE PERFECT PICTURE OF DEVOTION.

ily to bring up. He would scold and seem to tell her that it was all foolishness, that for his part he didn't want to hear a lot of chickens squawking around. He would seem to argue with her that a brood of chickens would be a dead give-away on them both, and they would be at once classed as old folks, while if they were alone in the world they would be spring chickens, and could go in young society, but the hen would scold back, and tell him he ought to be ashamed of himself to talk that way, and he would go off mad, and sulk around a spell, and then go to a neighbor's hen house and sometimes he wouldn't come back till the next day. The hen would be sorry she had spoken so cross, and would seem pained at his going away and would look anxiously for his return, and when he came back after being out in the rain all night, she would be solicitous after his health, and tell him he ought to wrap something around him, but he acted as though he didn't care for his health, and he would go out again and get chilled through. Finally the hen come off the nest with ten chickens, and the rooster seemed very proud, and when anybody came out to have a look at them he would crow, and seemed to say they were all his chickens, though the hen was a long time hatching them, and if it had been him that was setting on them he could have hatched them out in a week, or died a trying. But the exposure told on him, and he went into a decline, and one morning we found him dead. Do you know, I never see a hen that seemed to realize a calamity as she did. She looked pale, and her eyes looked red, and she seemed to be utterly crushed. If the chickens, which were so young they could not realize that they were little orphans, became noisy, and got to pulling and hauling over a worm, and conducted themselves in an unseemly manner she would talk to them in hen language, with tears in her eyes, and it was a picture of woe. But the next day a neighboring rooster got to looking through the fence from the alley, and trying to flirt with her. At first she was indignant, and seemed to tell him he ought to go about his business, and leave her alone, but the dude kept clucking, and pretty soon the widowed hen edged up toward the fence, and asked him to come in, but the hole in the fence was too small for him, and then the chickens went out in the alley, and the hen followed them out. I shall always think she told the chickens to go out, so she would have an excuse to go after them, and flirt with the rooster and I think it is a perfect shame. She is out in the alley half the time, and I could cuff her. It seems to me wrong to so soon forget a deceased rooster, but I suppose a hen can't be any more than human. Say, you don't want to buy a dead rooster do you? You could pick it and sell it to somebody that owes you, for a spring chicken."

WITH A PAPER PINNED ON ITS BREAST.

"No, I don't want any deceased poultry, that died of grief, and you better go home and watch your hen, or you will be bereaved some more," and the grocery man went out in the shed to see if the cat was over its fit, and when he came back the boy was gone, and after a while the grocery man saw a crowd in front of the store and he went out and found the dead rooster lying on the vegetable stand, with a paper pinned on its breast on which was a sign:

THIS RUSTER DIED OF COLIX
FOR SALE CHEAP
TO BOARDING HOUSE ONLY.

He took the dead rooster and threw it out in the street, and looked up and down the street for the bad boy, and went in and hid a raw hide where he could reach it handy.

CHAPTER XIX

ONE MORE JOKE ON THE OLD MAN

Uncle Ezra returns—The basket on the steps—The anonymous letter—"O, brother that I should live to see this day!" An ugly Dutch baby—The old man wheels the baby now—A frog in the old man's bed.

"I SEE your Pa wheeling the baby around a good deal lately," said the grocery man to the bad boy, as he came in the store one evening to buy a stick of striped peppermint candy for the baby, while his Pa stopped the baby wagon out on the sidewalk and waited for the boy, with an expression of resignation on his face.

"What's got into your Pa to be nurse girl this hot weather?"

"O, we have had a circus at our house," said the boy, as he came in after putting the candy in the baby's hand. "You see, Uncle Ezra came back from Chicago, where he had been to sell some cheese, and he stopped over a couple of days with us, and he said we must play one more joke on Pa before he went home. We played it, and it is a wonder I am alive because I never saw Pa so mad in my life. Now this is the last time I go into any joke on shares. If I play any more jokes I don't want any old uncle to give me away."

"What is it?" said the grocery man, as he took a stool and sat out by the front door beside the boy who was trying to eat a box of red raspberries on the sly.

"Well, uncle Ezra and me bribed the nurse girl to dress up the baby one evening in some old, dirty baby clothes, belonging to our wash woman's baby, and we put it in a basket and placed the basket on the front door step, and put a note in the basket and addressed it to Pa. We had the nurse girl stay out in front, by the basement stairs, so the baby couldn't get away and she rung the bell and got behind something. Ma and Pa, and Uncle Ezra and me were in the back parlor when the bell rung, and Ma told me to go to the door, and I brought in the basket, and set it down, and told Pa there was a note in it for him. Ma, she came up and looked at the note as Pa tore it open, and Uncle Ezra looked in the basket and sighed. Pa read a part of the note and stopped and turned pale, and sat down, then Ma read some of it, and she didn't feel very well, and she leaned against the piano and grated her teeth. The note was in a girl's handwriting, and was like this:

'Old Bald Headed Pet:—

You will have to take care of your child, because I cannot. Bring it up tenderly, and don't, for heaven's sake, send it to the Foundling Asylum. I shall go drown myself.

Your loving,

Almira.'"

"What did your Ma say?" said the grocery man, becoming interested.

"O, Ma played her part well. Uncle Ezra had told her the joke, and she said, ''Retch,' to Pa, just as the actresses do on the stage, and put her handkerchief to her eyes. Pa said it was 'false,' and Uncle Ezra said, 'O, brother, that I should live to see this day,' and I said, as I looked in the basket, 'Pa, it looks just like you, and I'll leave it to Ma.' That was too much, and Pa got mad in a minute. He always gets mad at me. But he went up and looked in the basket, and he said it was some Dutch baby, and was evidently from the lower strata of society, and the unnatural mother wanted to get rid of it, and he said he didn't know any 'Almira' at all. When he called it a Dutch baby, and called attention to its irregular features, that made Ma mad, and she took it up out of the basket and told Pa it was a perfect picture of him, and tried to put it in Pa's arms, but he wouldn't have it, and said he would call the police and have it taken to the poor house. Uncle Ezra took Pa in a corner and told him the best thing he could do would be to see 'Almira and compromise with her, and that made Pa mad, and he was going to hit Uncle Ezra with a chair. Pa was perfectly wild, and if he had a gun I guess he would have shot all of us. Ma took the baby up stairs and had the girl put it to bed, and

O, BROTHER, THAT I SHOULD LIVE TO SEE THIS DAY.

after Pa got mad enough Uncle Ezra told him it was all a joke, and it was his own baby, that we had put in the basket, and then he was madder than ever, and he told Uncle Ezra never to darken his door again. I don't know how he made up with Ma for calling it a Dutch baby from the Polack settlement, but anyway, he wheels it around every day, and Ma and Pa have got so they speak again."

"That is a mighty mean trick, and you ought to be ashamed of yourself. Where do you expect to fetch up when you die?" said the grocery man.

"I told Uncle Ezra it was a mean trick," said the boy, "but he said that wasn't a priming to some of the tricks Pa had played on him years ago. He says Pa used to play tricks on everybody. I may be mean, but I never played wicked jokes on blind people as Pa did when he was a boy. Uncle Ezra says once there was a party of four blind vocalists, all girls, gave an entertainment at the town where Pa lived, and they stayed at the hotel where Pa tended bar. Another thing I never sold rum, either, as Pa did. Well, before the blind vocalists went to bed Pa caught a lot of frogs and put them in the beds where the girls were to sleep, and when the poor blind girls got into bed the frogs hopped over them, and the way they got out was a caution. It is bad enough to have frogs hopping all over girls that can see, but for girls that are deprived of their sight, and don't know what anything is, except by the feeling of it, it looks to me like a pretty tough joke. I guess Pa is sorry now for what he did, 'cause when Uncle Ezra told the frog story, I brought home a frog and put it in Pa's bed. Pa has been afraid of paralysis for years, and when his leg, or anything gets asleep, he thinks that is the end of him. Before bedtime I turned the conversation onto paralysis, and told about a man about Pa's age having it on the West Side, and Pa was nervous, and soon after he retired I guess the frog wanted to get acquainted with Pa, 'cause he yelled six kinds of murder, and we went into his room. You know how cold a frog is? Well, you'd dide to see Pa. He laid still, and said his end had come, and Uncle Ezra asked him if it was the end with the head on or the feet, and Pa told him paralysis had marked him for a victim, and he could feel that his left leg was becoming dead. He said he could feel the cold, clammy hand of death walking up him, and he wanted Ma to put a bottle of hot water to his feet. Ma got the bottle of hot water and put it to Pa's feet, and the cork came out and Pa said he was dead, sure enough, now, because he was hot in the extremities and that a cold wave was going up his leg. Ma asked him where the cold wave was, and he told her, and she thought she would rub it, but she

WELL, HERE COMES OUR BABY WAGON.

began to yell the same kind of murder Pa did, and she said a snake had gone up her sleeve. Then I thought it was time to stop the circus, and I reached up Ma's lace sleeve and caught the frog by the leg and pulled it out, and told Pa I guessed he had taken my frog to bed with him, and I showed it to him, and then he said I did it, and he would maul me so I could not get up alone, and he said that a boy that would do such a thing would go to hell as sure as preachin' and I asked him if he thought a man who put frogs in the beds with blind girls, when he was a boy, would get to heaven, and then he told me to lite out, and I lit. I guess Pa will feel better when Uncle Ezra goes away, 'cause he thinks Uncle Ezra talks too much about old times. Well, here comes our baby wagon, and I guess Pa has done penance long enough, and I will go and wheel the kid a while. Say, you call Pa in, after I take the baby wagon, and tell him you don't know how he would get along without such a nice boy as me, and you can charge it in our next month's bill."

CHAPTER XX

FOURTH OF JULY MISADVENTURES

Trouble in the pistol pocket—The grocery man's cat—The bad boy a ministering angel—Asleep on the Fourth of July—Goes with his girl to the Soldiers' Home—Terrible Fourth of July misadventures—The girl who went out comes back a burnt offering.

"HERE, condemn you, you will pay for that cat," said the grocery man to the bad boy, as he came in the store all broke up, the morning after the 4th of July.

"What cat?" said the boy, as he leaned against the zinc ice box to cool his back, which had been having trouble with a bunch of fire crackers in his pistol pocket. We haven't ordered any cat from here. Who ordered any cat sent to our house? We get our sausage at the market," and the boy rubbed some cold cream on his nose and eyebrows where the skin was off.

"Yes, that is all right enough," said the grocery man, "but somebody who knew where that cat slept, in the box of sawdust, back of the store, filled it full of fire crackers, Wednesday forenoon, when I was out to see the procession, and never notified the cat, and touched them off, and the cat went through the roof of the shed, and she hasn't got hair enough left on her to put in tea. Now, you didn't show up all the forenoon, and I went and asked your Ma where you was, and she said you had been sitting up four nights straight along with a sick boy in the Third Ward, and you was sleeping all the forenoon the 4th of July. If that is so, that lets you out on the cat, but it don't stand to reason. Own up, now, was you asleep all the forenoon, the 4th while other boys were celebrating, or did you scorch my cat?" and the grocery man looked at the boy as though he would believe every word he said, if he *was* bad.

"Well," said the bad boy as he yawned as though he had been up all night, "I am innocent of setting up with your cat, but I plead guilty to sitting up with Duffy. You see, I am bad, and it don't make any difference where I am, and Duffy thumped me once when we were playing marbles, and I said I would get even with him some time. His Ma washes for us, and when she told me that her boy was sick with fever, and had nobody to stay with him while she was away, I thought it would be a good way to get even with Duffy when he was weak, and I went down there to his shanty and gave him his medicine, and read to him all day, and he cried 'cause he knew I ought to have mauled him, and that night I sat up with him while his Ma did the ironing, and Duffy was so glad that I went down every day and stayed there every night, and fired medicine down him, and let his Ma sleep, and Duffy has got mashed on me, and he says I will be an angel when I die. Last night makes five nights I have sat up with him, and he has got so he can eat beef tea and crackers. My girl went back on me 'cause she said I was sitting up with some other girl. She said that Duffy story was too thin, but Duffy's Ma was washing at my girl's house and she proved what I said, and I was all right again. I slept all the forenoon the 4th, and then stayed with Duffy till four o'clock, and got a furlough and took my girl to the Soldiers' Home. I had rather set up with Duffy, though."

"O, get out. You can't make me believe you had rather stay in a sick room and set up with a boy, than to take a girl to the 4th of July," said the grocery man as he took a brush and wiped the saw dust off some bottles of pepper-sauce that he was taking out of a box. "You didn't have any trouble with the girl, did you?"

"No,—not with her," said the boy, as he looked into the little round zinc mirror to see if his eyebrows were beginning to grow. "But her Pa is so unreasonable. I think a man ought to know better than to kick a boy right where he has had a pack of fire crackers explode in his pocket. You see, when I brought the girl back home, she was a wreck. Don't you ever take a girl to the 4th of July. Take the advice of a boy who has had experience. We hadn't more than got to the Soldiers' Home grounds before some boys who were playing tag grabbed hold of my girl's crushed-strawberry polonaise and ripped it off. That made her mad, and she wanted me to take offense at it, and I tried to reason with

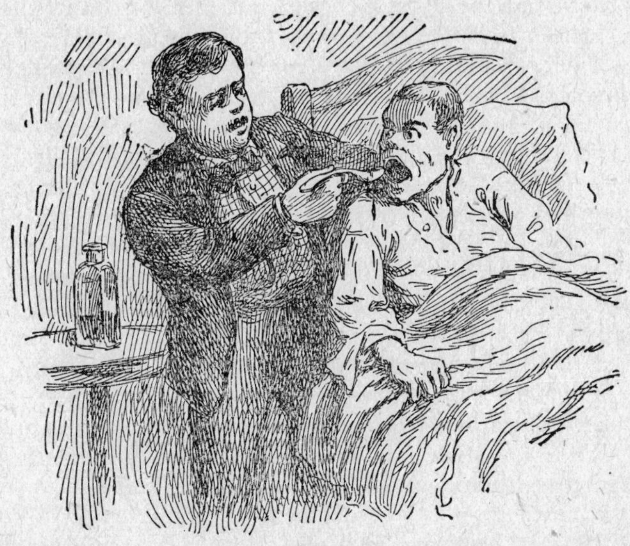

I THOUGHT IT WOULD BE A GOOD WAY TO GET EVEN WITH DUFFY.

the boys and they both jumped on me, and I see the only way to get out of it honorably, was to get out real spry, and I got out. Then we sat down under a tree, to eat lunch, and my girl swallowed a pickle the wrong way, and I pounded her on the back, the way Ma does when I choke, and she yelled, and a policeman grabbed me and shook me, and asked me what I was hurting that poor girl for, and told me if I did it again he would arrest me! Everything went wrong. After dark somebody fired a Roman candle into my girl's hat, and set it on fire, and I grabbed the hat and stamped on it, and spoiled the hair her Ma bought her. By gosh, I thought her hair was curly, but when the wig was off, her hair was as straight as could be. But she was purty, all the same. We got under another tree, to get away from the smell of burned hair, and a boy set off a nigger chaser, and it ran right at my girl's feet, and burned her stockings, and a woman put the fire out for her, while I looked for the boy that fired the nigger chaser, but I didn't want to find him. She was pretty near a wreck by that time, though she had all her dress left except the polonaise, and we went and sat under a tree in a quiet place, and I put my arm around her and told her never to mind the accidents, 'cause it would be dark when we got home, and just then a spark dropped down through the trees and fell in my pistol pocket, right next to her, where my bunch of fire crackers was, and they began to go off. Well, I never saw such a sight as she was. Her dress was one of these mosquito bar, cheese cloth dresses and it burned just like punk. I had presence of mind enough to roll her on the grass and put out the fire, but in doing that I neglected my own conflagration, and when I got her put out, my coat tail and trousers were a total loss. *My*, but she looked like a goose that had been picked, and I looked like a fireman that fell through a hatchway. My girl wanted to go home, and I took her home, and her Pa was setting on the front steps, and he wouldn't accept her, looking that way. He said he placed in my possession a whole girl, clothed in her right mind, and I had brought back a burnt offering. He teaches in our Sunday school, and knows how to talk pious, but his boots are offul thick. I tried to explain that I was not responsible for the fireworks, and that he could bring in a bill against the government and I showed him how I was bereaved of a coat tail and some pants, but he wouldn't reason at all, and when his foot hit me I thought it was the resurrection, sure, and when I got over the fence, and had picked myself up I never stopped till I got to Duffy's and I sat up with him, 'cause I thought her Pa was after me, and I thought he wouldn't enter a sick room and maul a watcher at the bedside of an invalid. But that settles it with me about celebrating. I don't care if we *did* whip the British, after declaring inde-

PA WENT TO DIG POTATOES FOR DINNER.

pendence, I don't want my pants burnt off. What is the declaration of independence good for to a girl who loses her polonaise, and has her hair burnt off, and a nigger chaser burning her stockings? No, sir, they may talk about the glorious 4th of July, but will it bring back that blonde wig, or re-tail my coat? Hereafter I am a rebel, and I will go out in the woods the way Pa does, and come home with a black eye, got in a rational way."

"What, did your Pa get a black eye, too? I hadn't heard about that," said the grocery man, giving the boy a handful of unbaked peanuts to draw him out. "Didn't get to fighting, did he?"

"No, Pa don't fight. It is wrong, he says, to fight, unless you are sure you can whip the fellow, and Pa always gets whipped, so he quit fighting. You see, one of the deacons in our church lives out on a farm, and his folks were going away to spend the 4th, and he had to do all the chores, so he invited Pa and Ma to come out to the farm and have a nice quiet time, and they went. There is nothing Pa likes better than to go out on a farm and pretend he knows everything. When the farmer got Pa and Ma out there he set them to work, and Ma shelled peas while Pa went to dig potatoes for dinner. I think it was mean for the deacon to send Pa out in the corn field to dig potatoes, and set the dog on Pa, and tree him in an apple tree near the bee hives, and then go and visit with Ma and leave Pa in the tree with the dog barking at him. Pa said he never knew how mean a deacon could be, until he had set on a limb of that apple tree all the afternoon. About time to do chores the farmer came and found Pa, and called the dog off, and Pa came down, and then the farmer played the meanest trick of all. He said city people didn't know how to milk cows, and Pa said he wished he had as many dollars as he knew how to milk cows. He said his spechulty was milking kicking cows, and the farmer gave Pa a tin pail and a milking stool and let down the bars, and pointed out to Pa 'The worst cow on the place.' Pa knew his reputation was at stake, and he went up to the cow and punched it in the flank and said, 'Hist, confound you.' Well, the cow wasn't a histing cow, but a histing bull, and Pa knew it was a bull as quick as he see it put down its head and beller, and Pa dropped the pail and stool, and started for the bars, and the bull after

Pa. I don't think it was right in Ma to bet two shillings with the farmer that Pa would get to the bars before the bull did, though she won the bet. Pa said he knew it was a bull just as soon as the horns got tangled up in his coat tail, and when he struck on the other side of the bars, and his nose hit the ash barrel where they made lye for soap, Pa said he saw more fireworks than he did at the Soldiers' Home. Pa wouldn't celebrate any more, and he came home after thanking the farmer for his courtesies, but he wants me to borrow a gun and go out with him hunting. We are going to shoot a bull and a dog and some bees, maybe, we will shoot the farmer, if Pa keeps on as mad as he is now. Well, we won't have another 4th of July for a year, and may be by that time my girl's polonaise and hair will grow out, and that bull may become gentle so Pa can milk it. Ta-ta."

CHAPTER XXI

WORKING ON SUNDAY

Turning a grindstone is healthy—"Not any grindstone for Hennery!"—This hypocrisy is played out—Another job on the old man—How the days of the week got mixed—The numerous funerals—The minister appears—The bad boy goes over the back fence.

"HELLO," said the grocery man to the bad boy as he came in looking sick at heart, and all broke up. "How is your muscle this morning?"

"All right enough," said the boy with a look of inquiry, as though wondering what was coming next. "Why?"

"O, nothing, only I was going to grind the hatchet, and some knives and things, this morning, and I thought maybe you would like to go out in the shed and turn the grindstone for me to develop your muscles. Turning the grindstone is the healthiest thing a boy can do."

"That is all right enough," said the bad boy, as he took up a sweet cracker, "but please take a good look at me. Do I look like a grindstone boy? Do I resemble a good little boy that can't say 'No,' and goes off and turns a grindstone half a day for some old duffer, who pays him by giving him a handful of green currents or telling him he will be a man some day, and the boys goes off one way, with a lame back, while the good man goes the other way with a sharp scythe, and a chuckle at the softness of the boy? You are mistaken in me. I have passed the grindstone period, and you will have to pick up another sardine who has never done circular work. Not any grindstone for Hennery, if you please."

"You are getting too smart," said the grocery man as he charged a pound of sweet crackers to the boy's father. "You don't have to turn the grindstone if you don't want to."

"That's what I thought," says the boy as he takes a handful of blueberries. "You grindstone sharps, who are always laying for a fool boy to give taffy to, and get him to break his neck, don't play it fine enough. You bear too hard on the grindstone. I have seen the time when a man could get me to turn the grindstone for him till the cows come home, by making me believe it was fun, and by telling

THEY MAKE A BOY BELIEVE HE IS BIGGER THAN GRANT.

me he never saw a boy that seemed to throw so much soul into turning a grindstone as I did, but I have found that such men are hypocrites. They inveigle a boy into their nest, like the spider does the fly, and at first they don't bear on hard, but just let the blade of the axe or scythe touch the grindstone, and they make a boy believe he is a bigger man than old Grant. They bet him he will get tired, and he bets that he can turn a grindstone as long as anybody, and when the boy has got his reputation at stake, then they begin to bear on hard, and the boy gets tired but he holds out, and when the tools are ground he says he is as fresh as a daisy, when he is tired enough to die. Such men do more to teach boys the hollowness of the world, and its tricky features, than anything, and they teach boys to know who are friends and who are foes. No, sir, the best way is to hire a grown person to turn your grindstone. I remember I turned a grindstone four hours for a farmer once, and when I got through he said I could go to the spring and drink all the water I wanted for nothing. He was the tightest man I ever saw. Why, tight! That man was tight enough to hold kerosene."

"That's all right. Who wanted you to turn the grindstone, anyway? But what is it about your Pa and Ma being turned out of church? I hear they scandalized themselves horribly last Sunday."

"Well, you see, me and my chum put up a job on Pa to make him think Sunday was only Saturday and Ma she fell into it, and I guess we are all going to get fired from the church for working on Sunday. You see they didn't go to meetin' last Sunday because Ma's new bonnet hadn't come, and Monday and Tuesday it rained and the rest of the week was so muddy no one called, or they could not get anywhere, so Monday I slid out early and got the daily paper, and on Tuesday my chum he got the paper off the steps and put Monday's paper in its place. I watched when they were reading it, but they did not notice the date. Then Wednesday we put Tuesday's paper on the steps and Pa said it seemed more than Tuesday, but Ma she got the paper of the day before and looked at the date and said it seemed so to her but she guessed they had lost a day somehow. Thursday we got Wednesday's paper on the steps, and Friday we rung in Thursday's paper, and Saturday my chum he got Friday's paper on the steps, and Ma said she guessed she would wash to-morrow, and Pa said he believed he would hoe in the garden and get the weeds out so it would look better to folks when they went by Sunday to church. Well, Sunday morning came, and with it Saturday's daily paper, and Pa barely glanced it over as he got on his overalls and went out in his shirt sleeves a hoeing in the front garden, and I and my chum helped Ma carry water to wash. She said it seemed the longest week she ever saw, but when we brought the water, and took a plate of pickles

IT WASN'T LONG BEFORE FOLKS BEGAN GOING TO CHURCH.

to the hired girl that was down with the mumps, we got in the lilac bushes and waited for the curtain to rise. It wasn't long before folks began going to church and you'd a dide laughing to see them all stop in front of where Ma was washing and look at her, and then go on to where Pa was hoeing weeds and stop and look at him and then drive on. After about a dozen teams had passed I heard Ma ask Pa if he knew who was dead, as there must be a funeral somewhere. Pa had just hoed into a bumble-bee's nest and said he did not know of any that was dead, but knew some that ought to be, and Ma she did not ask any foolish questions any more. After about twenty teams had stopped, Ma she got nervous and asked Deacon Smith if he saw anything green; he said something about desecration, and drove away. Deacon Brown asked Pa if he did not think he was setting a bad example before his boy; but Pa, he said he thought it would be a good one if the boy could only be hired to do it. Finally Ma got mad and took the tub behind the house where they could not see her. About four o'clock that afternoon we saw a dozen of our congregation headed by the minister, file into our yard, and my chum and I knew it was time to fly, so we got on the back steps where we could hear. Pa met them at the door, expecting some bad news; and when they were seated, Ma she came in and remarked that it was a very unhealthy year, and it stood people in hand to meet their latter end. None of them said a word until the elder put on his specs, and said it was a solemn occasion, and Ma she turned pale, and wondered who it could be, and Pa says, 'Don't keep us in suspense, who is dead?' and the elder said no one was dead; but they called as a duty they owed the cause to take action on them for working on Sunday. Ma, she fainted away, and they threw a pitcher of water down her back, and Pa said he guessed they were a pack of lunatics, but they all swore it was Sunday, and they saw Ma washing and Pa out hoeing, as they went to church, and they had called to take action on them. Then there was a few minutes low conversation I could not catch, and then we heard Pa kick his chair over and say it was more tricks of that darned boy. Then we knew it was time to adjourn, and I was just getting through the back fence as Pa reached me with a barrel stave, and that's what makes me limp some!"

"That was real mean in you boys," said the grocery man. "It will be hard for your Pa and Ma to explain that matter. Just think how bad they must feel."

"O, I don't know. I remember hearing Pa and Uncle Ezra tell how they fooled their father once, and got him to go to mill with a grist, on Sunday, and Pa said he would defy anybody to fool him on the day of the week. I don't think a man ought to tempt his little boy by defying him to fool his father. Well, I'll take a glass of your fifty cent cider and go," and soon the grocery man looked out of the window and found somebody had added a cipher to the 'Sweet cider, only five cents a glass,' making it an expensive drink, considering it was made of sour apples.

CHAPTER XXII

THE OLD MAN AWFULLY BLOATED

The old man begins drinking again—Thinks betting is harmless—Had to walk home from Chicago—The spectacles changed—A small suit of clothes—The old man awfully bloated—"Hennery your Pa is a mighty sick man"—The swelling suddenly goes down.

"COME in," said the grocery man to the bad boy, as the youth stood on the steps in an uncertain sort of a way, as though he did not know whether he would be welcome or not. "I tell you, boy, I pity you. I understand your Pa has got to drinking again. It is too bad. I can't think of anything that humiliates a boy, and makes him so ashamed, as to have a father that is in the habit of hoisting in too much benzine. A boy feels as though everybody was down on him, and I don't wonder that such boys often turn out bad. What started your Pa to drinking again?"

"O, Ma thinks it was losing money on the Chicago races. You see, Pa is great on pointers. He don't usually bet unless he has got a sure thing, but when he gets what they call a pointer, that is, somebody tells him a certain horse is sure to win, because the other horses are to be pulled back, he thinks a job has been put up, and if he thinks he is on the inside of the ring he will bet. He says it does not do any hurt to bet, if you win, and he argues that a man who wins lots of money can do a great deal of good with it. But he had to walk home from the Chicago races all the same, and he has been steaming ever since. Pa can't stand adversity. But I guess we have got him all right now. He is the scartest man you ever saw," and the boy took a can opener and began to cut the zinc under the stove, just to see if it would work as well on zinc as on tin.

"What, you haven't been dissecting him again, have

you?" said the grocery man, as he pulled a stool up beside the boy to hear the news. "How did you bring him to his senses?"

"Well, Ma tried having the minister talk to Pa, but Pa talked Bible, about taking a little wine for the stomach's sake, and gave illustrations about Noah getting full, so the minister couldn't brace him up, and then Ma had some of

HIS HAND LOOKED LIKE A HAM.

the sisters come and talk to him, but he broke them all up by talking about what an appetite they had for champagne punch when they were out in camp last summer, and they couldn't have any effect on him, and so Ma said she guessed I would have to exercise my ingenuity on Pa again. Ma has an idea that I have got some sense yet, so I told her that if she would do just as I said, me and my chum would scare Pa so he would swear off. She said she would, and we went to work. First, I took Pa's spectacles down to an optician, Saturday night, and had the glasses taken out and a pair put in their place that would magnify, and I took them home and put them in Pa's spectacle case. Then I got a suit of clothes from my chum's uncle's trunk, about half the size of Pa's clothes. My chum's uncle is a very small man, and Pa is corpulent. I got a plug hat three sizes smaller than Pa's hat, and the name out of Pa's hat and put it in the small hat. I got a shirt about half big enough for Pa, and put his initials on the thing under the bosom, and got a number fourteen collar. Pa wears seventeen. Pa had promised to brace up and go to church Sunday morning, and Ma put these small clothes where Pa could put them on. I told Ma, when Pa woke up, to tell him he looked awfully bloated, and excite his curiosity, and then send for me."

" You didn't play such a trick as that on a poor old man, did you?" said the grocery man as a smile came over his face.

"You bet. Desperate diseases require desperate remedies. Well, Ma told Pa he looked awfully bloated, and that his dissipation was killing him, as well as all the rest of the family. Pa said he guessed he wasn't bloated very much, but he got up and put on his spectacles and looked at himself in the glass. You'd a dide to see him look at himself. His face looked as big as two faces, through the glass, and his nose was a sight. Pa looked scared, and then he held up his hand and looked at that. His hand looked like a ham. Just then I came in, and I turned pale, with some chalk on my face, and I begun to cry, and I said, 'O, Pa, what ails you? You are so swelled up I hardly knew you.' Pa looked sick to his stomach, and then he tried to get on his pants. O, my, it was all I could do to keep from laughing to see him pull them pants on. He could just get his legs in, and when I got a shoe horn and gave it to him, he was mad. He said it was a mean boy that would give his Pa a shoe horn to put on his pants with. The pants wouldn't come around Pa into ten inches, and Pa said he must have eat something that disagreed with him, and he laid it to a watermelon. Ma stuffed her handkerchief in her mouth to keep from laffing, when she see Pa look at hisself. The legs of the pants were so tight Pa could hardly breathe, and he turned pale, and said: 'Hennery, your Pa is a mighty sick man,' and then Ma and me both laughed, and he said we wanted him to die so we could spend his life insurance in riotous living. But when Pa put on the condensed shirt, Ma she laid down on the lounge and fairly yelled, and I laughed till my side ached. Pa got it

TAKE IT AWAY! MY HEAD IS ALL WRONG TOO.

over his head, and got his hands in the sleeves, and couldn't get it either way, and he couldn't see us laugh, but he could hear us, and he said, 'It's darned funny, ain't it, to have a parent swelled up this way? If I bust you will both be sorry.' Well, Ma took hold of one side of the shirt, and I took hold of the other, and we pulled it on, and when Pa's head came up through the collar, his face was blue. Ma told him she was afraid he would have a stroke of apoplexy before he got his clothes on, and I guess Pa thought so too. He tried to get the collar on, but it wouldn't go half way around his neck, and he looked in the glass and cried, he looked so. He sat down in a chair and panted, he was so out of breath, and the shirt and pants ripped, and Pa said there was no use living if he was going to be a rival to a fat woman in the side show. Just then I put the plug hat on Pa's head, and it was so small it was going to roll off, when Pa tried to fit it on his head, and then he took it off and looked inside of it to see if it was his hat, and when he found his name in it, he said, 'Take it away. My head is all wrong too.' Then he told me to go for the doctor, mighty quick. I got the doctor and told him what we were trying to do with Pa, and he said he would finish the job. So the doc. came in, and Pa was on the lounge, and when the doc. saw him, he said it was lucky he was called just as he was or we would have required an undertaker. He put some pounded ice on Pa's head the first thing, ordered the shirt cut open, and we got the pants off. Then he gave Pa an emetic, and had his feet soaked, and Pa said, 'Doc., if you will bring me out of this I will never drink another drop.' The doc. told Pa that his life was not worth a button if he ever drank again, and left about half a pint of sugar pills to be fired into Pa every five minutes. Ma and me sat up with Pa all day Sunday, and Monday morning I changed the spectacles, and took the clothes home and along about noon Pa said he felt as though he could get up. Well, you never see a tickleder man than he was when he found the swelling had gone down so he could get his pants and shirt on, and he says that doctor is the best in this town. Ma says I am a smart boy, and Pa has taken the pledge, and we are all right. Say, you don't think there is anything wrong in a boy playing it on his Pa once in a while, do you?"

"Not much. You have very likely saved your Pa's life. No, sir, joking is all right when by so doing you can break a person of a bad habit," and the grocery man cut a chew of tobacco off a piece of plug that was on the counter, which the boy had soaked in kerosene, and before he had fairly got it rolled in his cheek, he spit it out and began to gag, and as the boy started leisurely out the door, the grocery man said, "Look-a-here, condemn you, don't you ever tamper with my tobacco again, or, by thunder, I'll maul you," and he followed the boy to the door, spitting cotton all the way; and, as the boy went around the corner, the grocery man thought how different a joke seemed when it was on somebody else. And then he turned to go in and rinse the kerosene out of his mouth, and found a sign on a box of new green apples, as follows:

COLIC OR CHOLERA INFANTUM
YOU PAYS YOUR MONEY
AND TAKES YOUR CHOICE.

CHAPTER XXIII

Ghosts don't steal wormy figs—A grand rehearsal—The minister murders Hamlet—The watermelon knife—The old man wanted to rehearse the drunken scene in Rip Van Winkle—No hugging allowed —Hamlet wouldn't have two ghosts—"How would you like to be an idiot?"

"I AM thy father's ghost," said a sheeted form in the doorway of the grocery, one evening, and the grocery man got behind the cheese box, while the ghost continued in a sepulchral voice "doomed for a certain time to walk the night," and, waving a chair round, the ghost strode up to the grocery man, and with the other ghostly hand reached into a box of figs.

"I AM THY FATHER'S GHOST."

"No, you ain't no ghost," said the grocery man, recognizing the bad boy. "Ghosts do not go prowling around groceries stealing wormy figs. What do you mean by this sinful masquerade business? My father never had no ghost!"

"O, we have struck it now," said the bad boy as he pulled off his mask and rolled up the sheet he had worn around him. "We are going to have amateur theatricals, to raise money to have the church carpeted, and I am going to boss the job."

"You don't say," answered tne grocery man, as he thought how much he could sell to the church people for a strawberry and ice cream festival, and how little he could sell for amateur theatricals. "Who is going into it, and what are you going to play?"

"Pa and Ma, and me, and the minister, and three choir singers, and my chum, and the minister's wife, and two deacon's, and an old maid are rehearsing, but we have not decided what to play yet. They all want to play a different play, and I am fixing it so they can all be satisfied. The minister wants to play Hamlet, Pa wants to play Rip Van Winkle, Ma wants to play Mary Anderson, the old maid wants to play a boarding school play, and the choir singers want an opera, and the minister's wife wants to play Lady Macbeth, and my chum and me want to play a double song and dance, and I am going to give them all a show. We had a rehearsal last night, and I am the only one able to be around to-day. You see they have all been studying different plays, and they all wanted to talk at once. We let the minister sail in first. He had on a pair of his wife's black stockings, and a mantle made of a linen buggy-lap blanket, and he wore a mason's cheese knife such as these fellows with poke bonnets and white feathers wear when they get an invitation to a funeral or an excursion. Well, you never saw Hamlet murdered the way he did it. His interpretation of the character was that Hamlet was a dude that talked through his nose and while he was repeating Hamlet's soliloquy, Pa, who had come in with an old hunting suit on, as Rip Van Winkle, went to sleep, and he didn't wake up till Lady Macbeth came in, in the sleep-walking scene. She couldn't find a knife, so I took a slice of watermelon and sharpened it for her, and she made a mistake in the one she was to stab, and she stabbed Hamlet in the neck with a slice of watermelon, and the core of the melon fell on Pa's face, as he lay asleep as Rip and when Lady Macbeth said, 'Out damned spot,' Pa woke up and felt the gob of watermelon on his face, and he thought he had been murdered, and Ma came in on a hop, skip and jump as 'Parthenia,' and threw her arms around a deacon who was going to play the grave digger, and began to call him pet names, and Pa was mad, and the choir singers they began to sing, 'In the North Sea lived a whale,' and then they quit acting. You'd a dide to see Hamlet. The piece of watermelon went down his neck, and Lady Macbeth went off and left it in the wound under his collar, and Ma had to pull it out, and Hamlet said the seeds and the juice was running down inside his shirt, and he said he wouldn't play if he was going to be stabbed with a slice of melon, so while his wife was getting the melon seeds out of his neck, and drying the juice on his shirt, I sharpened a cucumber for Lady Macbeth to use as a dagger, but Hamlet kicked on cucumbers, too, and I had more trouble than any stage manager ever had. Then Pa wanted to rehearse the drunken scene in Rip Van Winkle, where he hugs Gretchen and drinks out of a flask behind her back, and he got one of the choir singers to act as Gretchen, and I guess he would have been hugging till this time, and have swallowed the flask, if Ma had not taken him by the ear and said a little of that would go a good ways in an entertainment for the church. Pa said he didn't know as it was any worse than her prancing up to a grave digger and hugging him till the filling came out of his teeth, and then the minister decided that we wouldn't have any hugging at all in the play, and the choir girls said they wouldn't play, and the old maids struck, and the play came to a stand-still."

"Well, that beats anything I ever heard tell of. It's a shame for people outside the profession to do play acting, and I won't go to the entertainment unless I get a pass," said the grocery man. "Did you rehearse any more?"

"Yes, the minister wanted to try the ghost scene," said the boy, "and he wanted me to be the ghost. Well, they have two 'Markses' and two 'Topsies' in Uncle Tom's Cabin, and I thought two ghosts in Hamlet would about fill the bill for amateurs, so I got my chum to act as one ghost. I wanted to have something new in ghosts, so my chum and me got two pairs of Ma's long stockings, one pair red and one pair blue, and I put on a red one and a blue one, and my chum did the same. Then we got some ruffled clothes belonging to Ma, and put them on, and we put

MA SAID A LITTLE OF THAT WOULD GO A GOOD WAYS.

sheets over us, clear to our feet, and when Hamlet got to yearning for his father's ghost, I came in out of the bath room with the sheet over me, and said I was the huckleberry he was looking for, and my chum followed me out and said he was a twin ghost, also, and then Hamlet got on his ear and said he wouldn't play with two ghosts, and he went off pouting, and then my chum and me pulled off the sheets and danced a clog dance. Well, when the rest of the troop saw our make up, it nearly killed them. Most of them had seen ballet dancers, but they never saw them with different colored socks. The minister said the benefit was rapidly becoming a farce, and before we had danced half a minute Ma recognized her socks, and she came for me with a hot box, and made me take them off, and Pa was mad and said the dancing was the only thing that was worth the price of admission, and he scolded Ma, and the choir girls sided with Pa, and just then my chum caught his toe in the carpet and fell down, and that loosened the plaster overhead and about a bushel fell on the crowd. Pa thought lightning had struck the house, the minister thought it was a judgment on them all for play acting, and he began to shed his Hamlet costume with one hand and pick the plaster out of his hair with the other. The women screamed and tried to get the plaster out of their necks, and while Pa was brushing off the choir singers Ma said the rehearsal was adjourned, and they all went home, but we are going to rehearse again on Friday night. The play cannot be considered a success, but we will bring it out all right by the time the entertainment is to come off."

"By gum," said the grocery man, "I would like to have seen that minister as Hamlet. Didn't he look funny?"

"Funny! Well, I should remark. He seemed to predominate. That is, he was too fresh, too numerous, as it were. But at the next rehearsal I am going to work in an act from Richard the Third, and my chum is going to play the Chinaman of the Danites, and I guess we will take the cake. Say, I want to work in an idiot somewhere. How would you like to play the idiot? You wouldn't have to rehearse or anything—"

At this point the bad boy was seen to go out of the grocery store real spry, followed by a box of wooden clothes pins, that the grocery man had thrown after him.

CHAPTER XXIV

THE CRUEL WOMAN AND THE LUCKLESS DOG

The bad boy with a dog and a black eye—Where did you steal him? Angels don't break dog's legs—A woman who breaks dog's legs has no show with St. Peter—Another burglar scare—The grocery delivery man scared.

"HELLO!" said the grocery man to the bad boy, as he came in with a black eye, leading a hungry looking dog that was walking on three legs, and had one leg tied up with a red silk handkerchief. "What is this—a part of your amateur theater? Now you get out of here with that dog mighty quick. A boy that hurts dogs so they have to have their legs tied up, is no friend of mine," and the grocery man took up a broom to drive the dog out of doors."

"There, you calm yourself," says the boy to the grocery man, as the dog got behind the boy and looked up at the grocery man as though he was not afraid as long as the bad boy was around. "Set up the crackers and cheese, sausage, and pickles, and everything this dog wants to eat—he is a friend of mine—that dog is my guest, and those are my splints on his broken leg, and that is my handkerchief that my girl gave me, wound around it, and you touch that dog except in the way of kindness, and down comes your house." And the boy doubled up his fists as though he meant business.

"Poor doggie," said the grocery man, as he cut off a piece of sausage and offered it to the dog, which was declined with thanks, expressed by the wagging tail. "Where did you steal him?"

"I didn't steal him, and he is no cannibal. He won't eat your sausage!" and the boy put up his elbow as though to ward off an imaginary blow. "You see, this dog was following a pet dog that belonged to a woman, and she tried to shoo him away, but he wouldn't shoo. This dog did not know that he was a low born, miserable dog, and had no right to move in the society of an aristocratic pet dog, and he followed right along. He thought this was a free country, and one dog was as good as another, and he followed that woman and her pet dog right into her door yard. The pet dog encouraged this dog, and he went in the yard, and when the woman got up on the steps she threw a velocipede at this dog and broke his leg, and then she took up her pet and went in the house so she wouldn't hear this dog howl. She is a nice woman, and I see her go to meeting every Sunday with a lot of morocco books in her hands, and once I pumped the organ in the church where she goes, and she was so pious I thought she was an angel—but angels don't break dogs' legs. I bet when she goes up to the gate and sees St. Peter open the book and look for the charges against her she will tremble as though she had fits. And when St. Peter runs his finger down the ledger, and stops at the dog column, and turns and looks at her over his spectacles, and says, 'Madam, how about your stabbing a poor dog with a velocipede, and breaking its leg?' she will claim it was an accident; but she can't fool Pete. He is on to everybody's racket, and if they get in there, they have got to have a clean record."

"Say, look-a-here," said the grocery man, as he looked at the boy in astonishment as he unwound the handkerchief to dress the dog's broken leg, while the dog looked up in the boy's face with an expression of thankfulness and confidence that he was an able practitioner in dog bone-setting, "what kind of talk is that? You talk of heaven as though the books were kept like the books of a grocery, and you speak too familiarly of St. Peter."

"Well, I didn't mean any disrespect," said the boy, as he fixed the splint on the dog's leg, and tied it with a string, while the dog licked his hand, "but I learned in Sunday school that up there they watch even the sparrow's fall, and they wouldn't be apt to get left on a dog bigger than a whole flock of sparrows, 'specially when the dog's fall was accompanied with such noise as a velocipede makes when it falls down stairs. No, sir, a woman who throws a velocipede at a poor, homeless dog, and breaks its leg, may carry a car load of prayer books, and she may attend to all the

"SAY, LOOK-A-HERE," SAID THE GROCERY MAN.

sociables, but according to what I have been told, if she goes sailing up to the gate of New Jerusalem, as though she owned the whole place and expects to be ushered into a private box, she will get left. The man in the box office will tell her she is not on the list, and that there is a variety show below, where the devil is a star, and fallen angels are dancing the cancan with sheet iron tights, on brimstone lakes and she can probably crawl under the canvas but she can't get in among the angelic hosts until she can satisfactorily explain that dog story that is told of her. Possibly I have got a raw way of expressing myself, but I had rather take my chances if I should apply for admission up there, with this lame dog under my arm than to take hers with a pug dog that hain't got any legs broke. A lame dog and a clear conscience beats a pet dog, when your conscience feels nervous. Now I am going to lay this dog in a barrel of dried apples, where your cat sleeps, and give him a little rest, and I will give you four minutes to tell me all you know, and you will have three minutes on your hands with nothing to say. Unbutton your lip and give your teeth a vacation."

"Well, you *have* got gall. However, I don't know but you are right about that woman that hurt the dog. Still, it may have been her way of petting a strange dog. We should try to look upon the charitable side of people's eccentricities. But say, I want to ask you if you have seen anything of my man that delivers groceries. Saturday night I sent him over to your house to deliver some things, about ten o'clock, and he has not showed up since. What do you think has become of him?"

"Well, by gum, that accounts for it. Saturday night, about ten o'clock, we heard somebody in the back yard, around the kitchen door, just as we were going to bed, and Pa was afraid it was a burglar after the church money he had collected last Sunday. He had got to turn it over the next day, to pay the minister's expenses on his vacation, and it made him nervous to have it around. I peeked out of the window and saw the man, and I told Pa, and Pa got a revolver and began shooting through the wire screen to the kitchen window, and I saw the man drop the basket and begin to climb over the fence real sudden, and I went out and began to groan, as though somebody was dying in the alley, and I brought in the basket with the mackerel and green corn, and told Pa that from the groaning out there I guess he had killed the grocery delivery man, and I wanted Pa to go out and help me hunt for the body, but he said he was going to take the midnight train and go

THE MAN BEGAN TO CLIMB.

out West on some business, and Pa lit out. I guess your man was scared and went one way and Pa was scared and went the other. Won't they be astonished when they meet each other on the other side of the world? Pa will shoot him again when they meet if he gives Pa any sass. Pa says when he gets mad he had just as soon eat as to kill a man."

"Well, I guess my man has gone off to a Sunday pic-nic or something, and will come back when he gets sober, but how are your theatricals getting along?" asked the grocery man.

"O, that scheme is all busted," said the boy. "At least until the minister gets back from his vacation. The congregation has noticed a red spot on his hand for some time, and the ladies said what he needed was rest. They said if that spot was allowed to go on it might develop into a pimple, and the minister might die of blood poison, superinduced by overwork, and they took up a collection, and he has gone. The night they bid him good-bye, the spot on his hand was the subject of much comment. The women sighed and said it was lucky they noticed the spot on his hand before it had sapped his young life away. Pa said Job had more than four hundred boils worse than that, and he never took a vacation, and then Ma dried Pa up. She told Pa he had never suffered from blood poison, and Pa said he could raise cat boils for the market and never squeal. Ma see the only way to shut Pa up was to let him go home with the choir singer. So she bounced him off with her, and he didn't get home till most 'leven o'clock, but Ma she set up for him. Maybe what she said to Pa made him go West after peppering your burglar. Well, I must go home now, 'cause I run the family since Pa lit out. Say, send some of your most expensive canned fruits and things over to the house. Darn the expense." And the bad boy took the lame dog under his arm and walked out.

CHAPTER XXV

THE BAD BOY GROWS THOUGHTFUL

Why is lettuce like a girl?—King Solomon a fool—Think of any sane man having a thousand wives—He would have to have two hotels during vacation—300 blondes—600 brunettes, etc.—A thousand wives taking ice cream—I don't envy Solomon his thousand.

"WHAT are you sitting there like a bump on a log for?" asked the grocery man of the bad boy, as the youth had sat on a box for half-an-hour, with his hands in his pockets, looking at a hole in the floor, until his eyes were set like a dying horse. "What you thinking of, anyway? It seems to me boys set around and think more than they used to when I was a boy," and the grocery man brushed the wilted lettuce and shook it, and tried to make it stand up stiff and crisp, before he put it out doors; but the contrary lettuce which had been picked the day before, looked so tired that the boy noticed it.

"That lettuce reminds me of a girl. Yesterday I was in here when it was new, like the girl going to the picnic, and it was as fresh and proud, and starched up, and kitteny, and full of life, and sassy as a girl starting out for a picnic. To-day it has got back from the picnic, and, like the girl, the starch is all taken out, and it is limber, and languid, and tired, and can't stand up alone, and it looks as though it wanted to be laid at rest beside the rotten apples in the alley, rather than be set out in front of a store to be sold to honest people, and give them the gangrene of the liver," and the boy put on a health commissioner air that frightened the grocery man, and he threw the lettuce out the back door.

"You never mind about my lettuce," said the grocery

man, "I can attend to my affairs. But now tell me what you were thinking about here all the morning?"

"I was thinking what a fool King Solomon was," said the boy, with the air of one who has made a statement that has got to be argued pretty strong to make it hold water.

"Now, look-a-here," said the grocery man in anger, "I have stood it to have you play tricks on me, and have listened to your condemned foolishness without a murmur as long as you have confined yourself to people now living, but when you attack Solomon—the wisest man, the great king—and call him a fool, friendship ceases, and you must get out of this store. Solomon in all his glory, is a friend of mine, and no fool boy is going to abuse him in my presence. Now, you dry up!"

"Sit down on the ice box," said the boy to the grocery man, "what you need is rest. You are overworked. Your alleged brain is equal to wilted lettuce, and it can devise ways and means to hide rotten peaches under good ones, so as to sell them to blind orphans; but when it comes to grasping great questions, your small brain cannot comprehend them. Your brain may go up sideways to a great question and rub against it, but it cannot surround it, and grasp it. That's where you are deformed. Now, it is different with me. I can raise brain to sell to you grocery men. Listen. This Solomon is credited with being the wisest man, and yet history says he had a thousand wives. Just think of it. You have got one wife, and Pa has got one, and all the neighbors have one, if they have had any kind of luck. Does not one wife make you pay attention? Wouldn't two wives break you up? Wouldn't three cause you to see stars? How would ten strike you? Why, man alive, you do not grasp the magnitude of the statement that Solomon had a thousand wives. A thousand wives, standing side by side, would reach about four blocks. Marching by fours it would take them twenty minutes to pass a given point. The largest summer resort hotel only holds about five hundred people, so Sol would have had to hire two hotels if he took his wives out for a day in the country. If you would stop and think once in a while you would know more."

The grocery man's eyes had begun to stick out as the bad boy continued, as though the statistics had never been brought to his attention before, but he was bound to stand by his old friend Solomon, and he said, "Well, Solomon's wives must have been different from our wives of the present day."

"Not much," said the boy, as he saw he was paralyzing the grocery man. "Women have been about the same ever since Eve. She got mashed on the old original dude, and it stands to reason that Solomon's wives were no better than the mother of the human race. Statistics show that one woman out of every ten is red headed. That would give Solomon an even hundred red headed wives. Just that hundred red headed wives would be enough to make an ordinary man think that there is a land that is fairer than this. Then there would be, out of the other nine hundred,

"THAT LETTUCE REMINDS ME OF A GIRL."

about three hundred blondes, and the other six hundred would be brunettes, and maybe he had a few albinos, and bearded women, and fat women, and dwarfs. Now, those thousand women had appetites, desires for dress and style. the same as all women. Imagine Solomon saying to them: 'Girls, let's all go down to the ice cream saloon and have a dish of ice cream.' Can you, with your brain muddled with codfish and new potatoes, realize the scene that would follow? Suppose after Solomon's broom brigade had got seated in the ice creamery, one of the red headed wives should catch Solomon winking at a strange girl at another table. You may think Solomon did not know enough to wink, or that he was not that kind of a flirt, but he *must* have been or he could never have succeeded in marrying a thousand wives in a sparsely settled country. No, sir, it looks to me as though Solomon, in all his glory, was an old masher, and from what I have seen of men being bossed around with one wife, I don't envy Solomon his thousand. Why, just imagine that gang of wives going and ordering fall bonnets. Solomon would have to be a king or a Vanderbilt to stand it. Ma wears five dollar silk stockings, and Pa kicks awfully when the bill comes in. Imagine Solomon putting up for a few thousand pair of silk stockings. I am glad you will sit down and reason with me in a rational way about some of these Bible stories that take my breath away. The minister stands me off when I try to talk with him about such things, and tells me to study the parable of the Prodigal Son, and the deacons tell me to go and soak my head. There is darn little encouragement for a boy to try and figure out things. How would you like to have a thousand red headed wives come into the store this minute and tell you they wanted you to send carriages around to the house at three o'clock so they could go for a drive? Or how would you like to have a hired girl come rushing in and tell you to send up six hundred doctors, because six hundred of your wives had been taken with cholera morbus? Or—"

"O, don't mention it," said the grocery man, with a shudder. "I wouldn't take Solomon's place, and be the natural protector of a thousand wives if anybody would give me the earth. Think of getting up in a cold winter morning and building a thousand fires. Think of two thousand pair of hands in a fellow's hair! Boy, you have shown me that Solomon needed a guardian over him. He didn't have sense."

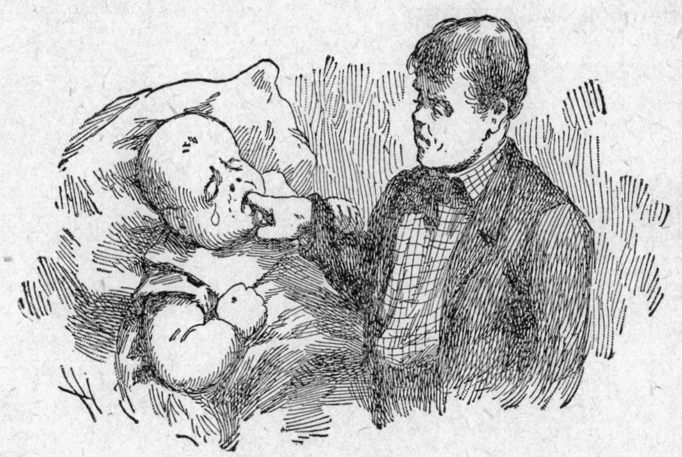

THE BABY IS TEETHING.

"Yes," says the boy, "and think of two thousand feet, each one as cold as a brick of chocolate ice cream. A man would want a back as big as the fence of a fair ground. But I don't want to harrow up your feelings. I must go and put some arnica on Pa. He has got home and says he has been to a summer resort on a vacation, and he is all covered with blotches. He says it is mosquito bites, but Ma thinks he has been shot full of bird shot by some watermelon farmer. Ma hasn't got any sympathy for Pa because he didn't take her along, but if she had been there she would have been filled with bird shot, too. But you musn't detain me. Between Pa and the baby I have got all that I can attend to.

The baby is teething, and Ma makes me put my fingers in the baby's mouth to help it cut teeth. That is a humiliating position for a boy as big as I am. Say, how many babies do you figure that Solomon had to buy rubber toothing rings for in all his glory?"

And the boy went out, leaving the grocery man reflecting on what a family Solomon must have had, and how he needed to be the wisest man to get along without a circus afternoon and evening.

CHAPTER XXVI

FARM EXPERIENCES

The bad boy works on a farm for a deacon—He knows when he has got enough—How the deacon made him flax around—And how he made it warm for the deacon.

"WANT to buy any cabbages?" said the bad boy to the grocery man, as he stopped at the door of the grocery, dressed in blue wamus, his breeches tucked in his boots, and an old hat on his head, with a hole that let out his hair through the top. He had got out of a democrat wagon, and was holding the lines hitched to a horse about forty years old, that leaned against the hitching post to rest. "Only a shilling apiece."

"O, go 'way," said the grocery man. "I only pay three cents apiece." And then he looked at the boy and said, "Hello, Hennery, is that you? I have missed you all the week, and now you come to me sudden, disguised as a granger. What does all this mean?

"It means that I have been the victim of as vile a conspiracy as ever was known since Cæsar was stabbed, and Marc Antony orated over his prostrate corpse in the Roman forum, to an audience of supes and scene shifters," and the boy dropped the lines on the sidewalk, said, "Whoa, gol darn you," to the horse that was asleep, wiped his boots on the grass in front of the store and came in, and seated himself on the old half bushel. "There, this seems like home again."

"What's the row?—who has been playing it on you?" And the grocery man smelled a sharp trade in cabbages, as well as other smells peculiar to the farm.

"Well, I'll tell you. Lately our folks have been constantly talking of the independent life of the farmer, and how easy it is, and how they would like it if I would learn to be a farmer. They said there was nothing like it, and several of the neighbors joined in and said I had the natural ability to be one of the most successful farmers in the state. They all drew pictures of the fun it was to work on a farm where you could get your work done and take your fish-pole and go off and catch fish, or a gun, and go out and kill game, and how you could ride horses, and pitch hay, and smell the sweet perfume, and go to husking bees, and dances, and everything, and they got me all worked up so I wanted to go to work on a farm. Then an old deacon that belongs to our church, who runs a farm about eight miles out of town, he came on the scene, and said he wanted a boy, and if I would go out and work for him he would be easy on me because he knew my folks, and we belonged to the same church. I can see it now. It was all a put up job on me, just like they play three card monte on a fresh stranger. I was took in. By gosh, I have been out there a week, and here's what there is left of me. The only way I got a chance to come to town was to tell the farmer I could sell cabbages to you for a shilling a piece. I knew you sold them for fifteen cents and I thought that would give me a shilling. So the farmer said he would pay me my wages in cabbages at a shilling apiece and only charge me a dollar for the horse and wagon to bring them in. So you only pay three cents. Here are thirty cabbages, which will come to ninety cents. I pay a dollar for the horse, and when I get back to the farm I owe the farmer ten cents, besides working a week for nothing. O, it is all right. I don't kick, but this ends farming for Hennery. I know when I have got enough of an easy life on a farm. I prefer a hard life, breaking stones on the streets, to an easy, dreamy life on a farm."

"They *did* play it on you, didn't they?" said the grocery man. "But wasn't the old deacon a good man to work for?"

"Good man nothing," said the boy, as he took up a piece of horseradish and began to grate it on the inside of his rough hand. "I tell you there's a heap of difference in a deacon in Sunday school, telling about sowing wheat and tares, and a deacon out on a farm in a hurry season, when there is hay to get in and wheat to harvest all at the same time. I went out to the farm Sunday evening with the deacon and his wife, and they couldn't talk too much about the nice time we would have, and the fun; but the deacon changed more than forty degrees in five minutes after we got to the farm. He jumped out of the wagon and pulled off his coat and let his wife climb out over the wheel, and yelled to the hired girl to bring out the milk pail, and told me to fly around and unharness the horse, and throw down a lot of hay for the work animals, and then told me to run down to the pasture and drive up a lot of cows. The pasture was half a mile away, and the cows were scattered around in the woods, and the mosquitoes were thick, and I got all covered with mud and burrs, and stung with thistles, and when I got the cattle near to the house, the old deacon yellod to me that I was slower than molasses in the winter, and then I took a club and tried to hurry the cows, and he yelled at me to stop hurrying, 'cause I would retard the flow of milk. By gosh I *was* mad. I asked for a mosquito bar to put over me the next time I went after the cows, and the people all laughed at me, and when I sat down on the fence to scrape the mud off my Sunday pants the deacon yelled like he does in the revival, only he said, 'Come, come, procrastination is the thief of time. You get up and hump yourself and go and feed the pigs.' He was so darn mean that I could not help throwing a burdock burr against the side of the cow he was milking, and it struck her right in the flank on the other side from where the deacon was. Well, you'd a dide to see the cow jump up and blat. All four of her feet were off the ground at a time, and I guess most of them hit the deacon on his Sunday vest, and the rest hit the milk pail, and the cow backed against the fence and bellered, and the deacon was all covered with milk and cow hair, and he got up and throwed the three legged stool at the cow and hit her on the horn and it glanced off and hit me on the pants just as I went over the fence to feed the pigs. I didn't know a deacon could talk so sassy at a cow, and come so near swearing without actually saying cuss words. Well, I lugged swill until I was homesick to my stomach, and then I had to clean off horses, and go to the neighbors about a mile away to borrow a lot of rakes to use the next day. I was so tired I almost cried, and then I had to draw two barrels of water with a well bucket, to cleanse for washing the next day, and by that time I wanted to die. It was most nine o'clock, and I began to think about supper, when the deacon said all they had was bread and milk for supper Sunday night, and I rasseled with a tin basin of skim milk, and some old back number bread, and wanted to go to bed, but the deacon wanted to know if I was heathen enough to want to go to bed without evening prayers. There was no one thing I was less mashed on than evening prayers about that minute, but I had to take a prayer half an hour long on top of that skim milk, and I guess it curdled the milk, for I hadn't been in bed more than half an hour before I had the worst colic a boy ever had, and I thought I should die all alone up in that garret, on the floor, with nothing to make my last hours pleasant but some rats playing with ears of seed corn on the floor, and mice running through some dry pea pods. But how different the deacon talked in the evening devotions from what he did when the cow was galloping on him in the barn yard. Well, I got through the colic and was just getting to sleep when the deacon yelled for me to get up and hustle down-stairs. I thought maybe the house was on fire, 'cause I smelled smoke, and I got into my trousers and came down stairs on a jump yelling 'Fire,' when the deacon grabbed me and told me to get down on my knees, and before I knew it he was into the morning devotions, and when he said 'Amen' and jumped and said for us to fire breakfast into us quick and get to work doing chores; I looked at the clock and it was just three o'clock in the morning, just the time Pa comes home and goes to bed in town, when he is running a political campaign. Well, sir, I had to jump from one thing to another from three o'clock in the morning till nine at night, pitching hay, driving reaper, raking and binding, shocking wheat, hoeing corn, and everything, and I never got a kind word. I spoiled my clothes, and I think another week would make a pirate

MUD, BURRS AND MOSQUITOES WERE THICK.

of me. But during it all I had the advantage of a pious example. I tell you, you think more of such a man as the deacon if you don't work for him, but only see him when he comes to town, and you hear him sing, 'Heaven is my Home,' through his nose. He even is farther from home than any place I ever heard of. He would be a good mate on a Mississippi river steamboat if he could swear, and I guess he could soon learn. Now you take these cabbages and give me ninety cents, and I will go home and borrow ten cents to make up the dollar, and send my chum back with the horse and wagon and my resignation. I was not cut out for a farmer. Talk about fishing, the only fish I saw was a salt white fish we had for breakfast one morning, which was salted by Noah, in the ark," and while the grocery man was unloading the cabbages the boy went off to look for his chum, and later the two boys were seen driving off to the farm with two fishing poles sticking out of the hind end of the wagon.

CHAPTER XXVII

DRINKING CIDER IN THE CELLAR

The deacon will not accept Hennery's resignation—He wants butter on his pancakes—His chum joins him—The skunk in the cellar—The poor boy gets the "ager."

"WELL, I swow, here comes a walking hospital," said the grocery man as the bad boy's shadow came in the store, followed by the boy, who looked sick and yellow, and tired, and he had lost half his flesh. "What's the matter with you? Haven't got the yellow fever, have you?" and the grocery man placed a chair where the invalid could fall into it.

"No, got the ager," said the boy as he wiped the perspiration off his upper lip, and looked around the store to see if there was anything in sight that would take the taste of quinine out of his mouth. "Had too much dreamy life of ease on the farm, and been shaking ever since. Darn a farm anyway."

"What, you haven't been to work for the deacon any more, have you? I thought you sent in your resignation," and the grocery man offered the boy some limberger cheese to strengthen him.

"O, take that cheese away," said the boy, as he turned pale and gagged. "You don't know what a sick person needs any more than a professional nurse. What I want is to be petted. You see I went out to the farm with my chum, and I took the fish poles and remained in the woods while he drove the horse to the deacon's; and he gave the deacon my resignation, and the deacon wouldn't accept it. He said he would hold my resignation until after harvest, and then act on it. He said he could put me in jail for breach of promise, if I quit work and left him without giving proper notice; and my chum came and told me, and so I concluded to go to work rather than have any trouble, and the deacon said my chum could work a few days for his board if he wanted to. It was pretty darn poor board for a boy to work for, but my chum wanted to be with me, so he stayed. Pa and Ma came out to the farm to stay a day or two to help. Pa was going to help harvest, and Ma was going to help the deacon's wife, but Pa wanted to carry the jug to the field, and lay under a tree while the rest of us worked, and Ma just talked the arm off the deacon's wife. The deacon and Pa laid in the shade and see my chum and me work, and Ma and the deacon's wife gossiped so they forgot to get dinner, and my chum and me organized a strike, but we were beaten by monopoly. Pa took me by the neck and thrashed out a shock of wheat with my heels, and the deacon took my chum and sat down on him, and we begged and they gave us our old situations back. But we got even with them that night. I tell you, when a boy tries to be good, and quit playing jokes on people, and then has everybody down on him, and has his Pa hire him out on a farm to work for a deacon that hasn't got any soul except when he is in church, and a boy has to get up in the night to get breakfast and go to work, and has to work until late at night, and they kick because he wants to put butter on his pancakes, and feed him skim milk and rusty fat pork, it makes him tough, and he would play a joke on his aged grandmother. After my chum and me got all the chores done that night, we sat out on a fence back of the house in the orchard, eating green apples in the moonlight, and trying to think of a plan of revenge. Just then I saw a skunk back of the house, right by the outside cellar door, and I told my chum that it would serve them right to drive the skunk down cellar and shut the door, but my chum said that would be too mean. I asked him if it would be any meaner than for the deacon to snatch us bald headed because we couldn't mow hay away fast enough for two men to pitch it, and he said it wouldn't, and so we got on each side of the skunk and sort of scared it down cellar, and then we crept up softly and closed the cellar doors. Then we went in the house and I whispered to Ma and asked her if she didn't think the deacon had some cider, and Ma she began to hint that she hadn't had a good drink of cider since last winter, and the deacon's wife said us boys could take a pitcher and go down cellar and draw some. That was too much. I didn't want

"WHOOSH."

any cider, anyway, so I told them that I belonged to a temperance society, and I should break my pledge if I drawed cider, and she said I was a good boy, for me never to touch a drop of cider. Then she told my chum where the cider barrel was, down cellar; but he ain't no slouch. He said he was afraid to go down cellar in the dark, and so Pa said he and the deacon would go down and draw the cider, and the deacon's wife asked Ma to go down, too, and look at the fruit and berries she had canned for winter, and they all went down cellar. Pa carried an old tin lantern with holes in it, to light the deacon to the cider barrel; and the deacon's wife had a taller candle to show Ma the canned fruit. I tried to get Ma not to go, 'cause Ma is a friend of mine, and I didn't want her to have anything to do with the circus; but she said she guessed she knew her business. When anybody says they guess they know their own business, that settles it with me, and I don't try to argue with them. Well, my chum and me sat there in the kitchen, and I stuffed a piece of red table cloth in my mouth to keep from laughing, and my chum held his nose with his finger and thumb, so he wouldn't snort right out. We could hear the cider run in the pitcher, and then it stopped, and the deacon drank out of the pitcher, and then Pa did, and then they drawed some more cider, and Ma and the deacon's wife were talking about how much sugar it took to can fruit, and the deacon told Pa to help himself out of a crock of fried cakes, and I heard the cover on the crock rattle, and just then I heard the old tin lantern rattle on the brick floor of the cellar, the deacon said 'Merciful goodness;' Pa said 'Helen and damnation, I am stabbed,' and Ma yelled 'Goodness sakes alive,' and then there was a lot of dishpans on the stairs begun to fall, and they all tried to get up cellar at once, and they fell over each other; and O my, what a frowy smell came up to the kitchen from the cellar. It was enough to kill anybody. Pa was the first to get to the head of the stairs and he stuck his head in the kitchen, and drew in a long breath, and said '*Whoosh!* Hennery, your Pa is a mighty sick man.' The deacon came up next, and he had run his head into a hanging shelf and broken a glass jar of huckleberries, and they were all over him, and he said, 'Give me air. Earth's but a desert drear.' Then Ma and the deacon's wife came up on a gallop, and they looked tired. Pa began to peel off his coat and vest and said he was going out to bury them, and Ma said he could bury her, too, and I asked the deacon if he didn't notice a faint odor of sewer gas coming from the cellar, and my chum said it smelled more to him as though something had crawled in the cellar and died. Well, you never saw a sicker crowd, and I felt sorry for Ma and the deacon, 'cause their false teeth fell out, and I knew Ma couldn't gossip and the deacon couldn't talk sassy without teeth. But you'd dide to see Pa. He was mad, and thought the deacon had put up the job on him, and he was going to knock the deacon out in two rounds, when Ma said there was no use of getting mad about a dispensation of providence, and Pa said one more such dispensation of providence would just kill him on the spot. They finally got the house aired, and my chum and me slept on the hay in the barn, after we had opened the outside cellar door so the animal could get out, and the next morning I had the fever and ague, and Pa and Ma brought me home, and I have been firing quinine down my neck ever since. Pa says it is malaria, but it is getting up before daylight in the morning and prowling around a farm doing chores before it is time to do chores, and I don't want any more farm. I thought at Sunday school last Sunday, when the superintendent talked about the odor of sanctity that pervaded the house on that beautiful morning, and looked at the deacon, that the deacon thought the superintendent was referring to him and Pa, but maybe it was an accident. Well, I must go home and shoot another charge of quinine into me," and the boy went out as if he was on his last legs, though he acted as if he was going to have a little fun while he did last.

PECK'S SUNSHINE

A COLLECTION OF ARTICLES GENERALLY CALCULATED TO THROW SUNSHINE INSTEAD OF CLOUDS ON THE FACES OF THOSE WHO READ THEM

BY

GEORGE W. PECK

AUTHOR OF
"PECK'S FUN," "PECK'S BAD BOY AND HIS PA,"
"PECK'S BOSS BOOK"

ILLUSTRATED BY HOPKINS

PECK'S SUNSHINE

CONTENTS

NOT GUILTY

Gentlemen of the Jury:

I stand before you charged with an attempt to "remove" the people of America by the publication of a new book, and I enter a plea of "Not Guilty." While admitting that the case looks strong against me, there are extenuating circumstances, which, if you will weigh them carefully, will go far towards acquitting me of this dreadful charge. The facts are that I am not responsible. I was sane enough up to the day that I decided to publish this book and have been since; but on that particular day I was taken possession of by an unseen power—a Chicago publisher—who filled my alleged mind with the belief that the country demanded the sacrifice, and that there would be money in it. If the thing is a failure, I want it understood that I was instigated by the Chicago man; but if it is a success, then, of course, it was an inspiration of my own.

The book contains nothing but good nature, pleasantly told yarns, jokes on my friends; and, through it all, there is not intended to be a line or a word can cause pain or sorrow—nothing but happiness.

Laughter is the best medicine known to the world for the cure of many diseases that mankind is subject to, and it has been prescribed with success by some of our best practitioners. It opens up the pores, and restores the circulation of the blood and the despondent patient that smiles is in a fair way to recovery. While this book is not recommended as an infallible cure for consumption, if I can throw the patient into the blues by the pictures, I can knock the blues out by vaccinating with the reading matter.

To those who are inclined to look upon the bright side of life, this book is most respectfully dedicated by the author.

GEO. W. PECK.

PECK'S SUNSHINE

FEMALE DOCTORS WILL NEVER DO

A St. Louis doctor factory recently turned out a dozen female doctors. As long as the female doctors were confined to one or two in the whole country, and these were experimental, the *Sun* held its peace, and did not complain; but now that the colleges are engaged in producing female doctors as a business, we must protest, and in so doing will give a few reasons why female doctors will not prove a paying branch of industry.

In the first place, if they doctor anybody it must be women and three-fourths of the women had rather have a male doctor. Suppose these colleges turn out female doctors until there are as many of them as there are male doctors, what have they got to practice on?

A man, if there was nothing the matter with him, might call in a female doctor; but if he was sick as a horse—and when a man is sick he is sick as a horse—the last thing he would have around would be a female doctor. And why? Because when a man wants a female fumbling around him he wants to feel well. He don't want to be bilious, or feverish, with his mouth tasting like cheese, and his eyes bloodshot, when a female is looking over him and taking an account of stock.

Of course, these female doctors are all young and good looking, and if one of them came into a sick room where a man was in bed, and he had chills and was as cold as a wedge, and she should sit up close to the side of the bed, and take hold of his hand, his pulse would run up to a hundred and fifty and she would prescribe for a fever when he had chilblains. Then if he died she could be arrested for malpractice. O, you can't fool us on female doctors.

A man who has been sick and had male doctors, knows just how he would feel to have a female doctor come tripping in and throw her fur lined cloak over a chair, take off her hat and gloves, and throw them on the lounge, and come up to the bed with a pair of marine blue eyes, with a twinkle in the corner, and look him in the wild, changeable eyes, and ask him to run out his tongue. Suppose he knew his tongue was coated so it looked like a yellow Turkish towel, do you suppose he would want to run out five or six inches of the lower end of it, and let that female doctor put her finger on it, to see how it was furred? Not much! He would put that tongue up into his cheek, and wouldn't let her see it for twenty-five cents admission.

We have all seen doctors put their hands under the bed-clothes and feel a man's feet to see if they were cold. If a female doctor should do that, it would give a man cramps in the legs.

A male doctor can put his hand on a man's stomach, and liver, and lungs, and ask him if he feels any pain there; but if a female doctor should do the same thing it would make a man sick, and he would want to get up and kick himself for employing a female doctor. O, there is no use talking, it would kill a man.

Now, suppose a man had heart disease, and a female doctor should want to listen to the beating of his heart. She would lay her left ear on his left breast, so her eyes and rosebud mouth would be looking right in his face, and her wavy hair would be scattered all around there, getting tangled in the buttons of his night shirt. Don't you suppose his heart would get in about twenty extra beats to the minute? You bet! And she would smile—we will bet ten dollars she would smile—and show her pearly teeth, and her ripe lips would be working as though she were counting the beats, and he would think she was trying to whisper to him, and—

Well, what would he be doing all this time? If he was not dead yet, which would be a wonder, his left hand would brush the hair away from her temple, and kind of stay there to keep the hair away, and his right hand would get sort of nervous and move around to the back of her head, and when she had counted the heart beats a few minutes and was raising her head, he would draw the head up to him and kiss her once for luck, if he was as bilious as a Jersey swamp angel, and have her charge it in the bill; and then a reaction would set in, and he would be as weak as a cat, and she would have to fan him and rub his head till he got over being nervous, and then make out her prescription after he got asleep. No; all of man's symptoms change when a female doctor is practicing on him, and she would kill him dead.

The *Sun* is a woman's rights paper, and believes in allowing women to do anything that they can do as well as men, and is in favor of paying them as well as men are paid for the same work, taking all things into consideration; but it is opposed to their trifling with human life, by trying to doctor a total stranger. These colleges are doing a great wrong in preparing these female doctors for the war path, and we desire to enter a protest in behalf of twenty million men who could not stand the pressure.

CROSSMAN'S GOAT

Mr. Crossman, of Marshall street, is a man who was once a boy himself, if his memory serves him, and no boy of his is going to ask him for anything that is in his power to purchase and be refused. But when his boy asked him to buy a goat Mr. Crossman felt hurt. It was not the expense of the goat that he looked at, but he never had felt that confidence in the uprightness of the moral character of a goat that he wanted to feel.

A goat he always associated in his mind with a tramp, and he did not feel like bringing among the truly good children of the neighborhood a goat. He told his boy that he was sorry he had lavished his young and tender affections on a goat, and hoped that he would try and shake off the feeling that his life's happiness would be wrecked if he should refuse to buy him a goat. The boy put his sleeve up over his eyes and began to shed water, and that settled it.

Mr. Crossman's religion is opposed to immersion, and when the infant baptism began his proud spirit was conquered, and he told the boy to lead on and he would buy the goat. They went over into the Polack settlement and a countess there, who takes in washing, was bereaved of the goat, while Mr. Crossman felt that he was a dollar out of pocket.

Now that he thinks of it, Mr. Crossman is confident that the old lady winked as he led the goat away by a piece of clothes line, though at the time he looked upon the affair as an honorable business transaction. If he had been buying a horse he would have asked about the habits of the animal, and would probably have taken the animal on trial. But it never occurred to him that there was any cheating in goats.

The animal finally pulled Mr. Crossman home, at the end of the clothes line, and was placed in a neighbor's barn at eventide to be ready for the morning's play, refreshed. About 6 o'clock in the morning, Mr. Crossman was looking out of his window when he saw the neighboring lady come out of the barn door head first, and the goat was just taking its head away from her polonaise in a manner that Mr. Crossman considered, with his views of propriety, decidedly impolite.

Believing there was some misunderstanding, and that the goat was jealous of a calf that was in the barn, and that the matter could be satisfactorily explained to the goat, Mr. Crossman put the other leg in his trousers, took a cistern pole and went to the front. The goat saw him coming, and rushed out into the yard and stood up on its hind feet and gave the grand hailing sign of distress, and as Mr. Crossman turned to see if any of the neighbors were up, he felt an earthquake strike him a little below where he had his suspenders tied around his body. Mr. Crossman repeated a portion of the beautiful Easter service and climbed up on an ash barrel, where he stood poking the goat on the ear with the cistern pole, when Mr. Crombie, who lives hard by, and who had come out to split some kindling wood, appeared on the scene.

Mr. Crombie is a man who grasps a situation at once, and though he is a man who deliberates much on any great undertaking, when he saw the lady behind the coal box, and Mr. Crossman on the ash barrel, he felt that there was need of a great mind right there, and he took his with him over the fence, in company with a barrel stave and a hatchet. He told Crossman that there was only one way to dea with a goat, and that was to be firm and look him right in the eye. He said Sep. Wintermute, at Whitewater, once had a goat that used to drive the boys all around, but he could do nything with him, by looking nir in the eye.

He walked toward the goat, with "his eyes sot," and Mr. Crossman says one spell he thought, by the way the goat looked sheepish, that Crombie was regular lion tamer, but just as he was about to paralyze the anima Mr. Crombie caught the strings of his drawers, which were dragging on the ground, in the nails of a barrel hoop, and as he stooped down to untangle them the goat kicked him with his head, at a point about two chains and three links in a northwesterly direction fro the small of his back. Crombie gave a sigh, said, "I die by the hand of an assassin," and jumped up on a wagon, with the barrel stave and hatchet, and the hoop tangled in his legs.

The goat had three of them treed, and was looking for other worlds to conquer, when Mr. Nowell, who was out for a walk, saw the living statues and came in to hear the news. Mr. Crossman said he didn't know what had got into the goat, unless it was a tin pail or a lawn mower that was in the barn, but he was evidently mad, and he advised Mr. Nowell to go for the police.

Nowell said a man that had raised cub bears had no right to be afraid of a goat. He said all you wanted to do, in subduing the spirit of animals, was to gain their confidence. He said he could, in two minutes, so win the affections of that goat that it would follow him about like a dog, and he went up and stroked the animal's head, scratched its ear, and asked them if they could not see they had taken the wrong course with the goat. He said a goat was a good deal like a human being. You could coax, but you could not drive. "Come, Billy," said he, as he moved off, snapping his fingers.

It is Mr. Nowell's unbiased opinion that Billy *did* come. Not that he saw Billy come, but he had a vague suspicion, from a feeling of numbness some two feet from the base of the brain, that William had arrived in that immediate vicinity, and while he was recalling his scattered thoughts and feeling for the pieces of spine that might have become detached from the original column, Billy came again and caught three of Mr. Nowell's fingers in the pile driver. That was talk enough between gentlemen, and Mr. Nowell got his back against a fence and climbed up on top backwards.

When he caught his breath he said that was the worst shock he ever experienced since he fell off the step ladder last summer. He said he had rather break a bear to ride any time.

At this point Mr. Crombie espied a letter carrier on the other side of the street, and called him over. He told the letter carrier if he would step into the yard and drive the goat in the barn they would all unite in a petition to have the salaries of letter carriers raised. There is no class of citizens more accommodating than our letter carriers, and this one came in and walked up to the goat and pushed the animal with his foot.

"This goat seems tame enough," said he, turning around to speak to Mr. Crossman. His words had not more than vaporized in the chill air before the goat had planted two trip hammer blows into the seat of government, and the letter carrier went into the barn, fell over a wheelbarrow, and the letters from his sack were distributed in a box stall.

It was a beautiful sight to look upon, and they would have been there till this time had it not been that the Countess happened to come along gathering swill, and the party made up a purse of three dollars for her if she would take the goat away.

She took a turnip top from her swill pail, offered it to the goat, and the animal followed her off, bleating and showing every evidence of contentment, and the gentlemen got down from the positions they had assumed, and they shook hands and each took a bloody oath that he would not tell about it, and they repaired to their several homes and used arnica on the spots where the goat had kicked them.

The only trouble that is liable to arise out of this is that the postmaster threatens to commence an action against Crossman for obstructing the mails.

A MEAN TRICK

PROBABLY the meanest trick that was ever played on a white man was played in Milwaukee, and the fact that there is no vigilance committee there is the only reason the perpetrators of the trick are alive. A business man had just purchased a new stiff hat, and he went into a saloon with half a dozen of his friends to fit the hat on his head. They all took beer, and passed the hat around so all could see it. One of the meanest men that ever held a county office went to the bar tender and had a thin slice of Limberger cheese cut off, and when the party were looking at the frescoed ceiling through beer glasses this wicked person slipped the cheese under the sweat leather of the hat, and the man put it on and walked out.

The man who owned the hat is one of your nervous

people, who is always complaining of being sick, and who feels as though some dreadful disease is going to take possession of him and carry him off. He went back to his place of business, took off his hat and laid it on the table, and proceeded to answer some letters. He thought he detected a smell, and, when his partner asked him if he didn't feel sick, he said he believed he did. The man turnel pale and said he guessed he would go home. He met a man on the sidewalk who said the air was full of miasma, and in the street car a man who sat next to him moved away to the end of the car, and asked him if he had just come from Chicago. The man with the hat said he had not, when the stranger said they were having a great deal of smallpox there, and he said he guessed he would get out and walk, and he pulled the bell and jumped off. The cold perspiration broke out on the forehead of the man with the new hat, and he took it off to wipe his forehead, when the whole piece of cheese seemed to roll over and breathe, and the man got the full benefit of it, and came near fainting away.

He got home and his wife met him and asked him what was the matter. He said he believed mortification had set in, and she took one whiff as he took off his hat, and said she should think it had. Where did you get into it?" said she. "Get into it?" said the man, "I have not got into anything, but some deadly disease has got hold of me, and I shall not live." She told him if any disease that smelled like that had got hold of him and was going to be chronic, she felt as though he would be a burden to himself if he lived very long. She got his clothes off, and soaked his feet in mustard water, and he slept. The man slept and dreamed that a smallpox flag was hung in front of his house and that he was riding in a butcher wagon to the pest house.

The wife sent for a doctor, and when the man of pills arrived she told him all about the case. The doctor picked up the patient's new hat, tried it on and got a sniff. He said the hat was picked before it was ripe. The doctor and the wife held a post-mortem examination of the hat, and found the slice of limberger. "Few and short were prayers they said." They woke the patient, and, to prepare his mind for the revelation that was about to be made, the doctor asked him if his worldly affairs were in a satisfactory condition. He gasped and said they were. The doctor asked him if he had made his will. He said he had not, but that he wanted a lawyer sent for at once. The doctor asked him if he felt as though he was prepared to shuffle off. The man said he had always tried to lead a different life, and had tried to be done by the same as he would do it himself, but that he might have made a misdeal some way, and he would like to have a minister sent for to take an account of stock. Then the doctor brought to the bedside the hat, opened up the sweat-leather, and showed the dying man what it was that smelled so, and told him he was as well as any man in the city.

The patient pinched himself to see if he was alive, and jumped out of bed and called for his revolver, and the doctor couldn't keep up with him on the way down town. The last we saw of the odoriferous citizen he was trying to bribe the bar-tender to tell him which one of those pelicans it was that put that slice of cheese in his hat-lining.

A FEMALE KNIGHT OF PYTHIAS

A WOMAN of Bay City, Michigan, disguised herself as a man and clerked in a store for a year, and then applied for membership in the Knights of Pythias and was initiated. During the work of the third degree her sex was discovered. It seems that in the third degree they have an India rubber rat and a celluloid snake, which run by clock work inside, and which were very natural indeed. The idea is to let them run at the candidate for initiation to see if he will flinch. When the snake ran at the girl she kept her nerve all right, but when the rat tried to run up her trousers leg she grabbed her imaginary skirts in both hands and jumped onto a refrigerator that was standing near (which is used in the work of the fourth degree) and screamed bloody murder. The girl is a member of the order, however, and there is no help for it. This affair may open the eyes of the members of secret societies and cause them to investigate. One lodge here, we understand, takes precaution against the admission of women by examining carefully the feet of applicants. If the feet are cold enough to freeze ice cream the candidate is black-balled.

THE TELESCOPE FISH-POLE CANE

THERE is one thing we want to set our faces against and try and break up, and that is the habit of young and middle aged persons going fishing on Sunday, when going on the Summer excursions to the country. The devil, or some other inventor, has originated a walking-stick that looks as innocent as a Sunday school teacher, but within it is a roaring lion, in the shape of a fish-pole. We have watched young fellows, and know their tricks. Sunday morning they say to their parents that they have agreed to go over on the West Side and attend early mass with a companion, just to hear the exquisite music, and, by the way, they may not be home to dinner. And they go from that home, with their new cane, looking as pious as though they were passing the collection plate. When they get around the corner they whoop it up for the depot, and shortly they are steaming out into the country. They have a lot of angle worms in an envelope in their vest pockets, and a restaurant colored man, who has been seen the night before, meets them at the depot and hands them a basket of sandwiches with a bottle sticking out.

Arriving at the summer resort, they go to the bank of the lake and take a boat ride, and when well out in the lake they begin to unbosom the cane. Taking the plug out of the end of it, they pull out a dingus and three joints of the fish-pole come out, and they tie a line on the end, put an angle worm on the hook, and catch fish. That is the kind of "mass" they are attending.

At night the train comes back to town, and the sunburnt young men, with their noses peeled, hand a basket to the waiting colored man, which smells of fish, and they go home and tell their parents they went out to Forest Home Cemetery in the afternoon, and the sun was awful hot. The good mother knows she smells fish on her son's clothes, but she thinks it is some new kind of perfumery, and she is silent.

An honest up-and-up fish-pole is a thing of beauty and a joy forever, if the fishing is good, but one of these deceptive, three card monte, political fish-poles, that shoves in and appears to be a cane, is incendiary, and ought to be suppressed. There ought to be a law passed to suppress a fish-pole that passes in polite society for a cane, and in such a moment as ye think not is pulled out to catch fish. There is nothing square about it, and the invention of that blasted stem winding fish-pole is doing more to ruin this country than all the political parties can overcome. If there was a law to compel the owners of those walking-sticks to put a sign on their canes, "This is a fish-pole," there would be less canes taken on these Sunday excursions in summer.

Look not upon the walking-stick when it is hollow, and pulls out, for at last it giveth thee away, young fellow.

THE SUN is in receipt of an invitation to attend the opening of a new hotel in an Iowa city, but it will be impossible to attend. We remember one Iowa hotel which we visited in 1869, when the Wisconsin editors stopped there on the way back from Omaha,—the time when a couple of bed bugs took Uncle David Atwood up on the roof and were going to throw him off, and they would have done it, only a party of cockroaches took his part and killed the bed bugs.

Sam Ryon will remember how there was a crop of new potatoes growing on the billiard room floor in the dirt, that were all blossomed out; and Charley Seymour can tell how he had to argue for an hour to convince the colored cook that the peculiar smell of the scrambled eggs was owing to some of them being rotten. There were four waiters to a hundred guests, and it was a sight long to be remembered to see Mrs. Seymour and Mrs. Atwood carry their broiled chicken back to the kitchen and pick the feathers off, while good Uncle McBride, of Sparta, got into an altercation over his fried fish because the fish had not been scaled; where it was said the only thing that was not sour was the vinegar, and where the only thing that was not too small was the bill, and where every room smelled like a morgue, and towels in the rooms had not taken a bath since 1827.

At this hotel the proprietor would take a guest's napkin to wipe his nose, and the barefooted waiter girl would slip up on the rare-done fried egg spilled on the dining-room floor, and wipe the yolk off her dress on a guest's linen coat tail. This is all we want of a hotel in that place.

BOYS WILL BE BOYS

Not many months ago there was a meeting of ministers in Wisconsin, and after the holy work in which they were engaged had been done up to the satisfaction of all, a citizen of the place where the conference was held invited a large number of them to a collation at his house. After supper a dozen of them adjourned to a room up stairs to have a quiet smoke, as ministers sometimes do, when they got to talking about old times, when they attended school and were boys together, and *The Sun* man, who was present, disguised as a preacher, came to the conclusion that ministers were rather human than otherwise when they are young.

One two-hundred pound delegate with a cigar between his fingers, blew the smoke out of the mouth which but a few hours before was uttering a supplication to the Most High to make us all good, punched a thin elder in the ribs with his thumb and said: "Jim, do you remember the time we carried the cow and calf up into the recitation room?"

For a moment "Jim" was inclined to stand on his dignity, and he looked pained, until they all began to laugh, when he looked around to see if any worldly person was present, and satisfying himself that we were all truly good, he said: "You bet your life I remember it. I have got a scar on my shin now where that d—blessed cow hooked me," and he began to roll up his trousers leg to show the scar. They told him they would take his word, and he pulled down his pants and said:

"Well, you see I was detailed to attend to the calf, and I carried the calf up stairs, assisted by Bill Smith—who is now preaching in Chicago; got a soft thing, five thousand a year, and a parsonage furnished, and keeps a team, and if one of those horses is not a trotter then I am no judge of horse flesh or of Bill, and if he don't put on an old driving coat and go out on the road occasionally and catch on for a race with some worldly-minded man, then I am another. You hear me—well, I never knew a calf was so heavy, and had so many hind legs. Kick! Why, bless your old alabaster heart, that calf walked all over me, from Genesis to Revelations. And, say, we didn't get much of a breeze the next morning, did we, when we had to clean out the recitation room?"

A solemn-looking minister, with red hair, who was present, and whose eyes twinkled some through the smoke, said to another:

"Charlie, you remember you were completely gone on the professor's niece who was visiting there from Poughkeepsie? What became of her?"

Charlie put his feet on the table, struck a match on his trousers, and said:

"Well, I wasn't gone on her, as you say, but just liked her. Not too well, you know, but just well enough. She had a color of hair that I could never stand—just the color of yours, Hank—and when she got to going with a printer I kind of let up, and they were married. I understand he is editing a paper somewhere in Illinois, and getting rich. It was better for her, as now she has a place to live, and does not have to board around like a country school ma'am, as she would if she had married me."

A dark-haired man, with a coat buttoned clear to the neck, and a countenance like a funeral sermon, with no more expression than a wooden decoy duck, who was smoking a briar-wood pipe that he had picked up on a what-not that belonged to the host, knocked the ashes out in a spittoon, and said:

"Boys, do you remember the time we stole that three-seated wagon and went out across the marsh to Kingsley's farm, after watermelons?"

Four of them said they remembered it well enough, and Jim said all he asked was to live long enough to get even with Bill Smith, the Chicago preacher, for suggesting to him to steal a bee-hive on the trip. "Why," said he, "before I had got twenty feet with that hive, every bee in it had stung me a dozen times. And do you remember how we played it on the professor, and made him believe that I had the chicken-pox? O, gentlemen, a glorious immortality awaits you beyond the grave for lying me out of that scrape."

The fat man hitched around uneasy in his chair and said they all seemed to have forgotten the principal event of that excursion, and that was how he tried to lift a bull dog over the fence by the teeth, which had become entangled in a certain portion of his wardrobe that should not be mentioned, and how he left a sample of his trousers in the possession of the dog, and how the farmer came to the college the next day with his eyes blacked, and a piece of trousers cloth done up in a paper, and wanted the professor to try and match it with the pants of some of the divinity students, and how he had to put on a pair of nankeen pants and hid his cassimeres in the boat house until the watermelon scrape blew over and he could get them mended.

Then the small brunette minister asked if he was not entitled to some credit for blacking the farmer's eyes. Says he: "When he got over the fence and grabbed the near horse by the bits, and said he would have the whole gang in jail, I felt as though something had got to be done, and I jumped out on the other side of the wagon and walked around to him and put up my hands and gave him 'one, two, three' about the nose, with my blessing, and he let go that horse and took his dog back to the house."

"Well," says the red haired minister, "those melons were green, anyway, but it was the fun of stealing them that we were after."

At this point the door opened and the host entered, and, pushing the smoke away with his hands, he said: "Well, gentlemen, are you enjoying yourselves?"

They threw their cigar stubs in the spittoon, the solemn man laid the briarwood pipe where he got it, and the fat man said:

"Brother Drake, we have been discussing the evil effects of indulging in the weed, and we have come to the conclusion that while tobacco is always bound to be used to a certain extent by the thoughtless, it is a duty the clergy owe to the community to discountenance its use on all possible occasions. Perhaps we had better adjourn to the parlor, and after asking divine guidance take our departure."

After they had gone the host looked at the cigar box, and came to the conclusion that somebody must have carried off some cigars in his pocket.

AN ARM THAT IS NOT RELIABLE

A YOUNG fellow about nineteen, who is going with his first girl and who lives on the West Side has got the symptoms awfully. He just thinks of nothing else but his girl, and when he can be with her—which is seldom, on account of the old folks—he is there, and when he cannot be there, he is there or thereabouts, in his mind. He has been trying for three months to think of something to give his girl for a Christmas present, but he couldn't make up his mind what article would cause her to think of him the most, so the day before Christmas he unbosomed himself to his employer and asked his advice as to the proper article to give. The old man is baldheaded and mean. "You want to give her something that will be a constant reminder of you?" "Yes," he said, "that was what was the matter." "Does she have any corns?" asked the old wretch. The boy said he had never inquired into the condition of her feet, and wanted to know what corns had to do with it. The old man said that if she had corns, a pair of shoes about two sizes too small would cause her mind to dwell on him a good deal. The boy said shoes wouldn't do. The old man hesitated a moment, scratched his head, and finally said:

"I have it! I suppose, sir, when you are alone with her, in the parlor, you put your arm around her waist; do you not, sir?"

The young man blushed and said that was about the size of it.

"I presume she enjoys that part of the discourse, eh?"

The boy said that, as near as he could tell, by the way she acted, she was not opposed to being held up.

"Then, sir, I can tell you of an article that will make her think of you in that position all the time, from the moment she gets up in the morning till she retires."

"Is there any attachment to it that will make her dream of me all night?" asked the boy.

"No, sir! Don't be a hog," said the bad man.

"Then what is it?"

The old man said one word, "Corset."

The young man was delighted, and he went to a store to buy a nice corset.

"What size do you want?" asked the girl who waited on him.

That was a puzzler. He didn't know they came in sizes. He was about to tell her to pick out the smallest size, when he happened to think of something.

"Take a tape measure and measure my arm; that will just fit."

The girl looked wise, as though she had been there herself, found that it was a twenty-two inch corset the boy wanted, and he went home and wrote a note and sent it with the corset to the girl. He didn't hear anything about it till the following Sunday, when he called on her. She received him coldly, and handed him the corset, saying, with a tear in her eye, that she had never expected to be insulted by him. He told her that he had no intention of insulting her; that he could think of nothing that would cause her to think of the gentle pressure of his arm around her waist as a corset, but if she felt insulted he would take his leave, give the corset to some poor family, and go drown himself.

He was about to go away, when she burst out crying, and sobbed out the following words, wet with salt brine:

"It was v-v-v-very thoughtful of y-y-you, but I *couldn't feel it!* It is f-f-four sizes too b-b-big! Why didn't you get number eighteen? You are silent, you cannot answer, enough!"

They instinctively found their way to the sofa; mutual explanations followed; he measured her waist again; saw where he had made a mistake by his fingers lapping over on the first turn, and he vowed by the beard of the prophet, he would change it for another, if she had not worn it and got it soiled. They are better now.

BOUNCED FROM CHURCH FOR DANCING

THE Presbyterian synod at Erie, Pa., has turned a lawyer named Donaldson out of the church. The charge against him was not that he was a lawyer, as might be supposed, but that he had danced a quadrille. It does not seem to us as though there could be anything more harmless than dancing a cold-blooded quadrille. It is a simple walk around, and is not even exercise. Of course, a man can, if he chooses, get in extra steps enough to keep his feet warm, but we contend that no quadrille, where they only touch hands, go down in the middle, and alamand left, can work upon a man's religion enough to cause him to backslide.

If it was this new "waltz quadrille" that Donaldson indulged in, where there is intermittent hugging, and where the head gets to whirling, and a man has to hang on to his partner quite considerable, to keep from falling all over himself, and where she looks up fondly into his eyes and as though telling him to squeeze just as hard as it seemed necessary for his convenience, we should not wonder so much at the synod hauling him over the coals for cruelty to himself, but a cold quadrille has no deviltry in it.

We presume the wicked and perverse Mr. Donaldson will join another church that allows dancing judiciously administered, and may yet get to heaven ahead of the Presbyterian synod, and he may be elected to some high position there, as Arthur was here, after the synod of Hayes and Sherman had bounced him from the Custom House for dancing the great spoils walk around.

It is often the case here, and we do not know why it may not be in heaven, that the ones that are turned over and shook up, and the dust knocked out of them, and their metaphorical coat tail filled with boots, find that the whirligig of time has placed them above the parties who smote them, and we can readily believe that if Donaldson gets a first-class position of power, above the skies, he will make it decidedly warm for his persecutors when they come up to the desk with their grip sacks and register and ask for a room with a bath, and a fire escape. He will be apt to look up at the key rack and tell them everything is full, but they can find pretty fair accommodations at the other house, down at the Hot Springs, on the European plan, by Mr. Devil, formerly of Chicago.

POLICE SEARCHING WOMEN

A NOVEL SCENE IN MILWAUKEE POLICE COURT

THERE is a movement on foot to provide for lady attendants at the Police Station, so that when a woman is arrested, and it is necessary to search her for concealed weapons, or money or incendiary documents, that duty can be performed by a person of the same sex as the prisoner. The *Sun* is anxious that this new departure be adopted at

"BUSHTLES ARE NEVER TWINS."

once, as it is very annoying for us to be called away from our business, every day or two, to aid the police—that is, of course, we are willing to be of assistance to anybody, but there *are* times—anybody will admit that.

The need of lady members of the police force was never illustrated any better than when the police arrested the women for passing counterfeit silver quarters, about six months ago. There was an oldish woman and a young woman, and when they were taken to the police office the reporters of the city papers were there, as usual, ready to lend a helping hand. The searching of the old lady was done in short order, by Detective Smith, who went about it in a business-like manner; but when it was time to search the young woman, and he looked into her soft, liquid eyes, and saw the emotion that she could not suppress, his heart failed him, and he sat down to write out his resignation. Tears came into his large, fawn-like eyes, and he called upon Mr. Northrop, correspondent of the Chicago *Times*, to assist him. Mr. Northrop had been inured to hardships, and knew much about the manner in which female persons conceal money, and being one of the "Willing Workers," he told Mr. Smith that he would help him.

The lady was told to remove her outward apparel, and to look steadily out of the window. She got behind a curtain-cord, and, in less time than it takes to write it, she threw her dress to the men, from her concealment behind the curtain-cord. The two men found a pocket in the dress, but to save them they couldn't find the pocket hole. The dress was turned the other side out forty times, to find the pocket hole.

Mr. Yenowine, of the *News*, who was present, said if they would hang the dress up on a hook he could find the pocket hole in the dark. He said there couldn't anybody fool him on finding a pocket hole in a dress.

The dress was hung in a closet, and Mr. Yenowine proceeded on the arctic exploring expedition, while Mr. Northrop and the detective were examining a corset that the young woman had thrown on the door, looking for bogus quarters. The *News* man, with all his knowledge of dress pockets, came out unsuccessful, and said he must have lost the combination, and accused the janitor of giving it away. Mr. Smith suggested that they cut the pocket off, but the district attorney, Mr. McKenney, said it would be clearly against the law. He said that would be burglary. In the meantime the young woman had kept on shucking herself, until Mr. Neiman, of the *Sentinel*. became faint and went out on the steps to get a breath of fresh air, from which position he looked through the window.

While the gentlemen were wondering if there were no rules of etiquette published that would make it easy and polite to search a woman for bogus two shilling pieces, the woman threw an article of female wearing apparel out on the floor for them to examine that fairly frightened them.

"Merciful heavens," said Mr. Yenowine, who was at that time a young and innocent person, unused to the ways of the world, "she has exploded."

Northrop poked it with his cane and said, "No, those always come off," and he put on an air of superiority over the boys which was annoying.

"What, always?" said Mr. Nieman, who had his fingers up before his face, and was blushing as though he had intermittent fever.

"Well, most always," said Mr. Northrop, who had taken it up and was examining it with a critic's eye.

"I presume those are a bustle, are they not?" said innocent Yenowine.

"Go aff, till the divil wid yer bushtle," said Mr. Smith, "I know bether. Gintlemen, I am a plain sphoken man, and for me age have seen many thrying situations, but if this was me lasht day on earth I should shwear that was no more a bushtle than I am. Bushtles are never twins."

Mr. Harger, of the *Wisconsin*, who had hidden behind the stove pipe, was asked by Mr. Smith what he thought they were, whether it might not be an infernal machine. Mr. Harger said he had never known one to explode. He said when he was reporting legislative proceedings the members drew those with their stationery, from the superintendent of public property, but he had no idea what they did with them.

At this point Mr. Aldrich, who had just come in, was asked to examine it and tell what it was. Mr. Aldrich took it up like a thing of life, and gazed upon it as though trying to recall something to his mind. Placing his finger, the one with the diamond ring on, to his corrugated forehead, he paused for a moment and finally gave his opinion that they were life preservers. He said that in Boston all women wore them, especially when they were out on excursions, or picnics. "See," says he, as he hefted it and made an indentation in it, which resumed its natural position as soon as he took his finger off, "it is filled with wind. Now, in case of accident, that would float a woman on top of water until she could be rescued. Let us demonstrate this matter by putting it on Mr. Boyington, of the *Sentinel,* and taking him to the morgue and placing him in the bath tub," and he proceeded to fasten the life preserver around the calf of Mr. Boyington's leg.

"Say, where are you putting it?" says Mr. B., as he struggled to keep from laughing right out. "You fellows don't know as much as Thompson's colt. If I know my own heart, and I think I do, a life preserver goes on under the vest."

Mr. Aldrich said he didn't pretend to know any more than anybody else. All he knew about these things personally was that he had seen them hanging up in stores, for sale, and one day when he was shopping he asked one of the lady clerks what it was hanging up there, and she had said it was a life preserver, and asked him if he wanted one, and he told her no, he was only inquiring for a friend of his, who rode a bicycle. He didn't know but it might be something that went with a bicycle.

All the time this discussion was going on we sat by the safe in the police office. We never were so sorry for a lot of innocent young men, never. The girl looked at us and winked, as much as to say, "Old man, why do you not come to the rescue of these young hoodlums, who don't know what they are talking about, and take the conceit out of them?" and so we explained to them in the best language we could command, the uses and abuses of the garment they were examining, and showed them how it went on, and how the invention of it filled a want long felt by our American people. They all admitted that we were right, and that it was a counterfeit well calculated to deceive, and we believe now that the woman was convicted of counterfeiting mainly on the testimony of the reporters. However that may be, we desire to impress upon the authorities the importance of employing ladies at the police office to examine women who are arrested for crime. The police cannot always depend on having a newspaper man around.

ABOUT HELL

An item is going the rounds of the papers, to illustrate how large the sun is, and how hot it is, which asserts that if an icicle a million miles long, and a hundred thousand miles through, should be thrust into one of the burning cavities of the sun, it would be melted in a hundredth part of a second, and that it would not cause as much "sissing" as a drop of water on a hot griddle.

By this comparison we can realize that the sun is a big thing, and we can form some idea of what kind of a place it would be to pass the summer months. In contemplating the terrible heat of the sun, we are led to wonder why those whose duty it is to preach a hell hereafter, have not argued that the sun is the place where sinners will go to when they die.

It is not our desire to inuagurate any reform in religious matters, but we realize what a discouraging thing it must be for preachers to preach hell and have nothing to show for it. As the business is now done, they are compelled to draw upon their imagination for a place of endless punishment, and a great many people, who would be frightened out of their boots if the minister could show them hell as he sees it, look upon his talk as a sort of dime novel romance.

They want something tangible on which they can base their belief, and while the ministers do everything in their power to encourage sinners by picturing to them the lake of fire and brimstone, where boat-riding is out of the question unless you paddle around in a cauldron kettle, it seems as though their labors would be lightened if they could point to the sun, on a hot day in August, and say to the wicked man that unless he gets down on his knees and says his now I lay me, and repents, and is sprinkled, and chips in pretty flush towards the running expenses of the church, and stands his assessments like a thoroughbred, that he will wake up some morning and find himself in the sun, blistered from Genesis to Revelations, thirsty as a harvest hand and not a brewery within a million miles, begging for a zinc ulster to cool his parched hind legs.

Such an argument, with an illustration right on the black-board of the sky, in plain sight, would strike terror to the sinner, and he would want to come into the fold *too* quick. What the religion of this country wants, to make it take the cake, is a hell that the wayfaring man, though a democrat or a greenbacker, can see with the naked eye. The way it is now, the sinner, if he wants to find out anything about the hereafter, has to take it second handed, from some minister or deacon who has not seen it himself, but has got his idea of it from some other fellow who maybe dreamed it out.

Some deacon tells a sinner all about the orthodox hell, and the sinner does not know whether to believe him or not. The deacon may have lied to the sinner some time in a horse trade, or in sending him goods, and beat him, and how does he know but the same deacon is playing a brace game on him on the hereafter, or playing him for a sardine?

Now, if the people who advance these ideas of heaven or hell, had a license to point to the moon, the nice, cool moon, as heaven, which would be plausible, to say the least, and say that it was heaven, and prove it, and could prove that the sun was the other place, which looks reasonable, according to all we have heard about t'other place, the moon would be so full there would not be standing room, and they would have to turn republicans away, while the sun would be playing to empty benches, and there would only be a few editors there who got in on passes.

Of course, during a cold winter, when the thermometer was forty or fifty degrees below zero, and everybody was blocked in, and coal was up to seventeen dollars a ton, the cause of religion would not prosper as much as it would in summer, because when you talked to a sinner about leading a different life or he would go to the sun, he would look at his coal pile and say that he didn't care a continental how soon he got there, but these discouragements would not be any greater than some that the truly good people have to contend with now, and the average the year round would be largely in favor of going to the moon.

The moon is very popular now, even, and if it is properly advertised as a celestial paradise, where only good people could get their work in, and where the wicked could not enter on any terms, there would be a great desire to take the straight and narrow way to the moon, and the path to the wicked sun would be grown over with sand burs, and scorched with lava, and few would care to take passage by that route. Anyway, this thing is worth looking into.

UNSCREWING THE TOP OF A FRUIT JAR

There is one thing that there should be a law passed about, and that is, these glass fruit jars, with a top that screws on. It should be made a criminal offense, punishable with death or banishment to Chicago, for a person to manufacture a fruit jar, for preserving fruit, with a top that screws on. Those jars look nice when the fruit is put up in them, and the housewife feels as though she was repaid for all her perspiration over a hot stove, as she looks at the glass jars of different berries on the shelf in the cellar.

The trouble does not begin until she has company, and decides to tap a little of her choice fruit. After the supper is well under way, she sends for a jar, and tells the servant to unscrew the top, and pour the fruit into a dish. The girl brings it into the kitchen, and proceeds to unscrew the top. She works gently at first, then gets mad, wrenches at it, sprains her wrist, and begins to cry, with her nose on the underside of her apron, and skins her nose on the dried pancake batter that is hidden in the folds of the apron.

Then the little housewife takes hold of the fruit can, smilingly, and says she will show the girl how to take off the top. She sits down on the wood-box, takes the glass jar between her knees, runs out her tongue, and twists. But the cover does not twist. The cover seems to feel as though it was placed there to keep guard over that fruit, and it is as immovable as the Egyptian pyramids. The little lady works until she is red in the face, and until her crimps all come down, and then she sets it away to wait for the old man to come home. He comes in tired, disgusted, and mad as a hornet, and when the case is laid before him, he goes out in the kitchen, pulls off his coat, and takes the jar.

He remarks that he is at a loss to know what women are made for, anyway. He says they are all right to sit around and do crochet work, but when strategy, brain, and muscle are required, then they can't get along without a man. He tries to unscrew the cover, and his thumb slips off and knocks the skin off the knuckle. He breathes a silent prayer and calls for the kerosene can, and pours a little oil into the crevice, and lets it soak, and then he tries again, and swears audibly.

Then he calls for a tack hammer, and taps the cover gently on one side, the glass jar breaks, and the juice runs down his trousers leg, on the table and all around. Enough of the fruit is saved for supper, and the old man goes up the back stairs to tie his thumb up in a rag, and change his pants.

All come to the table smiling, as though nothing had happened, and the house-wife don't allow any of the family to have any sauce for fear they will get broken glass into their stomachs, but the "company" is provided for generously, and all would be well only for a remark of a little boy, who, when asked if he will have some more of the sauce, says he "don't want no strawberries pickled in kerosene." The smiling little hostess steals a smell of the sauce, while they are discussing politics, and believes she does smell kerosene, and she looks at the old man kind of spunky, when he glances at the rag on his thumb and asks if there is no liminent in the house.

The preserving of fruit in glass jars is broken up in that house and four dozen jars are down cellar to lay upon the lady's mind till she gets a chance to send some of them to a charity picnic. The glass fruit jar business is played out unless a scheme can be invented to get the top off.

BUTTERMILK BIBBERS

THE immense consumption of buttermilk as a drink, retailed over the bars of saloons, has caused temperance people to rejoice. It is said that over two thousand gallons a day are sold in Milwaukee. There is one thing about buttermilk, in its favor, and that is, it does not intoxicate, and it takes the place of liquor as a beverage. A man may drink a quart of buttermilk, and while he may feel like a calf that has been sucking, and want to stand in a fence corner and bleat, or kick up his heels and run around a pasture, he does not become intoxicated and throw a beer keg through a saloon window.

Another thing, buttermilk does not cause the nose to become red, and the consumer's breath does not smell like the next day after a sangerfest. The complexion of the nose of a buttermilk drinker assumes a pale hue which is enchanting, and while his breath may smell like a baby that has nursed too much and got sour, the smell does not debar his entrance to a temperance society.

AN ÆSTHETIC FEMALE CLUB BUSTED

THE organization of the "Cosmos" Club, of Chicago women, for the purpose of discussing "æsthetic" business, ancient poetry and pottery ware, calls to mind the attempt to organize such a club here in Milwaukee. Our people here are too utterly full of business and domestic affairs to take to the "æsthetic" very generally, and the lady from Boston who tried to get up a class in the new wrinkle went away considerably disgusted. She called about fifty of our splendidest ladies together at the residence of one of them, and told them what the ladies of Eastern cities were doing in the study of higher arts. She elaborated considerably on the study of Norwegian literature, ceramics, bric-a-brac and so forth, and asked for an expression of the ladies present. One lady said she was willing to go into anything that would tend to elevate the tone of society, and make women better qualified for helpmates to their husbands, but she didn't want any Norwegian literature in hers. She said her husband ran for an office once and the whole gang of Norwegian voters went back on him and he was everlastingly scooped.

The Boston lady held up her hands in holy horror, and was going to explain to the speaker how she was off her base, when another lady got up and said she wanted to take the full course or nothing. She wanted to be posted in ancient literature and ceramics. She had studied ceramics some already, and had got a good deal of information. She had found that in case of whooping cough, goose oil rubbed on the throat and lungs was just as good as it was in case of croup, and she felt that with a good teacher any lady could learn much that would be of incalculable value, and she, for one, was going for the whole hog or none.

The Boston lady saved herself from fainting by fanning herself vigorously, and was about to show the two ladies that they had a wrong idea of æsthetics, when a lady from the West Side, who had just been married, got up and said she felt that we were all too ignorant of æsthetics, and they should take every opportunity to become better informed. She said when she first went to keeping house she couldn't tell baking powder that had alum in it from the pure article, and she had nearly ruined her husband's stomach before she learned anything. And speaking of bric-a-brac, she felt that every lady should learn to economize, by occasionally serving a picked up dinner of bric-a-brac that would otherwise be wasted.

The Boston lady found she could not speak understandingly, so she left her chair and went around to the different groups of ladies, who were talking earnestly, to get them interested. The first group of four that she broke in on were talking of the best way to renovate seal-skin cloaks that had been moth-eaten. One lady said that she had tried all the æsthetic insect powders that was advertised in the papers, and the moths would fairly get fat on it, and beg for more; but last spring she found out that moths were afraid of whisky.

Her husband worked in a wholesale whisky store and his garments became saturated with the perfume, and you couldn't hire a moth to go near him. So she got an empty whisky barrel and put in all her furs, and the moths never touched a thing. But she said the moths had a high old time all summer. They would get together in squads and go to the barrel and smell at the bung-hole, and lock arms and sashay around the room, staggering just as though there was an election, and about eleven o'clock they would walk up to a red spot in the carpet and take a lunch, just like men going to a saloon.

She said there was one drawback to the whisky barrel, as it gave her away when she first went out in company after taking her clothes out of the barrel. She wore her seal-skin cloak to the Good Templars' Lodge, the first night after taking it out, and they were going to turn her out of the Lodge on the ground that she had violated her obligation.

"You may talk about your Scandinavian literature," said she, turning to the Boston lady, "but when it comes to keeping moths out of furs, an empty whisky barrel knocks the everlasting socks off of anything I ever tried."

The Boston lady put on her æsthetic hat, and was about

to take her leave, satisfied that she had struck the wrong crowd, when a sweet little woman, with pouting lips, called her aside. The Boston lady thought she had found at last one congenial soul, and she said:

"What is it, my dear?"

The little lady hesitated a moment, and with a tear in her eye she asked:

"Madam, can you tell me what is good for worms? Fido has acted for a week as though he was ill, and—"

That settled it. The Boston lady went away, and has never been heard of since.

"A YOUNG fellow and his girl went out sleighing yesterday, and the lad returned with a frozen ear. There is nothing very startling in the simple fact of a frozen ear, but the idea is that it was the ear next to the girl that he was foolish enough to let freeze."

A girl that will go out sleigh-riding with a young man and allows his ears to freeze, is no gentleman, and ought to be arrested. Why, here in Milwaukee, on the coldest days, we have seen a young man out riding with a girl, and his ears were so hot they would fairly "sis," and there was not a man driving on the avenue but who would have changed places with the young man, and allowed his ears to cool. Girls cannot sit too close during this weather. The climate is rigorous.

FOOLING WITH THE BIBLE

REPORTS from the stationers show that there is no demand at all for the revised edition of the Bible, and had it not been for the newspapers publishing the whole affair there would have been very few persons that took the trouble to even glance at it, and it is believed that not one reader of the daily papers in a hundred read any of the Bible, and not one in ten thousand read all of it which was published. Who originated this scheme of revising the Bible we do not know, but whoever it was made a miscue. There was no one suffering particularly for a revision of the Bible. It was good enough as it was. No literary sharp of the present day has got any license to change anything in the Bible.

Why, the cheeky ghouls have actually altered over the Lord's Prayer, cut it biased, and thrown the parts about giving us this day our daily bread into the rag bag. How do they know that the Lord said more than he wanted to in that prayer? He wanted that daily bread in there, or He never would have put it in. The only wonder is that those revisers did not insert strawberry shortcake and ice cream in place of daily bread. Some of these ministers who are writing speeches for the Lord think they are smart. They have fooled with Christ's Sermon on the Mount until He couldn't tell it if He was to meet it in the Chicago *Times*.

This thing has gone on long enough, and we want a stop put to it. We have kept still about the piracy that has been going on in the Bible because people who are better than we are have seemed to endorse it, but now we are sick of it, and if there is going to be an annual clerical picnic to cut gashes in the Bible and stick new precepts and examples on where they will do the most hurt, we shall lock up our old Bible where the critters can't get at it, and throw the first book agent down stairs head first that tries to shove off on to us one of these new fangled, go-as-you-please Bibles, with all the modern improvements, and hell left out.

Now, where was there a popular demand to have hell left out of the Bible? Were there any petitions from the people sent up to this self-constituted legislature of pinchbeck ministers, praying to have hell abolished, and "hades" inserted? Not a petition. And what is this hades? Where is it? Nobody knows. They have taken away our orthodox hell, that has stood by us since we first went to Sunday school, and given us a hades. Half of us wouldn't know a hades if we should see it dead in the road, but they couldn't fool us any on hell.

No, these revisers have done more harm to religion than they could have done by preaching all their lives. They have opened the ball, and now, every time a second-class dominie gets out of a job, he is going to cut and slash into the Bible. He will think up lots of things that will sound better than some things that are in there, and by and by we shall have our Bibles as we do our almanacs, annually, with weather probabilities on the margins.

This is all wrong. Infidels will laugh at us, and say our old Bible is worn out, and out of style, and tell us to have our measure taken for a new one every fall and spring, as we do for our clothes. If this revision is a good thing, why won't another one be better? The woods are full of preachers who think they could go to work and improve the Bible, and if they don't shut down on this thing, they will take a hand in it. If a man hauls down the American flag, we shoot him on the spot and now we suggest that if any man mutilates the Bible, we run an umbrella into him and spread it.

The old Bible just filled the bill, and we hope every new one that is printed will lay on the shelves and get sour. This revision of the Bible is believed to be the work of an incendiary. It is a scheme got up by British book publishers to make money out of pious people. It is on the same principle that speculators get up a corner on pork or wheat. They got revision, and printed Bibles enough to supply the world, and would not let out one for love or money. None were genuine unless the name of this British firm was blown in the bottle.

Millions of Bibles were shipped to this country by the firm that was "long" on Bibles, and they were to be thrown on the market suddenly, after being locked up and guarded by the police until the people were made hungry for Bibles.

The edition was advertised like a circus, and doors were to be opened at six o'clock in the morning. American publishers who wanted to publish the Bible, too, got compositors ready to rush out a cheap Bible within twelve hours, and the Britons, who were running the corner on the Word of God, called these American publishers pirates. The idea of men being pirates for printing a Bible, which should be as free as salvation. The newspapers that had the Bibles telegraphed to them from the east, were also pirates.

O, revision is a three-card monte speculation; that is all it is.

A PECK AT THE CHEESE

GEO. W. PECK, of the *Sun*, recently delivered an address before the Wisconsin State Dairyman's Association. The following is an extract from the document:

Fellow Cremationists: In calling upon me, on this occasion, to enlighten you upon a subject that is dear to the hearts of all Americans, you have got the right man in the right place. It makes me proud to come to my old home and unfold truths that have been folded since I can remember. It may be said by scoffers, and it has been said to-day, in my presence, that I didn't know enough to even milk a cow. I deny the allegation; show me the allegator. If any gentleman present has got a cow here with him, and I can borrow a clothes wringer, I will show you whether I can milk a cow or not. Or, if there is a cheese mine here handy, I will demonstrate that I can—*runnet.*

The manufacture of cheese and butter has been among the earliest industries. Away back in the history of the world, we find Adam and Eve conveying their milk from the garden of Eden, in a one-horse wagon to the cool spring cheese factory, to be weighed in the balance. Whatever may be said of Adam and Eve to their discredit in the marketing of products of their orchard, it has never been charged that they stopped at the pump and put water in their milk cans. Doubtless you all remember how Cain killed his brother Abel because Abel would not let him do the churning. We can picture Cain and Abel driving mooly cows up to the house from the pasture in the southeast corner of the garden, and Adam standing at the bars with a tin pail and a three-legged stool, smoking a meerschaum pipe and singing "Hold the fort for I am coming through the rye," while Eve sat on the verandah altering over her last year's polonaise, and winking at the devil who stood behind the milk house singing, "I want to be an angel." After he got through milking he came up and saw Eve blushing, and he said, "Madam, cheese it," and she chose it.

But to come down to the present day, we find that cheese has become one of the most important branches of manufacture. It is next in importance to the silver interest. And, fellow cheese mongers, you are doing yourselves great injustice that you do not petition congress to pass a bill to remonetize cheese. There is more cheese raised in this country than there is silver, and it is more valuable. Suppose you had not eaten a mouthful in thirty days, and you should have placed on the table before you ten dollars stamped out of silver bullion on one plate and nine dollars stamped out of cheese bullion on another plate. Which would you take first? Though the face value of the nine cheese dollars would be ten per cent. below the face value of ten silver dollars, you would take the cheese. You could use it to better advantage in your business. Hence I say cheese is more valuable than silver, and it should be made legal tender for all debts, public and private, except pew rent. I may be in advance of other eminent financiers, who have studied the currency question, but I want to see the time come, and I trust the day is not far distant, when 412½ grains of cheese will be equal to a dollar in codfish, and when the merry jingle of slices of cheese shall be heard in every pocket.

Then every cheese factory can make its own coin, money will be plenty, everybody will be happy, and there never will be any more war. It may be asked how this currency can be redeemed? I would have an incontrovertible bond, made of Limberger cheese, which is stronger and more durable.

When this is done you can tell the rich from the poor man by the smell of his money. Nowadays many of us do not even get a smell of money, but in the good days which are coming the gentle zephyr will waft to us the able-bodied Limberger, and we shall know that money is plenty.

The manufacture of cheese is a business that a poor man can engage in as well as a rich man. I say it, without fear of successful contradiction, and say it boldly, that a poor man with, say 200 cows, if he thoroughly understands his business, can market more cheese than a rich man who owns 300 oxen. This is susceptible of demonstration. If my boy showed a desire to become a statesman, I would say to him, "Young man, get married, buy a mooley cow, go to Sheboygan county, and start a cheese factory."

Speaking of cows, did it ever occur to you, gentlemen, what a saving it would be to you if you should adopt mooley cows instead of horned cattle? It takes at least three tons of hay and a large quantity of ground feed annually to keep a pair of horns fat, and what earthly use are they? Statistics show that there are annually killed 45,000 grangers by cattle with horns. You pass laws to muzzle dogs, because one in ten thousand goes mad, and yet more people are killed by cattle horns than by dogs. What the country needs is more mooley cows.

Now that I am on the subject, it may be asked what is the best paying breed for the dairy. My opinion is divided between the south down and the cochin china. Some like one the best and some the other, but as for me, give me liberty or give me death.

There are many reforms that should be inaugurated in the manufacture of cheese. Why should cheese be made round? I am inclined to the belief that the making of cheese round is a superstition. Who had not rather buy a good square piece of cheese, than a wedge-shaped chunk, all rind at one end, and as thin as a Congressman's excuse for voting back pay at the other? Make your cheese square and the consumer will rise up and call you another.

Another reform that might be inaugurated would be to veneer the cheese with building paper or clapboards, instead of the time-honored piece of towel. I never saw cheese cut that I didn't think that the cloth around it had seen service as a bandage on some other patient. But I may have been wrong. Another thing that does not seem to be right, is to see so many holes in cheese. It seems to me that solid cheese, one made by one of the old masters, with no holes in it—I do not accuse you of cheating, but don't you feel a little ashamed when you see a cheese cut, and the holes are the biggest part of it? The little cells may be handy for the skipper, but the consumer feels the fraud in his innermost soul.

Among the improvements made in the manufacture of cheese I must not forget that of late years the cheese does not resemble the grindstone as much as it did years ago. The time has been when, if the farmer could not find his grindstone, all he had to do was to mortise a hole in the middle of a cheese, and turn it and grind his scythe. Before the invention of nitro-glycerine, it was a good day's work to hew off cheese enough for a meal. Time has worked wonders in cheese.

COLORED CONCERT TROUPES

Sometimes it seems as though the colored people ought to have a guardian appointed over them. Now, you take a colored concert troupe, and though they may have splendid voices, they do not know enough to take advantage of their opportunies. People go to hear them because they are colored people, and they want to hear old-fashioned negro melodies, and yet these mokes would tackle Italian opera and high toned music that they don't know how to sing.

They will sing these fancy operas, and people will not pay any attention. Along toward the end of the programme they will sing some old nigger song, and the house fairly goes wild and calls them out half a dozen times. And yet they do not know enough to make up a programme of such music as they can sing, and such as the audience want.

They get too big, these colored people do, and can't strike their level. People who have heard Kellogg, and Marie Roze, and Gerster, are sick when a black cat with a long red dress comes out and murders the same pieces the prima donnas have sung. We have seen a colored girl attempt a selection from some organ-grinder opera, and she would howl and screech, and catch her breath and come again, and wheel and fire vocal shrapnel, limber up her battery and take a new position, and unlimber and send volleys of soprano grape and canister into the audience, and then she would catch on to the highest note she could reach and hang to it like a dog to a root, till you would think they would have to throw a pail of water on her to make her let go, and all the time she would be biting and shaking like a terrier with a rat, and finally gave one kick at her red trail with her hind foot, and back off the stage looking as though she would have to be carried on a dustpan, and the people in the audience would look at each other in pity and never give her a cheer, when, if she had come out and patted her leg, and put one hand up to her ear, and sung, "Ise a Gwine to See Massa Jesus Early in de Mornin'," they would have split the air wide open with cheers and called her out five times.

The fact is, they haven't got sense.

There was a hungry-looking, round-shouldered, sick-looking colored man in that same party, that was on the programme for a violin solo. When he came out the people looked at each other, as much as to say, "Now we will have some fun." The moke struck an attitude as near Ole Bull as he could with his number eleven feet and his hollow chest, and played some diabolical selections from a foreign cat opera that would have been splendid if Wilhelmjor Ole Bull had played it, but the colored brother couldn't get within a mile of the tune. He rasped his old violin for twenty minutes and tried to look grand, and closed his eyes and seemed to soar away to heaven,—and the audience wished to heaven he had,—and when he became exhausted and squeezed the last note out, and the audience saw that he was in a profuse perspiration, they let him go and did not call him back. If he had come out and sat on the back of a chair and sawed off "The Devil's Dream," or "The Arkansaw Traveler," that crowd would have cheered him till he thought he was a bigger man than Grant

But he didn't have any sense.

If some one will send a marked copy of the paper to some of these colored concert troupes, and they will take the hint, and sing nigger songs, they will make a heap of money, where now they have to live on a free lunch route.

COULDN'T GET AWAY FROM HIM

A GOOD many may have wondered why we so suddenly quit speeding our horse on the avenue. For two or three days we couldn't go down the avenue enough, and there is no person but will admit that our old pile driver trotted real spry. We did not get the idea that he was the fastest horse that ever was, but he seemed real soon. It takes a good deal of executive ability for a man who has a third-class horse to keep from going down the road with horses that are too fast. One must be a good judge, and when he finds a horse that he can beat, stick to him.

We got the thing down pretty fine, but one day a man drove along beside us, going up, who seemed bound to get into conversation. He was a red-faced man, with these side-bar whiskers, evidently a German. He was driving a sorrel horse to a long sled, with a box on behind the seat, a sort of delivery sleigh. He had a barrel in the sleigh, filled with intestines from a slaughter house, two baskets full of the same freight, a cow's head, and two sheep heads. He was evidently owner of a sausage factory somewhere, and as he kept along beside us his company was somewhat annoying. Not that we were proud, but we feared the people on the avenue would think we were a silent partner in a sausage factory, and that we were talking business.

The man was real entertaining in his conversation, but the load he had was not congenial, and we were glad when the foot of the hill was reached, so we could turn around and go down, and get away from him. We turned and

"NICE RACE, AIN'T IT, MR. BECK?"

spit on our hands, and he began to pull up on the old horse, and he began to get his legs untangled and to go. We forgot about the sausage butcher, as we went down, the fresh air making every nerve get up and git.

Suddenly the nose of a sorrel horse began to work up by where we sat, and we looked around, and may we never live to make a million dollars if it wasn't the red-faced sausage man, intestines, cow's head, basket and all, and his old horse was coming for all that was out. We blush for our sex. It would look nice to get in the papers that we had been racing our blue-blooded thoroughbred against a sausage butcher, wouldn't it? Our plan was formed in an instant. Great generals form plans suddenly, and we took out the whip and touched our horse on a raw spot, intending to go right away from the fertilizer.

The horse seemed to smell the load behind him, and to have his pride touched, for he snorted and let out another link. We don't know as anyone would believe it, but the faster our beautiful and costly steed went, the faster that homely and cheap butcher horse climbed. People by the hundreds all along the line were watching the race. The baskets of sausage covers were slewing around from one side of his sled to the other, and we expected every moment one of them would flop over into our cutter.

Matters were becoming desperate, and we gave the horse one more cut and went the last block at a fearful rate, but the butcher was right beside us so one mosquito bar would have covered us, and we came out neck and neck, the Dutchman a little ahead because his horse was unchecked, and the crowd yelled for the butcher. We turned to go up, when the butcher came up alongside just as a carriage of beautiful ladies were passing, and as they turned up their noses at his load, he said:

"Dot vas a nice race, ain't it, Mister Beck?"

We could have killed him in cold blood. Not that we dislike to be beaten. We have always been beaten. It isn't that. But we don't want to trot horses with no delivery wagon. We are not calculated for associating, in the horse arena, with a load of slaughter house refuse. It is asking too much. We are willing to race with Deacon Van Schaick, or brother Antisdel, or Elder Hyde, or Elder Gordon, or any of those truly good men in whom there is no guile and in whose cutters there is no foreign matter, but as long as reason maintains her throne we shall never go upon the track again with a butcher.

There should be a law passed making it a penal offense for a person with a delivery wagon to tackle onto a man who drives a thoroughbred. It is wrong, and will lead to trouble. We have not given up racing entirely, but hereafter we shall look the avenue over very close for butchers before we let out our four-legged telescope. A butcher is just as good as anybody, understand us, but they must keep their distance. We don't want to look into the hind end of no cutter that is filled with slaughter house ornaments, and we won't. It is not pride of birth, or anything of that kind, but such people ought to drive on Wells street, or have slower horses.

DOGS AND HUMAN BEINGS

LORILLARD, the New York tobacco man, had a poodle dog stolen and has offered a reward of five hundred dollars for the arrest of the thief, and he informs the reporter that he will spend $10,000, if necessary, for the capture and conviction of the thief. [Applause.]

The applause marked in there will be from human skye terriers, who have forgotten that only a few weeks ago several hundred girls, who had been working in Lorillard's factory, went on a strike because, as they allege, they were treated like dogs. We doubt if they were treated as well as this poodle was treated. We doubt, in case one of these poor, virtuous girls was kidnapped, if the great Lorillard would have offered as big a reward for the conviction of the human thief as he has for the conviction of the person who has eloped with his poodle.

We hope that the aristocracy of this country will never get to valuing a dog higher than it does a human being. When it gets so that a rich person would not permit a poodle dog to do the work in a tobacco factory that a poor girl does to support a sick mother, hell had better be opened for summer boarders. When girls work ten hours a day stripping nasty tobacco, and find at the end of the week that the fines for speaking are larger than the wages, and the fines go for the conviction of thieves who steal the girl's master's dog, no one need come around here lecturing at a dollar a head and telling us there is no hell.

When a poor girl, who has gone creeping to her work at daylight, looks out of her window at noon to see her master's carriage go by, in which there is a five hundred dollar dog with a hundred dollar blanket on, and a collar set with diamonds, lolling on satin cushions and the girl is fined ten cents for looking out of the window, you don't want to fool away any time trying to get us to go to a heaven where such heartless employers are expected.

It is seldom the *Sun* gets on its ear, but it can say with great fervency, "Damn a man that will work poor girls like slaves, and pay them next to nothing, and spend ten thousand dollars to catch a dog thief!" If these sentiments are sinful, and for expressing them we are a candidate for fire and brimstone, it is all right, and the devil can stoke up and make up our bunk when he hears that we are on the through train.

It seems now—though we may change our mind the first day at the fire—as though we had rather be in hades with a hundred million people who have always done the square thing, than to be in any heaven that will pass a man in who has starved the poor and paid ten thousand dollars to catch a dog thief. We could have a confounded sight better time, even if we had our ulster all burned off. It would be worth the price of admission to stand with our back to the fire, and as we began to smell woolen burning near the pistol pocket, to make up faces at the ten-thousand-dollar-dog millionaires that were putting on style at the other place.

ANDREWS' *Bazar* says: "Gathered waists are very much worn."

If the men would gather the waists carefully and not squeeze so like blazes, they would not be worn so much. Some men go to work gathering a waist just as they would go to work washing sheep, or raking and binding. They ought to gather as though it was eggs done up in a funnel-shaped brown paper at a grocery.

THE Black River Falls *Independent* says: If you have any old pants to give to the poor, take or send them to the Ladies' Relief Society."

Well, we have got plenty of them: but, bless you, doubt if any member of the Ladies' Relief Society could wear them. They don't hook up.

ARTHUR WILL KEEP A COW

IT is announced by telegraph from the country's capitol at Washington that Gen. Arthur will keep a cow at the White House during his term, to furnish milk for the family, rather than be obliged to depend upon a milk man who is in the habit of selling a mixed drink, though the customers prefer to take it straight. There is nothing that will do more to convince people of the true simplicity of a President than

for him to keep a cow. No man who habitually associates with a cow, and stirs up a bran mash, and watches her plow her nose down to the bottom in search of a potato paring, can be wholly bad. If the President selects a good, honest cow we have no fears that he will be a tyrant in his administration of affairs. A man is very apt to absorb many of the characteristics and traits of the cow that he milks. If she is a good natured, honest, law abiding cow, that "hoists" at the word of command, stands firm and immovable while being milked, and "gives down" freely, so that the fingers are not cramped, and she does not switch her tail in the face of the milker, the man will be a good natured, generous, kindly dispositioned, and honest man; but if the cow is one of those communists, one of those plaguey all-round obstructionists, and has to be tied to the manger, and you have to hold one leg to keep her from kicking over the pail, and she tries to run a horn into your gizzard, and your nerves are unstrung for fear she is thinking of some deviltry to play on you, the man whose duty it is to draw the milk from her udder will become harsh, suspicious, cruel, tricky, and mean; and he will grind the face of the poor.

The country will hope that Mr. Arthur, in selecting a cow, will use more judgment than in selecting a cabinet, and will bring his great mind to bear on the subject as though he appreciated the situation. We trust he will not buy a cow of a democrat. There may be good cows owned by democrats, but they are not for sale, and a democrat would sell him a kicking cow that was farrow, just to injure his administration. Let him go to some friend in his own party, some man who is interested in the success of his administration, and state his case, and if possible get a cow on trial.

This policy is wise from the fact that he could thus see if the cow was going to hold out as a good milker. Some cows give a good mess of milk when they first go to a new place, but in a week they let down and the first thing you know they dry up entirely. Mr. Arthur wants to look out for this. The country is full of bold, bad men, who would palm off a kicking cow, or one that was not a stayer, onto their best friends.

Another thing, we would advise Mr. Arthur not to use a milking stool with one leg, but to get one with three legs. It is undignified in any man to stretch out on a barn floor, with a one-legged milk stool kicking him in the pistol pocket, a pail of milk distributing itself over his person, and a frightened cow backed up in a stall threatening to hook his daylights out and it would be more undignified in a President of the United States. Get a three-legged stool, by all means, or use an empty soap box to set on.

If all this unsolicited but well-meant advice is taken, the country will be in no danger from Arthur's decision to keep a cow, and we shall hope to see him on some fine morning next summer, as the sun is tingeing the eastern horizon with its golden beams, and the songs of birds float over the Capitol at Washington—driving his cow to pasture down by the Potomac, singing merrily as he slaps her on the rump with a piece of barrel stave, or we will accept an invitation to visit his barn and show him how to mix a bran mash that will wake to ecstacy the aforesaid cow, and cause her milk to flow like back-pay from the treasury. When it comes to cows we deserve a cabinet position.

SHALL THERE BE HUGGING IN THE PARKS?

THE law-abiding people of this community were startled on Tuesday, and the greatest indignation prevailed at an editorial article in the *Sentinel* denouncing the practice of hugging in the public parks. The article went on to show that the placing of seats in the parks leads to hugging, and the editor denounced hugging in the most insane manner possible.

The *Sun* does not desire to enter politics, but when a great constitutional question like this comes up, it will be found on the side of the weak against the strong.

The *Sentinel* advises the removal of the seats from the park because hugging is done on them. Great heavens! has it come to this? Are the dearest rights of the American citizen to be abridged in this summary manner? Let us call the attention of that powerful paper to a clause in the Declaration of Independence, which asserts that "All men are created free and equal, endowed with certain inalienable rights, among which are life, liberty and the pursuit of happiness." When the framers of that great Declaration of Independence were at work on that clause, they must have had in view the pastime of hugging in the parks.

Hugging is certainly a "pursuit of happiness." People do not hug for wages—that is, except on the stage. Nobody is obliged to hug. It is a sort of spontaneous combustion, as it were, of the feelings, and has to have proper conditions of the atmosphere to make it a success. Parties who object to hugging are old, usually, and have been satiated, and are like a lemon that has done duty in circus lemonade. If they had a job of hugging, they would want to hire a man to do it for them.

A man who objects to a little natural, soul-inspiring hugging on a back seat in a park, of an evening, with a fountain throwing water all over little cast-iron cupids, has probably got a soul, but he hasn't got it with him. To the student of nature there is no sight more beautiful than to see a flock of young people take seats in the park, after the sun has gone to bed in the west, and the moon has pulled a fleecy cloud over her face for a veil, so as not to disturb the worshipers.

A couple, one a male and the other a female, will sit far apart on the cast-iron seat for a moment, when the young lady will try to fix her cloak over her shoulders, and she can't fix it, and then the young man will help her, and when he has got it fixed he will go off and leave one arm around the small of her back. He will miss his arm, and wonder where he left it, and go back after it, and in the dark he will feel around with the other hand to find the hand he left, and suddenly the two hands will meet they will express astonishment, and clasp each other, and be so glad that they will begin to squeeze, and the chances are that they will cut the girl in two, but they never do. Under such circumstances a girl can exist on less atmosphere than she can when doing a washing.

There is just about so much hugging that has to be

done, and the *Sentinel* should remember that very many people have not facilities at their homes for such soul-stirring work, and they are obliged to flee to the parks, or to the woods, where the beneficent city government has provided all the modern improvements.

Hugging is as necessary to the youth of the land as medicine to the sick, and instead of old persons, whose days of kittenhood are over, throwing cold water upon the science of hugging, they should encourage it by all legitimate means.

When, in strolling through the parks, you run on to a case of sporadic hugging, instead of making a noise on the gravel walk, to cause the huggists to stop it, you should trace your steps noiselessly, get behind a tree, and see how long they can stand it without dying. Instead of removing the cast-iron seats from the parks, we should be in favor of furnishing reserved seats for old people, so they can sit and watch the hugging.

It doesn't do any hurt to hug.

People think it is unhealthy, but nobody was ever known to catch cold while hugging. It is claimed by some that young people who stay out nights and hug, are not good for anything the next day. There is something to this, but if they didn't get any hugging they wouldn't be worth a cent any time. They would be all the time looking for it.

No, good Mr. *Sentinel,* on behalf of fifty thousand young people who have no organ to make known their wants, we ask you to stay your hand, and do not cause the seats to be removed from the parks. Remember how many there are who have yet to learn the noble art of hugging, and give them a chance.

THE BOB-TAILED BADGER

THE last legislature having nothing else to do, passed a law providing for a change in the coat-of-arms of the State. There was no change, particularly, except to move the plows and shovels around a little, put on a few more bars of pig lead, put a new fashioned necktie on the sailor who holds the rope, the emblem of lynch law, tuck the miner's breeches into his boots a little further, and amputate the tail of the badger. We do not care for the other changes, as they were only intended to give the engraver a job, but when an irresponsible legislature amputates the tail of the badger, the emblem of the democratic party, that crawls into a hole and pulls the hole in after him, it touches us in our patriotism.

The badger, as nature made him, is a noble bird, and though he resembles a skunk too much to be very proud of, they had no right to cut off his tail and stick it up like a sore thumb. As it is now the new comer to our Garden of Eden will not know whether our emblem is a Scotch terrier smelling into the archives of the State for a rat, or a defalcation, or a *sic semper Americanus scunch.* We do not complain that the sailor with the Pinafore shirt on, on the new coat-of-arms, is made to resemble Senator Cameron, or that the miner looks like Senator Sawyer. These things are of minor importance, but the docking of that badger's tail, and setting it up like a bob-tail horse, is an outrage upon every citizen of the State, and when the democrats get into power that tail shall be restored to its normal condition if it takes all the blood and treasure in the State, and this work of the republican incendiaries shall be undone. The idea of Wisconsin appearing among the galaxy of States with a bob-tailed badger is repugnant to all our finer feelings.

CANNIBALS AND CORK LEGS

GREAT results are expected from an experiment recently tried by the American Missionary Society. Last fall they sent as missionary to the cannibal islands a brother who had lost both arms and both legs in a railroad accident. He was provided with cork limbs, and his voice being in good condition it was believed he could get in his work with the heathen as well as though he was a whole man. The idea was to allow the cannibals to kill him and eat him, believing that the heathen would see the error of their ways and swear off on human flesh.

A report has been received which is very encouraging. It seems that the cannibals killed the good missionary, and cut off his arms and legs for a sort of stew, or "boyaw," thus falling directly into the trap set for them by the missionary society. The missionary stationed at the next town, who furnishes the society with the data, says it was the most laughable thing he ever witnessed, to see the heathen chew on those cork limbs. They boiled them all day and night, keeping up a sort of a go-as-you-please walk around, or fresh meat dance, and giving a sacred concert about like our national "Whoop it up, Liza Jane," and when they stuck a fork into the boiling limbs, and found that the "meat" seemed water soaked, they set the table and sounded the loud timbrel for breakfast.

The surviving missionary says he shall never forget the look of pain on the face of a buck cannibal as he bit into the elbow joint of the late lamented and struck a brass hinge. He picked it out as an American would pick a buckshot out of a piece of venison, and laid it beside his plate in an abstracted manner, and began to chew on the cork elbow. Any person who has ever tried to draw a cork out of a beer bottle with his teeth can realize the feelings of these cannibals as they tried to draw sustenance from the remains of the cork man. They were saddened, and it is safe to say they are incensed against the missionary society.

Whether they will conclude that all Americans have become tough, and quit trying to masticate them, is not known, though that is the object sought to be attained by the society. One of the cannibals said he knew, when those legs and arms would not stay under water when they were boiling, and had to be loaded down with stones, that the meat wasn't right, but his wife told him "Some pork *would* bile so."

The experiment is worth following up, and we suppose

hereafter there will be a great demand for men with cork arms and legs to be sent as missionaries. After a few such experiences the cannibals may see the error of their ways and become Christians, and eat dog sausage and Limberg cheese.

THE MINISTERIAL PUGILISTS

THOSE who read the account of the trial of Rev. Carhart, at Oshkosh, are about as sick of true goodness as men can be. They open the ecclesiastical court by singing "A charge to keep I have," and then Brother Haddock, after a prayer has been delivered, does not keep his charges, but fires them at the presiding elder. Good old tunes are sung previous to calling witnesses to testify to alleged three card monte acts of a disciple of Christ. Sanctimonious looking men pray for divine guidance, and then try to prove that a dear brother has bilked another dear brother out of several hundred dollars on Texas lands, and that he tried to trade a wagon at double what it was worth to settle the matter.

They sing, "Take me just as I am," and then try to prove that the one who made charges against the other is not altogether holy, because he is alleged to have confessed to passing the night in a room with a female church member, in silent devotion, when he swears it is a lie—that he only laid on a lounge.

Prominent Methodists collect at the bull-fight in Oshkosh, take sides with one or the other and lay their bottom prayer that their champion will come out on top, with not a stripe polluted nor a star erased.

One side sings, "Jesus caught me when a stranger," and the other side smiles and winks and whispers that they are glad he was caught.

They sing, "Rock of ages, cleft for me," and proceed to cleave the rock of each other's character. They cast one eye heavenward in prayer, while with the other they watch the other side to see that they don't steal the testimony.

Someone starts "Little drops of water," and big drops of perspiration appear on truly good foreheads for fear proof will be adduced to show that money has been obtained under false pretenses.

And this goes by the name of religion!

There should be honor among ministers. Both of the principals in this suit should be bounced. If the charges are true, Carhart should emigrate. If they are not true, Haddock should emigrate.

MUSIC ON THE WATERS

Our readers have no doubt noticed in the papers that the Goodrich Transportation Company had secured a band from Waupun to make music on the boats of that line between Milwaukee and Chicago this summer. Well, there is trouble going on in consequence. Mr. Hurson, of the Goodrich line, entrusted the organization of the band to Mr. Nick Jarvis, of Waupun, a gentleman whose reputation as a scientific pounder of the bass drum has received encomiums from the crowned heads of Oshkosh and Hazen's cheese factory.

Having such confidence in Mr. Jarvis, Mr. Hurson gave him a roving commission, with authority to secure the best talent in the known world. He organized the band, and then it occurred to Mr. Jarvis that the musicians had always been accustomed to playing on land, and they might be sick on the water, so he took measures to accustom them to a seafaring life before leaving Waupun. He got them to practicing in a building, and hired some boys to throw water up on the side of the house, to see if they would be seasick. The band fellows would have stood the sea first rate, only the villains who had been hired to throw the water used a lot of dirty stuff they found back of a hotel, which smelled powerful.

A number of the band members felt the swash of the waves against the bulwarks of the house, and smelled what they supposed to be salt sea air, and they leaned out of the windows and wanted to throw up their situations, but a German in the party had a lemon and some cheese, which was given around to taste and smell, and they came out of it all right.

Mr. Jarvis' next idea, to accustom the prairie sailors to the vasty deep, was to take them out on the mill pond at Waupun in a skiff. They got out in the middle of the pond, and were playing a selection from the opera of "Solid Muldoon," when a boy who had slipped into the boat with a fish-pole, got a bite from a bullhead, which caused the vessel to roll, and the utmost confusion prevailed. Ordering the snare drum player to "Cut away the main bobstay, and belay the cornet," Mr. Jarvis took the bass drum between his teeth and jumped overboard, followed by the band, and they waded ashore.

On Monday last the band arrived in Milwaukee and reported on board the Goodrich steamer, in the river, ready for business. They were told to go as they pleased until evening, when they would be expected to play before the boat started, and also on the trip to Chicago. The men sat around on deck all the afternoon, and smelled of the river. It smelled different from any salt water they ever snuffed, and they wanted to go home.

At seven o'clock the band played a few tunes as the boat lay in the river, and finally she let go her ropes and steamed down toward the lake, the band whooping it up to the "Blue Danube." As the boat struck blue water, and her bow raised out about sixteen feet and began to jump, the cornet player stopped to pour water out of his horn, and lean against a post. He was as pale as death, and the tuba player stopped to see what ailed the cornet player, and to lean over the railing to see a man down stairs. The baritone had eaten something that did not agree with him, and he stopped playing and laid down in a life boat, the alto became cold around the extremities and quit playing and went to the smoke stack to warm himself, the b-flat began to perspire and quit playing and fanned himself with the cymbals, and all of the horn blowers were e-flat and b-flat on the deck in less than two minutes.

The captain noticed that there was some discrepancy in the music and came on deck to see about it. Wading through the brass horns he came up to where the band had been, and found Nick Jarvis beating blazes out of the bass drum and Harve Hill carving the Blue Danube out of the snare drum, and that was all the music there was. The captain asked Jarvis what kind of a riot that was, and he told him it was the best they could do under the circumstances.

MUSIC ON THE WATERS.

Restoratives were applied to the members, and they braced up enough to start in on "Rocked in the Cradle of the Deep," but they couldn't play it through, owing to dyspepsia. The captain got them into the cabin to play for the young folks to dance, but the only thing they could play without getting sick was "Home Again, from a Foreign Shore," and the bass drum had to do it all. The horn blowers were out looking at the starlight, leaning over the railing, as the stars were reflected in the water.

At Racine it took some time to load, owing to rough water, and in the midst of it all a pale man, with a snare drum on his arm, rolled up against the captain. It was Harve Hill. He held his hand over his mouth and in a voice choked with emotion and fried potatoes he said:

"Captain, I am a poor man, but if you will land this boat and save me, I will give you nine dollars."

The captain decided to dispense with the music the rest of the night, and let the band get on its sea legs.

At Chicago, the next morning, Jarvis, who had got a little sick, too, tried to induce the captain to allow the band to walk back to Milwaukee on the shore, beside the boat. He said they could play any tune that ever was played, on land, and the passengers could hear it just as well, if the boat kept alongside of the band. The captain wouldn't let them off, and they have been kept on the boat all the week, so that now they are old sailors, and can play all right. But it was pretty tough the first night. Waupun is organizing a reception for the band when it comes home.

WOMAN-DOZING A DEMOCRAT

A FEARFUL tale comes to us from Columbus. A party of prominent citizens of that place took a trip to the Dells of Wisconsin one day last week. It was composed of ladies and gentlemen of both political parties, and it was hoped that nothing would occur to mar the pleasure of the excursion.

When the party visited the Dells, Mr. Chapin, a lawyer of democratic proclivities, went out upon a rock overhanging a precipice, or words to that effect, and he became so absorbed in the beauty of the scene that he did not notice a republican lady who left the throng and waltzed softly up behind him. She had blood in her eye and gum in her mouth, and she grasped the lawyer, who is a weak man, by the arms, and hissed in his ear:

"Hurrah for Garfield, or I will plunge you headlong into the yawning gulf below!"

It was a trying moment. Chapin rather enjoyed being held by a woman, but not in such a position that, if she let go her hold to spit on her hands, he would go a hundred feet down, and become as flat as the greenback party, and have to be carried home in a basket.

In a second he thought over all the sins of his past life, which was pretty quick work, as anybody will admit who knows the man. He thought of how he would be looked down upon by Gabe Bouck, and all the fellows, if it once got out that he had been frightened into going back on his party.

He made up his mind that he would die before he would hurrah for Garfield, but when the merciless woman pushed him towards the edge of the rock, and said, "Last call! Yell, or down you go!" he opened his mouth and yelled so they heard it in Kilbourn City:

"Hurrah for Garfield! Now lemme go!"

Though endowed with more than ordinary eloquence, no remark that he had ever made before brought the applause that this did. Everybody yelled, and the woman smiled as pleasantly as though she had not crushed the young life out of her victim, and left him a bleeding sacrifice on the altar of his country, but when she realized what she had done her heart smote her, and she felt bad.

Chapin will never be himself again. From that moment his proud spirit was broken, and all during the picnic he seemed to have lost his cud. He leaned listlessly against a tree, pale as death, and fanned himself with a skimmer. When the party had spread the lunch on the ground and gathered around, sitting on the ant-hills, he sat down with them mechanically, but his appetite was gone, and when that is gone there is not enough of him left for a quorum.

Friends rallied around him, passed the pickles, and drove the antmires out of a sandwich, and handed it to him on a piece of shingle, but he either passed or turned it down

He said he couldn't take a trick. Later on, when the lemonade was brought on, the flies were skimmed off of some of it, and a little colored water was put in to make it look inviting, but his eyes were set. He said they couldn't fool him. After what had occurred, he didn't feel as though any democrat was safe. He expected to be poisoned on account of his politics, and all he asked was to live to get home.

Nothing was left undone to rally him, and cause him to forget the fearful scene through which he had passed. Only once did he partially come to himself, and show an interest in worldly affairs, and that was when it was found that he had sat down on some raspberry jam with his white pants on. When told of it, he smiled a ghastly smile, and said they were all welcome to his share of the jam.

They tried to interest him in conversation by drawing war maps with three-tined forks on the jam, but he never showed that he knew what they were about until Mr. Moak, of Watertown, took a brush, made of cauliflower preserved in mustard, and shaded the lines of the war map on Mr. Chapin's trousers, which Mr. Butterfield had drawn in the jam. Then his artistic eye took in the incongruity of the colors, and he gasped for breath, and said:

"Moak, that is played out. People will notice it."

But he relapsed again into semi-unconsciousness, and never spoke again, not a great deal, till he got home.

He has ordered that there be no more borrowing of sugar and drawings of tea back and forth between his house and that of the lady who broke his heart, and he has announced that he will go without sauerkraut all winter rather than borrow a machine for cutting cabbage of a woman that would destroy the political prospects of a man who had never done a wrong in his life.

He has written to the chairman of the Democratic State Central Committee to suspend judgment on his case, until he can explain how it happened that a dyed-in-the-wool democrat hurrahed for Garfield.

A LIVELY TRAIN LOAD

LAST week a train load of insane persons were removed from the Oshkosh Asylum to the Madison Asylum. As the train was standing on the sidetrack at Watertown Junction it created considerable curiosity. People who have ever passed Watertown Junction have noticed the fine old gentleman who comes into the car with a large square basket, peddling popcorn. He is one of the most innocent and confiding men in the world. He is honest, and he believes that everybody else is honest.

He came up to the depot with his basket, and seeing the train he asked Pierre, the landlord there, what train it was. Pierre, who is a most diabolical person, told the old gentleman that it was a load of members of the legislature and female lobbyists going to Madison. With that beautiful confidence which the popcorn man has in all persons, he believed the story, and went in the car to sell popcorn.

Stopping at the first seat, where a middle-aged lady was sitting alone, the popcorn man passed out his basket and said, "Fresh popcorn." The lady took her foot down off the stove, looked at the man a moment with eyes glaring and wild, and said, "It is—no, it cannot be—and yet it *is* me long lost Duke of Oshkosh," and she grabbed the old man by the necktie with one hand and pulled him down into the seat, and began to mow away corn into her mouth. The popcorn man blushed, looked at the rest of the passengers to see if they were looking, and said, as he replaced the necktie knot from under his left ear and pushed his collar down, "Madame, you are mistaken. I have never been a Duke of Oshkosh. I live here at the Junction." The woman looked at him as though she doubted his statement, but let him go.

He proceeded to the next seat, when a serious looking man rose up and bowed; the popcorn man also bowed and smiled as though he might have met him before. Taking a paper of popcorn and putting it in his coat tail pocket, the serious man said, "I was honestly elected President of the United States in 1876, but was counted out by the vilest conspiracy that ever was concocted on the earth, and I believe you are one of the conspirators," and he spit on his hands and looked the popcorn man in the eye. The popcorn man said he never took any active part in politics, and had nothing to do with that Hayes business at all. Then the serious man sat down and began eating the popcorn, while two women on the other side of the car helped themselves to the corn in the basket.

The popcorn man held out his hand for the money, when a man two seats back came forward and shook hands with him, saying: "They told me you would not come, but you have come, Daniel, and now we will fight it out. I will take this razor and you can arm yourself at your leisure." The man reached into an inside pocket of his coat, evidently for a razor, when the popcorn man started for the door, his eyes sticking out two inches. Every person he passed took a paper of popcorn, one man grabbed his coat and tore one tail off, another took his basket away, and as he rushed out on the platform the basket was thrown at his head, and a female voice said, "I will be ready when the carriage calls at 8."

As the old gentleman struck the platform and began to arrange his toilet he met Fitzgerald, the conductor, who asked him what was the matter. He said Pierre told him that crowd was going to the legislature, "But," says he, as he picked some pieces of paper collar out of the back of his neck, "if those people are not delegates to a democratic convention, then I have been peddling popcorn on this road ten years for nothing, and don't know my business." Fitz told him they were patients going to the Insane Asylum.

The old man thought it over a moment, and then he picked up a coupling pin and went looking for Pierre. He says he will kill him. Pierre has not been out of the house since. This Pierre is the same man that lent us a runaway horse once.

HOW SHARPER THAN A HOUND'S TOOTH

YEARS age we swore on a stack of red chips that we would never own another dog. Six promising pups that had been presented to us, blooded setters and pointers, had gone the way of all dog flesh, with the distemper and dog buttons, and by falling in the cistern, and we had been bereaved *via* dog misfortunes as often as John R. Bennett, of Janesville, has been bereaved on the nomination for attorney general. We could not look a pup in the face but it would get sick, and so we concluded never again to own a dog.

The vow has been religiously kept since. Men have promised us thousands of pups, but we have never taken them. One conductor has promised us at least seventy-five pups, but he has always failed to get us to take one. Dog lovers have set up nights to devise a way to induce us to accept a dog. We held out firmly until last week. One day we met Pierce, the Watertown Junction hotel man, and he told us he had a greyhound pup that was the finest bread dog—we think he said bread dog, though it might have been a sausage dog he said—anyway he told us it was blooded, and that when it grew up to be a man—that is, figuratively speaking—when it grew up to be a dog full size, it would be the handsomest canine in the Northwest.

We kicked on it entirely at first, but when he told us hundreds of men who had seen the pup had offered him thousands of dollars for it, but that he had rather give it to a friend than sell it to a stranger, we weakened, and told him to send it in.

Well—(excuse us while we go into a corner and mutter a silent remark)—it came in on the train Monday, and was taken to the barn. It is the confoundedest looking dog that a white man ever set eyes on. It is about the color of putty, and about seven feet long, though it is only six months old. The tail is longer than a whip lash, and when you speak sassy to that dog, the tail will begin to curl around under him, amongst his legs, double around over his neck and back over where the tail originally was hitched to the dog, and then there is tail enough left for four ordinary dogs.

It is the longest tail we have ever seen in one number. If that tail was cut up into ordinary tails, such as common dogs wear, there would be enough for all the dogs in the Seventh ward, with enough left for a white wire clothes line. When he lays down his tail curls up like a coil of telephone wire, and if you take hold of it and wring you can hear the dog at the central office. If that dog is as long in proportion, when he gets his growth, and his tail grows as much as his body does, the dog will reach from here to the Soldiers' Home.

His head is about as big as a graham gem and runs down to a point not bigger than a cambric needle, while his ears are about as big as a thumb to a glove, and they hang down as though the dog didn't want to hear anything. How a head of that kind can contain brains enough to cause a dog to know enough to go in when it rains is a mystery. But he seems to be intelligent.

If a man comes along on the sidewalk, the dog will follow him off, follow him until he meets another man, and then he follows *him* till he meets another, and so on until he has followed the entire population. He is not an aristocratic dog, but will follow one person just as soon as another, and to see him going along the street, with his tail coiled up, apparently oblivious to every human sentiment, it is touching.

His legs are about the size of pipe stems, and his feet are as big as a base ball base. He wanders around, following a boy, then a middle aged man, then a little girl, then an old man(and finally, about meal time, the last person he follows seems to go by the barn and the dog wanders in and looks for a buffalo robe or a harness tug to chew. It does not cost anything to keep him, as he has only eaten one trotting harness and one fox skin robe since Monday, though it may not be right to judge of his appetite. as he may be a little off his feed.

Pierce said he would be a nice dog to run with a horse, or under a carriage. Why, bless you, he won't go within twenty feet of a horse, and a horse would run away to look at him; besides, he gets right under a carriage wheel, and when the wheel runs over him he complains, and sings Pinafore.

What under the sun that dog is ever going to be good for is more than we know. He is too lean and bony for sausage. A piece of that dog as big as your finger in a sausage would ruin a butcher. It would be a dead give away. He looks as though he might point game, if the game was brought to his attention, but he would be just as liable to point a cow. He might do to stuff and place in a front yard to frighten burglars. If a burglar wouldn't be frightened at that dog nothing would scare him.

Anyway, now we have got him, we will bring him up, though it seems as though he would resemble a truss bridge or a refrigerator car, as much as a dog, when he gets his growth. For fear he will follow off a wagon track we tie a knot in his tail. Parties who have never seen a very long dog can call at the barn about meal time and see him.

A SEWING MACHINE GIVEN TO THE BOSS GIRL

IN response to a request from W. T. Vankirk, George W. Peck presented the Rock County Agricultural Society with a sewing machine, to be given to the "Boss combination girl" of Rock County. With the machine he sent the following letter, which explains his meaning of a "Combination girl," etc.:

MILWAUKEE, June 7, 1881.

W. T. VANKIRK—*Dear Sir:* Your letter, in reference to my giving some kind of a premium to somebody, at your County Fair, is received, and I have been thinking it over. I have brought my massive intellect to bear upon the subject, with the following result:

I ship you to-day, by express, a sewing machine, complete, with cover, drop leaf, hemmer, tucker, feller, drawers, and everything that a girl wants, except corsets and tall stockings. Now, I want you to give that to the best "Combination girl" in Rock County, with the compliments of the *Sun.*

What I mean by a "combination," is one that in the opinion of your Committee has all the modern improvements, and a few of the old-fashioned faults, such as health, etc. She must be good-looking, that is, not too handsome, but just handsome enough. You don't want to give this machine to any female statue, or parlor ornament, who don't know how to play a tune on it, or who is as cold as a refrigerator car, and has no heart concealed about her person. Our girl, that is, our "Fair Girl," that takes this machine, must be "The boss." She must be jolly and good-natured, such a girl as would make the young man that married her think that Rock County was the next door to heaven, anyway. She must be so healthy that nature's roses will discount any preparation ever made by man, and so well-formed that nothing artificial is needed to—well, Van, you know what I mean.

You want to pick out a thoroughbred, that is, all wool, a yard wide—that is, understand me, I don't want the girl to be a yard wide, but just right. Your Committee don't want to get "mashed" on some ethereal creature whose belt is not big enough for a dog collar. This premium girl wants to be able to do a day's work, if necessary, and one there is no danger of breaking in two if her intended should hug her.

After your Committee have got their eyes on a few girls that they think will fill the bill, then they want to find out what kind of girls they are around their home. Find if they honor their fathers and their mothers, and are helpful, and care as much for the happiness of those around them as they do for their own. If you find one who is handsome as Venus—I don't know Venus, but I have heard that she takes the cake—I say, if you find one that is perfect in everything, but shirks her duties at home, and plays, "I Want to Be an Angel," on the piano, while her mother is mending her stockings, or ironing her picnic skirts, then let her go ahead and be an angel as quick as she wants to, but don't give her the machine. You catch the idea?

Find a girl who has the elements of a noble woman; one whose heart is so large that she has to wear a little larger corset than some, but one who will make her home happy, and who is a friend to all; one who would walk further to do a good deed, and relieve suffering, than she would to patronize an ice cream saloon, one who would keep her mouth shut a month before she would say an unkind word, or cause a pang to another. Let your Committee settle on such a girl, and she is as welcome to that machine as possible.

Now, Van, you ought to have a committee appointed at once, and no one should know who the committee is. They should keep their eyes out from now till the time of the Fair, and they should compare notes once in a while. You have got some splendid judges of girls there in Janesville, but you better appoint married men. They are usually more unbiased. They should not let any girl know that she is suspected of being the premium girl, until the judgment is rendered, so no one will be embarrassed by feeling that she is competing for a prize.

Now, Boss, I leave the constitution and the girls in your hands; and if this premium is the means of creating any additional interest in your Fair, and making people feel good natured and jolly, I shall be amply repaid.

Your friend,
GEO. W. PECK.

DON'T APPRECIATE KINDNESS

ONE of the members of the Humane Society, who lives in an aristocratic ward, had been annoyed at hearing sounds from a stable near his residence, which indicated that a boy who had charge of a horse was in the habit of pounding the animal vigorously every morning, while cleaning off the dirt. It seemed to the humane man that the boy must use a barrel stave or fence board to curry off the horse, and the way the animal danced around the barn was terrible.

It occurred every morning, and the humane man made up his mind that it was his duty to put a stop to it. He went to the barn one morning, just as the cotillion commenced. Looking through a knot hole he saw the horse tied so his head was away up to the top of the barn, so he could not use his teeth to defend himself. The boy stood with a curry comb in one hand and a piece of plank in the other, and he warmed the horse with both, and the animal kicked for all that was out.

The humane man thought this was the worst case of cruelty to animals that ever was, and he rapped for admission. The boy, covered with perspiration, horse tail, stable refuse and indignation, opened the door, and the humane man proceeded to read him a lecture about cruelty to dumb animals, called him a fiend in human form, and told him that kindness was what was necessary, instead of a club.

The boy couldn't get in a word edgeways for a while, but when the man had exhausted his talk the boy told him that kindness might work on ordinary horses, but this horse was the meanest animal in the world. He would bite and kick without any provocation, and the present owner couldn't sell him or give him away. He said that the only way he could be curried was to tie him up at both ends and the only way he could be harnessed was to toss the harness on him with a pitch fork.

The horse, with his head tied up so high that he could not use it, looked down at the humane man with one eye filled with emotion—the other eye had been knocked out years ago—and seemed to be thanking the kind-hearted citizen for interfering in the matinee and causing hostilities to be suspended.

The humane man was touched by the intelligent look of the horse, and insisted that the animal be untied and allowed its freedom. The boy said he didn't dare untie him, for he would kick the side of the barn out, but the man insisted that he should release the horse, and went up to his head to do so, when the boy went through the manure hole in the side of the barn.

What happened when the humane citizen untied the halter will perhaps never be definitely known, but no sooner had the boy struck the ground through the hole,

"MEANEST ANIMAL IN THE WORLD."

than there was a sound of revelry in the barn, there came a yell from the crevices, there seemed to be a company of cavalry drilling on the barn floor, there was a sound as of cloth tearing and then it appeared as though something was climbing up the inside of the barn, and after which the hind heels of the horse could be heard playing the snare drum on the manger. The boy roused the neighbors and they armed themselves and entered the barn. They found the horse in the stall, with its head where its tail should be, with its mouth full of pantaloons cloth, and kicking away as though its heart would break.

And the humane man, where, oh, where was he? Ask of the winds that far around with fragments of hat and coat tail strewed the barn floor.

"Shoot the horse," said a faint voice from the upper part of the barn, and every eye was turned in that direction. The humane man was up there, clinging to a cross piece. He had evidently gone up the ladder which led to the hay loft, a little ahead of the horse, and as he clung to the cross piece, his coat tail gone, and the vital part of his pantaloons and some skin gone to that bourne from whence no pantaloons seat returns, his bald head covered with dust and cobwebs, he was a picture of meekness.

The crowd got the horse into another stall, head first, and put bars across, and the humane man came down from his perch. Seizing a barn shovel, and spitting on his hands, he asked his friends to wait and watch him curry off that horse just a minute for luck. He said he only wanted to live just long enough to maul every rib out of the animal, and if he was forgiven for interfering in somebody else's business this time he would try and lead a different life in the future.

They put a horse blanket around his wounds and led him home, and he has given the boy five dollars to pound the horse an hour every morning for the next thirty days. You can't make that man believe that a horse has any intelligence.

RELIGION AND FIRE

NEWSPAPER reports of the proceedings of the Sunday School Association encamped on Lake Monona, at Madison, give about as many particulars of big catches of fish as of sinners. The delegates divide their time catching sinners on spoon-hooks and bringing pickerel to repentance. Some of the good men hurry up their prayers, and while the

"Amen" is leaving their lips they snatch a fish-pole in one hand and a baking-powder box full of angle worms in the other, and light out for the Beautiful Beyond, where the rock bass turn up sideways, and the wicked cease from troubling.

Discussions on how to bring up children in the way they should go are broken into by a deacon with his nose peeled coming up the bank with a string of perch in one hand, a broken fish-pole in the other, and a pair of dropsical pantaloons dripping dirty water into his shoes.

It is said to be a beautiful sight to see a truly good man offering up supplications from under a wide-brimmed fishing hat, and as he talks of the worm that never, or hardly ever dies, red angle worms that have dug out of the piece of paper in which they were rolled up are crawling out of his vest pocket. The good brothers compare notes of good places to do missionary work, where sinners are so thick you can knock them down with a club, and then they get boats and row to some place on the lake where a local liar has told them the fish are just sitting around on their haunches waiting for some one to throw in a hook.

This mixing religion with fishing for black bass and pickerel is a good thing for religion, and not a bad thing for the fish. Let these Christian statesmen get "mashed" on the sport of catching fish, and they will have more charity for the poor man who, after working hard twelve hours a day for six days, goes out on a lake Sunday and soaks a worm in the water and appeases the appetite of a few of God's hungry pike, and gets dinner for himself in the bargain. While arguing that it is wrong to fish on Sunday, they will be brought right close to the fish, and can see better than before, that if a poor man is rowing a boat across a lake on Sunday, and his hook hangs over the stern, with a piece of liver on, and a fish that nature has made hungry tries to steal his line and pole and liver, it is a duty he owes to society to take that fish by the gills, put it in the boat and reason with it, and try to show it that in leaving its devotions on a Sunday and snapping at a poor man's only hook, it was setting a bad example.

These Sunday school people will have a nice time, and do a great amount of good, if the fish continue to bite, and they can go home with their hearts full of the grace of God, their stomachs full of fish, their teeth full of bones, and if they fall out of the boats, and their suspenders hold out, they may catch a basin full of eels in the basement of their pantaloons. But we trust they will not try to compete with the local sports in telling fish stories. That would break up a whole Sunday school system.

A DOCTOR OF LAWS

A DOCTOR at Ashland is also a justice of the peace, and when he is called to visit a house he don't know whether he is to physic or to marry. Several times he has been called out in the night, to the country, and he supposed some one must be awful sick, and he took a cart load of medicines, only to find somebody wanted marrying. He has been fooled so much that when he is called out now he carries a pill-bag and a copy of the statutes, and tells them to take their choice.

He was called to one house and found a girl who seemed feverish. She was sitting up in a chair, dressed nicely, but he saw at once that the fatal flush was on her cheek, and her eyes looked peculiar. He felt of her pulse, and it was beating at the rate of two hundred a minute. He asked her to run out her tongue, and she run out eight or nine inches of the lower end of it. It was covered with a black coating, and he shook his head and looked sad. She had never been married any before, and supposed that it was necessary for a justice who was going to marry a couple to know all about their physical condition, so she kept quiet and answered questions.

She did not tell him that she had been eating huckleberry pie, so he laid the coating on her tongue to some disease that was undermining her constitution. He put his ear on her chest and listened to the beating of her heart, and shook his head again. He asked her if she had been exposed to any contagious disease. She didn't know what a contagious disease was, but on the hypothesis that he had reference to sparking, she blushed and said she had but only two evenings, because John had only just got back from the woods where he had been chopping, and she had to sit up with him.

The doctor got out his pill-bags and made some quinine powders, and gave her some medicine in two tumblers, to be taken alternately, and told her to soak her feet and go to bed, and put a hot mustard poultice on her chest, and some onions around her neck.

She was mad and flared right up, and said she wasn't very well posted, and lived in the country, but if she knew her own heart she would not play such a trick as that on a new husband.

The doctor got mad, and asked her if she thought he didn't understand his business; and he was about to go and let her die, when the bridegroom came in and told him to go ahead with the marrying. The doc. said that altered the case. He said next time he came he should know what to bring, and then she blushed, and told him he was an old fool anyway, but he pronounced them man and wife, and said the prescription would be five dollars, the same as though there had been somebody sick.

But the doc. had cheek. Just as he was leaving he asked the bridegroom if he didn't want to ride up to Ashland with him; it was only eighteen miles and the ride would be lonesome, but the bride said not if the court knew herself, and the bridegroom said now he was there he guessed he would stay. He said he didn't care much about going to Ashland, anyway.

THE DIFFERENCE IN HORSES

THERE has been a great change in livery horses within the last twenty years. Years ago, if a young fellow wanted to take his girl out riding, and expected to enjoy himself, he had to hire an old horse, the worst in the livery stable, that would drive itself, or he never could get his arm around his girl to save him. If he took a decent looking team, to put on style, he had to hang on to the lines with both hands, and if he even took his eyes off the team to look at the suffering girl beside him, with his mouth, the chances were that the team would jump over a ditch, or run away, at the conclusion. Riding out with girls was shorn of much of its pleasure in those days.

We knew a young man that was going to put one arm around his girl if he did not lay up a cent, and it cost him over three hundred dollars. The team ran away, the buggy was wrecked, one horse was killed, the girl had her hind leg broken, and the girl's father kicked the young man all over the orchard, and broke the mainspring of his watch.

It got so that the livery rig a young man drove was an index to his thoughts. If he had a stylish team that was right up on the bit, and full of vinegar, and he braced himself and pulled for all that was out, and the girl sat back in the corner of the buggy, looking as though she should faint away if a horse got his tail over a line, then people said that couple was all right, and there was no danger that they would be on familiar terms.

But if they started out with a slow old horse that looked as though all he wanted was to be left alone, however innocent the party might look, people knew just as well as though they had seen it, that when they got out on the road, or when night came on, that fellow's arm would steal around her waist, and she would snug up to him—Oh, pshaw, you have heard it before.

Well, late years the livery men have "got onto the racket," as they say at the church sociables. They have found that horses that know their business are in demand, and so horses are trained for this purpose. They are trained on purpose for outdoor sparking. It is not an uncommon thing to see a young fellow drive up to a house where his girl lives with a team that is just tearing things. They prance, and champ the bit, and the young man seems to pull on them as though his liver was coming out. The horses will hardly stand still long enough for the girl to get in, and they start off and seem to split the air wide open and the neighbors say, "Them children will get all smashed up one of these days."

The girl's mother and father see the team start, and their minds experience a relief as they reflect that "As long as John drives that frisky team there can't be no hugging a-going on." The girl's older sister sighs and says, "That's so," and goes to her room and laughs right out loud.

It would be instructive to the scientists to watch that team for a few miles. The horses fairly foam, before they get out of town, but striking the country road, the fiery steeds come down to a walk, and they mope along as though they had always worked on a hearse. The shady woods are reached and the carriage scarcely moves, and the horses seem to be walking in their sleep. The lines are loose on the dash board, and the left arm of the driver is around the pretty girl, and they are talking low. It is not necessary to talk loud, as they are so near each other that the faintest whisper can be heard.

But a change comes over them. A carriage appears in front, coming towards them. It may be some one that knows them. The young man picks up the lines, and the horses are in the air, and as they pass the other carriage it almost seems as though the team is running away, and the girl that was in sweet repose a moment before acts as though she wanted to get out. After passing the intruder the walk and conversation are resumed.

If you meet the party on the Whitefish Bay road at 10 o'clock at night, the horses are walking as quietly as oxen, and they never wake up until coming into town, and then he pulls up the team and drives through town like a cyclone, and when he drives up to the house the old man is on the steps and he thinks John must be awful tired trying to hold that team. And he is.

It is thought by some that horses have no intelligence, but a team that knows enough to take in a sporadic case of buggy sparking has got sense. These teams come high but the boys have to have them.

ADDICTED TO LIMBURG CHEESE

During the investigation of Chief Kennedy one witness testified to something that ought to make it hot for the chief. When men stoop to do things that Mr. Chapin testified to, an outraged public sentiment has got to step in. Mr. Chapin testified—and he is a man whose word is as good as our note—he said he met Kennedy in a street car, and his breath smelled of limburg cheese. That is enough. Carry his remains out.

Any man who will appear in a public place among folks, with his breath smelling of limburg cheese, has got his opinion of us. It is simply damnable. We can see how a man who likes limburg cheese is liable, though he may have sworn off, to return to the mustard cup and after the first taste, fill his skin full of cheese, arguing that one may as well die for an old sheep as a lamb.

It is a well known fact, agreed to by all scientists, that a single mouth full will tarnish an otherwise virtuous breath as much as a whole cheese. One mouth full of cheese leads to another, and we are prepared to believe that if the chief smelled of the cheese at all, he was full of it.

Men can not be too careful of cheese. If a man feels that he is going to commit the dastardly act of eating limburg cheese he has time to go out to a glue factory, or a slaughter house, or the house of correction, or some other place whose offense is rank.

The desire to eat cheese does not come upon a man suddenly, like the desire to take a drink, or stand off a creditor, and he is not taken possession of by the demon of appetite and pulled to the nearest saloon by a forty horse power devil, as the man who has the jim jams.

The cheese does its work more quietly. It whispers to him about 11 o'clock A. M. and says there is nothing like cheese. He stands it off, and again in the afternoon the cheese takes possession of him, and leads him on step by step, by green fields, and yet he does not fall. But about 9 o'clock P. M. the air seems full of cheese, and he smells it wherever he goes, and finally, after resisting for ten hours, he goes and orders a cheese sandwich.

Now, when the feeling first comes on, and he shuts his eyes and imagines he sees limburg cheese, if the victim would go and buy a slice and go away out in the country, by the fertilizer factory, he could eat his cheese and no one but the workmen in the fertilizer factory could complain. That is what ought to be done when a man is addicted to cheese.

But this chief of police has stood up in the face of public opinion, eaten limburg cheese with brazen effrontery that would do credit to a lawyer, and has gone into a public conveyance, breathing pestilence and cheese. There is no law on our statute books that is adequate to punish a man who will thus trample upon the usages of society.

However, the conviction of Kennedy of eating limburg cheese will be the means of acquitting him of the other charge, that of conversing with a lewd woman. We doubt if there is a lewd woman, though she be terribly lewd, who would allow a man to come within several blocks of her who had been eating the deceased cheese.

If we were in Kennedy's place we would admit the cheese, and then bring ten thousand women to swear whether they would remain in the same room with a man who had been eating that cheese. There are men who *do* eat cheese, bad men, the wicked classes, who go into the presence of females, but that is one thing which causes so many suicides among the poor fallen girls. When we hear that another naughty but nice looking girl has been filling her skin full of paregoric and is standing off a doctor with a stomach pump, we instinctively feel as though some man with a smell of cheese about his garments had been paying attention to her, and she had become desperate.

If they discharge the chief on that cheese testimony it will be a lesson to all men hereafter.

TERRIBLE TIME ON THE CARS

THERE is something about the average Chicago young man that gives him away, and gives away anybody that gets in with him. He is full of practical jokes, and is a bad egg on general principles.

Last week Mr. Eppenetus Hoyt, of Fond du Lac, went to Chicago on a visit. He is a pious gentleman, whose candor would carry conviction to the mind of the seeker after righteousness, and his presence at the prayer meeting, at the sociable or the horse-race, is an evidence that everything will be conducted on the square.

Mr. Hoyt knew a young man named Johnny Darling, who was attending Rush Medical College, and through him was permitted to visit the dissecting-room, and gaze upon the missionary work being done there. Mr. Hoyt was introduced to a number of the wicked young men who were carving the late lamented, and after he got accustomed to the climate he rather enjoyed the performance.

Whether young Mr. Darling told the boys that Mr. Hoyt was "fresh" or not, will, perhaps, never be known; but, as Mr. Hoyt passed around among the slabs where they were at work, each made a contribution from the "stiff" he was at work upon to Mr. Hoyt's coat pockets unbeknown to him. While one was calling his attention tc a limb that he was dissecting, another would cut off an ear, or a finger, or a nose, or dig out an eye, and drop the same into Mr. Hoyt's overcoat pockets. Finally, he bid the boys good-bye, thanked them for their courtesies in showing him around, told them if they ever came to Fond du Lac his pew in church was at their disposal, and he skipped for the train and got on board.

The seats were all occupied, and a middle aged lady, with a slim face and spectacles, and evidently an old maid, allowed him to sit beside her. The car was warm, and it was not long before the "remains" began to be heard from. He was talking to the lady about the "sweet by-and-by," and the hope of a glorious immortality beyond the grave, and of the inducements held out by the good book to those who try to lead a different life here on earth, when he smelled something. The lady had been smelling it for some miles back, and she had got her eye on Mr. Hoyt, and had put her handkerchief to her nose. He took a long breath and said to the lady:

"The air seems sort o' fixed here in this car, does it not?" and he looked up at the transom.

"Yes," said the lady, as she turned pale, and asked him to let her out of the seat, "it is very much fixed, and I believe *that you are the man that fixed it!*" and she took her satchel and went to the rear of the car, where she glared at him as though he was a fat rendering establishment.

Mr. Hoyt devoted a few moments to silent prayer, and then his attention was called to a new married couple, in the seat behind him. They had been having their heads close together, when suddenly the bride said:

"Hennery, have you been drinking?"

He vowed by all that was great and glorious that he had not, when she told him there was something about his breath that reminded her of strong drink, or a packing-house.

He allowed that it was not him, but admitted that he had noticed there was something wrong, though he didn't know but that it was some of her teeth that needed filling.

They were both mad at the insinuations of the other,

and the bride leaned on the window and cried, while the groom looked the other way, and acted cross.

Mr. Hoyt was very much annoyed at the smell.

The smell remained, and people all around him got up and went to the forward end of the car, or to the rear, and there were a dozen empty seats when the conductor came in, and lots of people standing up. The conductor got one sniff, and said:

"Whoever has got that piece of limberger cheese in his pocket, will have to go in the emigrant car!"

They all looked at Hoyt, and the conductor went up to him and asked him if he didn't know any better than to be carrying around such cheese as that.

Hoyt said he hadn't got no cheese.

The conductor insisted that he had, and told him to turn his pockets wrong side out.

Hoyt jabbed his hands into his pockets, and felt something cold and clammy. He drew his hands out empty, turned pale, and said he didn't have any cheese.

The conductor insisted on his feeling again, and he brought to the surface a couple of human ears, a finger, and a thumb.

"What in the name of the Apostles have you got there?" says the conductor. "Do you belong to any canning establishment that sends canned missionary to the heathen cannibals?"

Hoyt told the conductor to come in the baggage car, and he would explain it all; and as he passed by the passengers, with both hands full of the remains, the passengers were ready to lynch Hoyt. He told the conductor where he had been, and the boys had played it on him, and the fingers and things were thrown beside the track, where some one will find them and think a murder has been committed.

Afterwards Hoyt went into the car and tried to apologize to the old maid, but she said if he didn't go away from her she would scream. Hoyt would always rather go away than have a woman scream.

He is trying to think of some way to get even with the boys of Rush Medical College.

CHANGED SATCHELS

THERE was one of those old fashioned mistakes occurred on the train from Monroe to Janesville a week or so ago. A traveling man and a girl who was going to Milton College sat in adjoining seats, and their satchels were exactly alike. and the traveling man took the wrong satchel and got off at Janesville, and the girl went on to Milton.

The drummer went down to Vankirk's grocery and put his satchel on the counter, and asked Van how his liver was getting along, while he picked a piece off a codfish and ate it, and then smelled of his fingers and said, "Whew!" Van said his liver was "not very torpid, thank you; how are you fixed for tea?" The drummer said he wished he had as many dollars as he was fixed for tea, and began to open his sample case. Van cut off a piece of cheese and was eating it while he walked along toward the drummer.

When the case was opened the drummer fell over against a barrel of brooms, and grasping a keg of maple syrup for support, turned pale and said he'd be dashed. Van looked in the sample case, and said, "Fixed for tea! I should think you was, but it wasn't that kind of tea I want."

There was a long female night-shirt, clapboarded up in front with trimming and starch, and buttoned from Genesis to Revelations. Van took a butter tryer and lifted it out, and there was more than a peck measure full of stuff that never belonged in no grocery. Van said: "If you are traveling for a millinery house I will send a boy to direct you to a millinery store"

The drummer wiped the perspiration from his face with a coffee sack and told Van he would give him a million dollars if he never would let the house in Milwaukee know about it, and he chucked the things back in. "What is this?" said Van, as he held up a pair of giddy looking affairs that no drummer ever wore on his own person. "Don't ask *me,*" says the drummer. "I am not a married man."

He took the satchel and went to Milton on the next train. The girl had opened the satchel which fell to her in the division to show her room-mate how to make a stitch in crochet, and when the brown sugar, coffee, tea, rice, bottles of syrup, maccaroni and a pack of cards came in sight, she fairly squealed. Along after dinner the drummer called and asked for an exchange, and they exchanged, and it was hard to tell which blushed the most.

THE NAUGHTY BUT NICE CHURCH CHOIR

You may organize a church choir and think you have got it down fine, and that every member of it is pious and full of true goodness, and in such a moment as you think not you will find that one or more of them are full of the old Harry, and it will break out when you least expect it. There is no more beautiful sight to the student of nature than a church choir. To see the members sitting together, demure, devoted and pious looking, you think that there is never a thought enters their mind that is not connected with singing anthems, but sometimes you get left.

There is one church choir in Milwaukee that is about as near perfect as a choir can be. It has been organized for a long time, and has never quarreled, and the congregation swears by it. When the choir strikes a devotional attitude it is enough to make an ordinary christian think of the angel band above, only the male singers wear whiskers, and the females wear fashionable clothes.

You would not think that this choir played tricks on each other during the sermon, but sometimes they do. The choir is furnished with the numbers of the hymns that are to be sung, by the minister, and they put a book mark in the book at the proper place. One morning they all got up to sing, when the soprano turned pale as an ace of spades dropped out of her hymn book, and the alto nearly fainted when a queen of hearts dropped at her feet, and the rest of the pack was distributed around in the other books. They laid it onto the tenor, but he swore, while the minister was preaching, that he didn't know one card from another.

One morning last summer, after the tenor had been playing tricks all spring on the rest of the choir, the soprano brought a chunk of shoemaker's wax to church. The tenor was arrayed like Solomon, in all his glory, with white pants, and a Seymour coat. The tenor got up to see who the girl was who came in with the old lady, and while he was up the soprano put the shoemaker's wax on the chair, and the tenor sat down on it. They all saw it, and they waited for the result. It was an awful long prayer, and the church was hot, the tenor was no iceberg himself, and shoemaker's wax melts at ninety-eight degrees Fahrenheit.

The minister finally got to the amen, and read a hymn, the choir coughed and all rose up. The chair that the tenor was in stuck to him like a brother, and came right along and nearly broke his suspenders. It was the tenor to bat, and as the great organ struck up he pushed the chair off his person, looked around to see if he had saved his pants, and began to sing, and the rest of the choir came near bursting. The tenor was called out on three strikes by the umpire, and the alto had to sail in, and while she was singing the tenor began to feel of first base to see what was the matter. When he got his hand on the shoemaker's warm wax his heart smote him, and he looked daggers at the soprano, but she put on a pious look and got her mouth ready to sing "Hold the Fort."

Well, the tenor sat down on a white handkerchief before he went home, and he got home without anybody seeing him, and he has been, as the old saying is, "laying" for the soprano ever since to get even.

It is customary in all first-class choirs for the male singers to furnish candy for the lady singers, and the other day the tenor went to a candy factory and had a peppermint lozenger made with about half a teaspoonful of cayenne pepper in the center of it. On Christmas he took his lozenger to church and concluded to get even with the soprano if he died for it.

Candy had been passed around, and just before the hymn was given out in which the soprano was to sing a solo, "Near My God to Thee," the wicked wretch gave her the loaded lozenger. She put it in her mouth and nibbed off the edges, and was rolling it as a sweet morsel under her tongue, when the organ struck up and they all arose. While the choir was skirmishing on the first part of the verse and getting scooped for the solo, she chewed what was left of the candy and swallowed it.

Well, if a democratic torch-light procession had marched unbidden down her throat she couldn't have been any more astonished. She leaned over to pick up her handkerchief and spit the candy out, but there was enough pepper left around the selvage of her mouth to have pickled a peck of chow-chow. It was her turn to sing, and as she rose and took the book, her eyes filled with tears, her voice trembled, her face was as red as a spanked lobster, and the way she sung that old hymn was a caution. With a sweet tremolo she sang, "A Charge to Keep I Have," and the congregation was almost melted to tears.

As she stopped, while the organist got in a little work, she turned her head, opened her mouth and blew out her breath with a "Whoosh," to cool her mouth. The audience saw her wipe a tear away, but did not hear the sound of her voice as she "whooshed." She wiped out some of the pepper with her handkerchief and sang the other verses with a good deal of fervor, and the choir sat down, all of the members looking at the soprano.

She called for water. The noble tenor went and got it for her, and after she had drank a couple of quarts, she whispered to him: "Young man, I will get even with you for that peppermint candy if I have to live a thousand years, and don't you forget it," and then they all sat down and looked pious, while the minister preached a most beautiful sermon on "Faith." We expect that tenor will be blowed through the roof some Sunday morning, and the congregation will wonder what he is in such a hurry for.

SENSE IN LITTLE BUGS

There is a cockroach that makes its home on our desk that has got more sense than a delinquent subscriber. He—if it is a he one; we are not clear as to that—comes out and sits on the side of the paste-dish, and draws in a long breath. If the paste is fresh he eats it, and wiggles his polonaise as much as to thank us, and goes away refreshed. If the paste is sour, and smells bad, he looks at us with a mournful expression, and goes away looking as though it was a mighty mean trick to play on a cockroach, and he runs about as though he was offended. When a package of wedding cake is placed on the desk he is the first one to find it out, and he sits and waits till we cut the string, when he goes into it and walks all over the cake till he strikes the bridal cake, when he gets onto it, stands on his head and seems to say, "Yum, yum," and is tickled as a girl with a fresh beau.

There is human nature in a cockroach. When a man comes in and sits around with no business, on our busy day, and asks questions, and stays and keeps us from working, the cockroach will come out and sit on the inkstand and look across at the visitor as much as to say:

"Why don't you go away about your business and leave the poor man alone, so he can get out some copy, and not keep us all standing around here doing nothing?"

But when the paper is out, and there is a look of cheerfulness about the place, and we are anxious to have friends call, the cockroach flies around over the papers and welcomes each caller as pleasantly as he can, and seems to enioy it.

One day the paste smelled pretty bad, and we poured about a spoonful of whisky in it, and stirred it up. The cockroach came out to breakfast, and we never saw a person that seemed to enjoy the meal any more than the cockroach did. It seemed as though he couldn't get enough paste. Pretty soon he put one hand to his head and looked cross-eyed. He tried to crawl down off the paste-dish, and fell over himself and turned a flip-flap on the blotting paper. Then he looked at us in a sort of mysterious way, winked one eye as much as to say:

"You think you are smart, don't you, old baldy?"

Then he put one hand to his forehead as if in meditation, and staggered off into a drawer, coming out presently with his arm around another cockroach, and he took him to the paste-pot, and *he* filled up, too, and then they locked arms and paraded up and down on the green cloth of the desk, as though singing, "We won't go home till morning," and they kicked over the steel pens, and acted a good deal like politicians after a caucus.

Finally, some remark was made by one of them that didn't suit, and they pitched in and had the worst fight that ever was, after which one rushed off as if after a policeman, and the other staggered into his hole, and we saw no more of our cockroach till the next morning, when he came out with one hand on his head and the other on his stomach, and after smelling of the paste and looking sick, he walked off to a bottle of seltzer water and crawled up to the cork and looked around with an expression so human that we uncorked the bottle and let him in, and he drank as though he had been eating codfish. Since that day he looks at us a little suspicious, and when the paste smells a little peculiar he goes and gets another cockroach to eat some of it first, and he watches the effect.

Now, you wouldn't believe it, but that cockroach can tell, the minute he sees a man, whether the man has come in with a bill, or has come in to pay money. We don't know how he does it, but when the man has a bill the cockroach begins to look solemn and mournful, and he puts his hands to his eyes as though weeping. If a man comes in to pay money, the cockroach looks glad, and a smile plays around his mouth, and he acts kitteny. He acts the most human when ladies come into the office. If a book agent comes in, he makes no attempt to show his disgust.

One day an old person came in with a life of Garfield and laid it on the table, opened to the picture of the candidate, and left it. The cockroach walked through the violet ink and got his feet all covered, and then he walked all over that book, and left his mark. The woman saw the tracks,

"WON'T GO HOME TILL MORNING."

and thought we had signed our name, and she said she was sorry we had written our signature there, because she had another book for subscriber's names.

When a handsome lady comes in, the cockroach is in his element, and there is a good deal of proud flesh about him. He puts his thumbs in the arm-holes of his vest and walks around.

One day we put our face up to a deaf young lady to speak to her, and the cockroach looked straight the other way, and seemed to be looking over an old copy of the *Christian*

Statesman; but when he found we only yelled at the lady, he winked as much as to say:

"Well, how did *I* know?"

O, that cockroach is a thoroughbred!

SUMMER RESORTING

THE other day a business man who has one of the nicest houses in the nicest ward in the city, and who has horses and carriages in plenty, and who usually looks as clean as though just out of a band box and as happy as a schoolma'am at a vacation picnic, got on a street car near the depot, a picture of a total wreck. He had on a long linen duster, the collar tucked down under the neck band of his shirt, which had no collar on, his cuffs were sticking out of his coat pocket, his eyes looked heavy, and where the dirt had come off with the perspiration he looked pale, and he was cross as a bear.

A friend who was on the car, on the way up town, after a day's work, with a clean shirt on, a white vest and a general look of coolness, accosted the traveler as follows:

"Been summer resorting, I hear?"

The dirty-looking man crossed his legs with a painful effort, as though his drawers stuck to his legs and almost peeled the bark off, and answered:

"Yes, I have been out two weeks. I have struck ten different hotels, and if you ever hear of my leaving town again during the hot weather, you can take my head for a soft thing," and he wiped a cinder out of his eye with what was once a clean handkerchief.

"Had a good, cool time, I suppose, and enjoyed yourself," said the man who had not been out of town.

"Cool time, hell," said the man, who has a pew in two churches, as he kicked his limp satchel of dirty clothes under the car seat. "I had rather been sentenced to the house of correction for a month."

"Why, what's the trouble?"

"Well, there is no trouble, for people who like that kind

of fun, but this lets me out. I do not blame people who live in Southern States for coming North, because they enjoy things as a luxury that we who live in Wisconsin have as a regular diet, but for a Chicago or Milwaukee man to go into the country to swelter and be kept awake nights is bald lunacy. Why, since I have been out I have slept in a room a size smaller than the closet my wife keeps her linen in, with one window that brought in air from a laundry, and I slept on a cot that shut up like a jack-knife and always caught me in the hinge where it hurt.

"At another hoted I had a broken-handled pitcher of water that had been used to rinse clothes in, and I can show you the indigo on my neck. I had a piece of soap that smelled like a tannery, and if the towel was not a recent damp diaper then I have never raised six children.

"At one hotel I was the first man at the table, and two families came in and were waited on before the Senegambian would look at me, and after an hour and thirty minutes I got a chance to order some roast beef and baked potatoes, but the perspiring, thick-headed pirate brought me some boiled mutton and potatoes that looked as though they had been put in a wash-tub and mashed by treading on them barefooted. I paid twenty-five cents for a lemonade made of water and vinegar, with a piece of something on top that might be lemon peel, and it might be pumpkin rind.

"The only night's rest I got was one night when I slept in a car seat. At the hotel the regular guests were kept awake till 12 o'clock by number six headed boys and girls dancing until midnight to the music of a professional piano boxer, and then for two hours the young folks sat on the stairs and yelled and laughed, and after that the girls went to bed and talked for two hours more, while the boys went and got drunk and sang 'Allegezan and Kalamazoo.'

"Why, at one place I was woke up at 3 o'clock in the morning by what I thought was a chariot race in the hall outside, but it was only a lot of young bloods rolling ten pins down by the rooms, using empty wine bottles for pins and China cuspidores for balls. I would have gone out and shot enough drunken galoots for a mess, only I was afraid a cuspidore would carom on my jaw. Talk about rest, I would rather go to a boiler factory.

"Say, I don't know as you would believe it, but at one place I sent some shirts and things to be washed, and they sent to my room a lot of female underclothes, and when I kicked about it to the landlord he said I would have to wear them, as they had no time to rectify mistakes. He said the season was short and they had to get in their work, and he charged me Fifth Avenue Hotel prices with a face that was child-like and bland, when he knew I had been wiping on diapers for two days instead of towels.

"But I must get off here and see if I can find water enough to bathe all over. I will see you down town after I bury these clothes."

And the sticky, cross man got off, swearing at summer hotels and pirates. We don't see where he could have been traveling.

THE GOSPEL CAR

Because there are cars for the luxurious, and smoking cars for those who delight in tobacco, some of the religious people of Connecticut are petitioning the railway companies to fit up "Gospel cars." Instead of the card tables they want an organ and piano, they want the seats arranged facing the center of the car, so they can have a full view of whoever may conduct the services; instead of spittoons they will have a carpet, and instead of cards they want Bibles and Gospel song books.—*Chicago News.*

There is an idea for you. Let some railroad company fit up a Gospel car according to the above prescription, and run it, and the porter on that car would be the most lonesome individual on the train. The Gospel hymn books would in a year appear as new as do now the Bibles that are put up in all cars. Of the millions of people who ride in the trains, many of them pious Christians, who has ever seen a man or woman take a Bible off the iron rack and read it a single minute? And yet you can often see ministers and other professing Christians in the smoking car, puffing a cigar and reading a daily paper.

Why, it is all they can do to get a congregation in a church on Sunday; and does any one suppose that when men and women are traveling for business or pleasure—and they do not travel for anything else—that they are going into a "Gospel car" to listen to some sky pirate who has been picked up for the purpose, talk about the prospects of landing the cargo in heaven?

Not much!

The women are too much engaged looking after their baggage, and keeping the cinders out of their eyes, and keeping the children's heads out of the window, and keeping their fingers from being jammed, to look out for their immortal souls. And the men are too much absorbed in the object of their trip to listen to gospel truths. They are thinking about whether they will be able to get a room at he hotel or whether they will have to sleep on a cot.

Nobody can sing gospel songs on a car, with their throats full of cinders, and their eyes full of dust, and the chances are if anybody should strike up, "A charge to keep I have," some pious sinner who was trying to take a nap in the corner of the gospel car would say:

"O, go and hire a hall!"

It would be necessary to make an extra charge of half a dollar to those who occupied the gospel car, the same as is charged on the parlor car, and you wouldn't get two persons on an average train full that would put up a nickel.

Why, we know a Wisconsin Christian, worth a million dollars, who, when he comes up from Chicago to the place where he lives, hangs up his overcoat in the parlor car, and then goes into the forward car and rides till the whistle blows for his town, when he goes in and gets his coat and never pays thirty-five cents to the conductor, or ten cents to the porter. Do you think a gospel car would catch him for half a dollar? He would see you in Hades first.

The best way is to take a little eighteen carat religion

along into the smoking car, or any other car you may happen to be in.

A man—as we understand religion from those who have had it—does not have to howl to the accompaniment of an asthmatic organ, pumped by a female with a cinder in her eye and smut on her nose, in order to enjoy religion, and he does not have to be in the exclusive company of other pious people to get the worth of his money. There is a great deal of religion in sitting in a smoking car, smoking dog-leg tobacco in a briar-wood pipe, and seeing happy faces in the smoke that curls up—faces of those you have made happy by kind words, good deeds or half a dollar put where it will drive away hunger, instead of paying it out for a reserved seat in a gospel car. Take the half dollar you would pay for a seat in a gospel car and go into the smoker, and find some poor emigrant that is going west to grow up with the country, after having been beaten out of his money at Castle Garden, and give it to him and see if the look of thankfulness and joy does not make you feel better than to listen to a discussion in the gospel car, as to whether the children of Israel went through the Red sea with life preservers or wore rubber hunting boots.

Take your gospel-car half dollar and buy a vegetable ivory rattle of the train boy and give it to the sick emigrant mother's pale baby, and you make four persons happy—the baby, the mother, the train boy and yourself.

We know a man who gave a dollar to a prisoner on the way to State prison, to buy tobacco with, who has enjoyed more good square religion over it than he could get out of all the chin music and saw-filing singing he could hear in a gospel car in ten years. The prisoner was a bad man from Oshkosh, who was in a caboose in charge of the sheriff, on the way to Waupun. The attention of the citizen was called to the prisoner by his repulsive appearance, and his general don't-care-a-damative appearance. The citizen asked the prisoner how he was fixed for money to buy tobacco in prison. He said he hadn't a cent, and he knew it would be the worst punishment he could have to go without tobacco. The citizen gave him the dollar and said:

"Now, every time you take a chew of tobacco in prison, just make up your mind to be square when you get out."

The prisoner reached out his hand-cuffed hands to take the dollar, the hands trembling so that the chains rattled, and a great tear as big as a shirt button appeared in one eye—the other eye had been gouged out while "having some fun with the boys" at Oshkosh—and his lips trembled as he said:

"So help me God, I will!"

That man has been boss of a gang of hands in the pinery for two winters, and has a farm paid for on the Central Railroad, and is "squar."

That is the kind of practical religion a worldly man can occasionally practice without having a gospel car.

INCIDENTS AT THE NEWHALL HOUSE FIRE

THERE were a great many ludicrous scenes about the Newhall House during the fire of last Saturday morning. When the people were notified that there was a fire in the house, but that the danger was not great, though it was thought best to give them all plenty of time to prepare for the worst, many jumped right out of bed and started down stairs.

When we arrived on the scene our first inquiry was for the safety of the lady members of the Rice Surprise Party, the young women who had been cutting up on the stage all the week with so little apparel. We did not expect to find them in a greater state of barefootedness than they were when we saw them last, but in some instances they were.

We were kindly yet firmly informed by Mr. Rankin that the ladies had been rescued. It seemed that everybody wanted to save the girls. Mr. Rankin knew this, and he knew if the young and thoughtless gentlemen were allowed to rescue the girls it would cause remark. He said he was an old line democrat, and that his days of kitfenhood were over, and that it was proper that he should superintend the removal of the girls.

Mr. McKittrick, the conductor, argued the matter with him. He said he had been running a train a good many years, and had seen all phases of humanity, and that he was inured to a life of hardship, and had seen many sad sights, in the sleeping cars, and he insisted that he be allowed to superintend the removal of the girls.

The discussion became warm, and finally they compromised by agreeing that McKittrick should rush into the rooms and drag them out of the fire and smoke and hand them to Mr. Rankin at the foot of the first pair of stairs, who would dispose of them in safety. They both agreed that the first outside vandal who laid a hand on them should die.

The first trouble they had was with Prof. Haskins. He came out of his room with nothing on but his glasses, an ascension robe and one boot. He rushed through the hall, and while in front of the room of the girl who wore the black tights with the crochet work on the limbs he ventured a joke. He is the telegraph manager and he said, "There is a line down here," as a two-inch stream struck him about the alleged pistol pocket. The girl, who was tying her wardrobe up in a napkin, heard him and said, "There is no *lying down* here, not much." Prof. Haskins was shocked that any female should thus mistake him for a democrat, and falling over a zinc trunk head first, he went back to his room to send his son Harry out to help.

Mr. McKittrick rushed into a room and grabbed a corset in his arms and handed it down stairs to Rankin. There is no person who can fool Rankin. He threw the corset back, saying: "There is no girl in this. Never mind the wearing apparel, save the girls." After handing down a few of the female clog dancers a cloud appeared on the horizon, and it was discovered that it was Hawley Cole. He said he came in to save the effects of the theatre. McKittrick threw him a pair of busted tights that he found in a room, and said, "This is one of the effects of the theatre."

Just at this point a girl with a waterproof on came along the hall and Mr. Cole asked her if she didn't want to be rescued. She said she had been carried down stairs six times already by a big granger, and she would shoot the next man that attempted to rescue her. She said there was no danger, and wanted to know why the big galoots did not go and help put the fire out.

On inquiry it was found that the girl had been carried down stairs six times and left on the sidewalk. She de-

scribed the man who carried her out, and said he was excited, and no sooner would she get up stairs than he would grab her and carry her down again, until she was almost froze. He told her the last time that he had saved six girls from a fiery grave.

THE WAY WOMEN BOSS A PILLOW

Among the recent inventions is a pillow holder. It is explained that the pillow holder is for the purpose of holding a pillow while the case is being put on. We trust this new invention will not come into general use, as there is no sight more beautiful to the eyes of man than to see a woman hold a pillow in her teeth while she gently manipulates the pillow case over it.

We do not say that a woman is beautiful with her mouth full of pillows. No one can ever accuse us of saying that, but there is something home-like and old-fashioned about it that can not be replaced by any invention.

We know that certain over-fastidious women have long clamored for some new method of putting on a pillow case, but these people have either lost their teeth, or the new ones do not grasp the situation. They have tried several new methods, such as blowing the pillow case up, and trying to get the pillow in before the wind got out, and they have tried to get the pillow in by rolling up the pillow case until the bottom is reached, and then placing the pillow on end and gently unrolling the pillow case, but all these schemes have their drawbacks.

The old style of chewing one end of the pillow, and holding it the way a retriever dog holds a duck, till the pillow case is on, and then spanking the pillow a couple of times on each side, is the best, and it gives the woman's jaws about the only rest they get during the day.

If any invention drives this old custom away from us, and we no more see the matrons of our land with their hair full of feathers and their mouths full of striped bed-ticking, we shall feel that one of the dearest of our institutions has been ruthlessly torn from us, and the fabric of our national supremacy has received a sad blow, and that our liberties are in danger.

THE DEADLY PAPER BAG

THERE is a woman on the West Side who has learned a lesson that will last her a lifetime. She has been for years wearing these paper bags, such as the green grocers use, for bustles. The paper is stiff, and sticks out splendid, and makes the dress look well. Last Sunday morning while she was dressing, her young son got in the room and blew the paper bag full of wind and tied a string around the mouth of it, and left it in a chair. The good lady took it and tied it on and dressed herself for church. She bribed her husband to go to church with her, though he is a sort of Bob Ingersoll christian.

As they went down the aisle the minister was reading a hymn about "Sounding the Loud Hosanna," and the lady went into the pew first, and sat down while her husband was putting his hat on the floor. There was a report like distant thunder. You have heard how these confounded paper bags explode when boys blow them up, and crush them between their hands.

Well, it was worse than that, and everybody looked at the innocent husband, who was standing there a perfect picture of astonishment. He looked at his wife as much as to say: "Now, this is the last time you will catch me in church, if you are going to play any of your tricks on me. You think you can scare me into getting religion?"

The minister stopped reading the hymn and looked over his spectacles at the new comers as though it would not surprise him if that bad man should blow the church up. The poor lady blushed and looked around as much as to say, "I did not know it was loaded," and she looked the hymn book through for the hymn, and as the choir rose to sing she offered one side of the book to her husband, but he looked mad and pious, and stood at the other end of the pew and looked out of the stained glass window.

After the service they started home together, and as they turned the first corner he said to his wife, "Well, you played hell on your watch, didn't you?" She told him there was no such thing as hell in the Bible now, but that she would make that boy think there had been no revision of the Bible that left hell out, when she got home. We only get the story from the husband.

He said he didn't know what it was that made the noise

until they got home, and after a little skirmishing around his wife held up a bursted paper bag, and asked the boy if he blew that bag up. He said he did, but he did not know there was anything wrong about it. The boy and his mother and a press board paid a visit to the back kitchen, and there was a sound of revelry. Boys will be boys.

THE VIRGINIA DUEL

THE proposed duel between Senator Mahone and Jubal Early did not come off, for reasons that have not been made public. It is well known that Mahone is the thinnest man in Virginia. We do not allude to his politics, or his ability, in speaking of his being thin, but to his frame. He does not make a shadow. He could hide behind a wire fence. Gen. Early, after challenging Mahone, went to practicing at a piece of white wire clothes line, hung to the limb of a tree, but he could not hit it, and he felt that all the advantage would be on Mr. Mahone's side, so he asked Mahone to do the only thing in his power that would make the thing even, and that was to eat a quantity of dried apples the day before the duel, in order to swell his stomach out so that a gentleman could stand some show of hitting him.

Gen. Early pledged himself, on the honor of a Virginia gentleman, that he would not shoot at Mahone's stomach, but would aim at it, and then make a line shot either above or below.

Mahone replied that, while he appreciated the advantage he had over his opponent, and was willing to do anything reasonable to make the thing even, he could not consistently eat dried apples, as they would certainly kill him. He was willing to take his chances on the bullets of his opponent, because statistics showed that dueling was the most healthy business a man could engage in; and he pointed to the number of duelists that were now living at a ripe old age, who had fought hundreds of duels and never received a scratch or scratched an opponent, but on the other hand he could produce proof to show that many people had been injured, if not killed, by an over-indulgence in dried apples.

Mr. Mahone said he thought it was late in the day for him to produce any proof as to his own bravery, but in the face of the fact that he would be pointed at as one who had not sand, he should have to decline to eat dried apples in order to make himself a target.

Gen. Early said he appreciated the delicacy of his honorable and high-toned opponent, and respected his feelings, and would not insist on the dried apple act, but that he would go into training to reduce himself in flesh to the size of Mahone, and hoped that the affair might be declared off until he could diet himself. He said he should at once begin a course of treatment to reduce his flesh, by boarding at a summer resort hotel that he had heard of, where the desired effect might be produced.

So the duel is postponed for the present. Both Mahone and Early are high-toned gentlemen, and they will do nothing rash.

THE DIFFERENCE

One of the great female writers on dress reform, in trying to illustrate how terrible the female dress is, says:

"Take a man and pin three or four table-cloths about him, fastened back with elastic and looped up with ribbons, draw all his hair to the middle of his head and tie it tight, and hairpin on five pounds of other hair and a big bow of ribbon. Keep the front locks on pins all night, and let them tickle his eyes all day, pinch his waist into a corset, and give him gloves a size too small and shoes the same, and a hat that will not stay on without torturing elastic, and a little lace veil to blind his eyes whenever he goes out to walk, and he will know what a woman's dress is."

Now you think you have done it, don't you, sis? Why, bless you, that toggery would be heaven compared to what a man has to contend with. Take a woman and put a pair of men's four-shilling drawers on her that are so tight that when they get damp, from perspiration, sis, they stick so you can't cross your legs without an abrasion of the skin, the buckle in the back turning a somersault and sticking its points into your spinal meningitis; put on an undershirt that draws across the chest so you feel as though you must cut a hole in it, or two, and which is so short that it works up under your arms, and allows the starched upper shirt to sand paper around and file off the skin until you wish it was night, the tail of which will not stay tucked more than half a block, though you tuck, and tuck, and tuck; and then fasten a collar made of sheet zinc, two sizes too small for you, around your neck; put on vest and coat, and liver pad and lung pad and stomach pad, and a porous plaster, and a chemise shirt between the two others, and rub on some liniment, and put a bunch of keys and a jack-knife and a button-hook and a pocket-book and a pistol and a plug of tobacco in your pockets, so they will chafe your person, and then go and drink a few whisky cocktails, and walk around in the sun with tight boots on, sis, and then you will know what a man's dress is.

Come to figure it up, it is about an even thing, sis—isn't it?

SPURIOUS TRIPE

Another thing that is being largely counterfeited is tripe. Parties who buy tripe cannot be too careful. There is a manufactory that can make tripe so natural that no person on earth can detect the deception. They take a large sheet of rubber about a sixteenth of an inch thick for a background, and by a process only known to themselves veneer it with a Turkish towel, and put it in brine to soak. The unsuspecting boarding-house keeper, or restaurant man, buys it and cooks it, and the boarder or transient guest calls for tripe. A piece is cut off the damnable tripe with a pair of shears used in a tin-shop for cutting sheet iron, and it is handed to the victim. He tries to cut it, and fails; he tries to gnaw it off, and if he succeeds in getting a mouthful, that settles him. He leaves his tripe on his plate, and it is gathered up and sewed on the original piece, and is kept for another banquet.

The tripe is expensive, owing to royalty that has to be paid to the rubber company, and often the boarder succeeds in eating off some of the towel, so it has to be veneered over again; but take it the year round, and the tripe pays its way in a boarding-house.

A CASE OF PARALYSIS

ABOUT as mean a trick as we ever heard of was perpetrated by a doctor at Hudson last Sunday. The victim was a justice of the peace named Evans. Mr. Evans is a man who has the alfiredest biggest feet east of St. Paul, and when he gets a new pair of shoes it is an event that has its effect on the leather market.

Last winter he advertised for sealed proposals to erect a pair of shoes for him, and when the bids were opened it was found that a local architect in leather had secured the contract, and after mortgaging his house to a Milwaukee tannery, and borrowing some money on his diamonds of his "uncle," John Comstock, who keeps a pawnbrokery there, he broke ground for the shoes.

Owing to the snow blockade and the freshets, and the trouble to get hands who would work on the dome, there were several delays, and Judge Evans was at one time inclined to cancel the contract, and put some strings in box cars and wear them in place of shoes, but sympathy for the contractor, who had his little awl invested in the material and labor, induced him to put up with the delay.

On Saturday the shoes were completed, all except laying the floor and putting on a couple of bay windows for corns, and conservatories for bunions, and the judge concluded to wear them on Sunday. He put them on, but got the right one on the left foot, and the left one on the right foot. As he walked down town the right foot was continually getting on the left side, and he stumbled over himself, and he felt pains in his feet. The judge was frightened in a minute. He is afraid of paralysis, all the boys know it, and when he told a wicked republican named Spencer how his feet felt, that degraded man told the judge that it was one of the surest symptoms of paralysis in the world, and advised him to hunt a doctor.

The judge pranced off, interfering at every step, skinning his shins, and found Dr. Hoyt. The doctor is one of the worst men in the world, and when he saw how the shoes were put on he told the judge that his case was hopeless unless something was done immediately. The judge turned pale, the sweat poured out of him, and taking out his purse he gave the doctor five dollars and asked him what he should do. The doctor felt his pulse, looked at his tongue, listened at his heart, shook his head, and then told the judge that he would be a dead man in less than sixty years if he didn't change his shoes.

The judge looked down at the vast expanse of leather, both sections pointing inwardly, and said, "Well, dam a fool," and "changed cars" at the junction. As he got them on the right feet, and hired a raftsman to tie them up for him, he said he would get even with the doctor if he had to catch the smallpox. Oh, we suppose they have more fun in some of these country towns than you can shake a stick at.

MALE AND FEMALE MASHING

THERE has been a great deal of talk in the papers about arresting "mashers," that is, young men who stand on the corners and pulverize women, and a great many good people got the idea that it was unsafe to travel the streets. This is not the case. A woman might travel all day and half the night and not be insulted. Of course, once in a great while, a woman will be insulted by a man, the same as a man will be by a woman.

No woman, unless she throws out one eye, kind of cunning, is in danger of having a male man throw out his other eye the same way. There has got to be two parties to a mashing match, and one must be a woman. Too many women act sort of queer just for fun, and the poor male man gets to acting improper before he realizes the enormity of the crime, and then it is everlastingly too late.

But a female masher, one who is thoroughly bad, like the male loafers that have been driven from the corners, is a terror. She will insult a respectable man and laugh at his blushes. One of them was arrested the other day for playing her act on a policeman who was disguised as a respectable granger from Stevens Point. These female mashers are a tornado.

Why, one of them met a respectable church member the other night, and asked him how his liver complaint was. He was a man who had been troubled with the liver complaint, and supposing she was some acquaintance, he stopped on the corner and talked with the pullet for about ten minutes, explaining to her the course of treatment he had used to cure him, and dozens of people passing by that knew him, and knew that she was clear off.

Finally she asked him if he wouldn't take her to a restaurant and buy her a spring chicken and a small bottle. He told her if she would come up to his house she should have a hen, and there were lots of bottles, both large and small, that she was welcome to. She told him to go to hades, and he went in a drug store and asked a clerk who that lady was he had been talking with, and when the clerk, who knew her, told him she was a road agent, a street walker, a female masher, the old man had to sit down on a box of drugs and fan himself with his hat.

We mention this to show that ladies are not the only portion of the population that is liable to be accosted and insulted. The other night a respectable merchant was going to the opera with a friend from the country, when a couple of sirens met them and one said to the other, "Look at his nibs," and she locked arms with him and asked him if he was not her own darling. He said his name was not "Nibs," and he would have to look at his memorandum book before he could tell whether he was her darling or not, but from the smell of gin about her person he would blush to extemporize.

We do not give his exact language, but in the heat of debate he shook her and told her if she ever clawed on him again he would everlastingly go and tell her parents. And while he was talking with her the other one had seated herself beside his country friend on a salt barrel in front of a grocery and was feeling in his vest pocket to see if he had any cloves.

A female masher is much worse than a male masher, as you can imagine. Who ever heard of a male masher feeling in an unprotected female's vest pocket for cloves? Oh, the men are simply unprotected, and at the mercy of wicked, designing women, and the police ought to protect them.

THE USES OF THE PAPER BAG

A First ward man was told by his wife to bring home a quart of oysters on New Year's night, to fry for supper. He drank a few prescriptions of egg nog, and then took a paper bag full of selects and started for home. He stopped at two or three saloons, and the bag began to melt, and when he left the last saloon the bottom fell out of the bag and the oysters were on the sidewalk.

We will leave the man there, gazing upon the wreck, and take the reader to the residence where he is expected.

A red-faced woman is putting the finishing touches to the supper table, and wondering why her husband does not come with the oysters. Presently a noise as of a lead pencil in the key-hole salutes her ear, and she goes to the door and opens it, and finds him taking the pencil out of the key-hole. Not seeing any oysters, she asks him if he has forgotten the oysters.

"Forgot noth(hic)ing," says he.

He walks up to the table and asks for a plate, which is given him by the unsuspicious wife.

"Damsaccident you ever(hic)see," said the truly good man, as he brought his hand out of his overcoat pocket, with four oysters, a little smoking tobacco, and a piece of cigar-stub.

"Slipperysoysterssev(hic)er was," said he, as he run his hand down in the other pocket, bringing up five oysters, a piece of envelope, and a piece of wire that was used as a bail to the pail.

"Got all my pock(hic)ets full," said he, as he took a large oyster out of his vest pocket. Then he began to go down in his pants pocket, and finding a hole in it, he said:

"Six big oys(hic)ters gone down my trousers leg. S'posi'll find them in my boot," and he sat down to pull off his boot, when the lady took the plate of oysters and other stuff into the kitchen and threw them in the swill, and then she put him to bed, and all the time he was trying to tell her how the bag busted just as he was in front of All Saints Ca-(hic)thedral.

THREE distinct charges of heresy will be made against Rev. Dr. Thomas, of Chicago, at the trial next month. The amount of heresy that is going on in this country, and particularly among ministers, is truly alarming. The names of his partners in guilt are not mentioned, probably out of respect for their families. A minister that goes around practicing heresy ought to be watched, and when caught at it he should be bounced. There is no excuse for *heresy*, though a minister will occasionally meet a mighty attractive *her*, but he should say: "Git thee forninst me, Susan, and when I have a convenient reason I will send the police after thee."

THERE should be an amendment to the constitution of the United States making it lawful for an ex-President to walk on grass. We have no great admiration for Hayes, but when we read that at Cleveland he was ordered off the grass by a thirteen dollar a month soldier, and had to shin it over a fence real spry to save the shoulder of his pants from assault by a cheap bayonet, it makes us feel ashamed, and we blush for America. The spectacle of a man who has occupied the White House, and been the chief attraction of county fairs, being compelled to put his stomach on a fence, and flop over, heels over appetite, like a boy playing tag, to keep from being jabbed in a vital part, makes us sick.

THE NEW COAL STOVE

WE never had a coal stove around the house until last Saturday. Have always used pine slabs and pieces of our neighbor's fence. They burn well, too, but the fence got all burned up, and the neighbor said he wouldn't build a new one, so we went down to Jones' and got a coal stove.

You see, we didn't know anything about coal stoves. We filled the stove about half full of pine fence, and, when the stuff got well to going, we filled the artesian well on the top with coal. It simmered and sputtered about five or ten minutes, and all went out, and we put on an overcoat and a pair of buckskin mittens and "went out too"—to supper. We remarked, in the course of the final meal, that Jones was a "froad" for recommending such a confounded refrigerator to a man to get warm by.

After supper we took a piece of ice and rubbed our hands warm, and went in where that stove was, resolved to make her draw and burn if it took all the pine fence in the First ward. Our better-half threw a quilt over her, and shiveringly remarked that she never knew what real solid comfort was until she got a coal stove.

Stung by the sarcasm in her remark, we turned every

dingus on the stove that was movable, or looked like it had anything to do with the draft, and pretty soon the stove began to heave up heat. It was not long before she stuttered like the new Silsby steamer. Talk about your heat! In ten minutes that room was as much worse than a Turkish bath as hades is hotter than Liverman's ice-house. The perspiration fairly fried out of a tin water cooler in the next room. We opened the doors, and snow began to melt as far up Vine street as Hanscombe's house, and people all round the neighborhood put on linen clothes. And we couldn't stop the confounded thing.

We forgot what Jones told us about the dampers, and she kept a biling. The only thing we could do was to go to bed, and leave the thing to burn the house up if it wanted to. We stood off with a pole and turned the damper every way, and at every turn she just sent out heat enough to roast an ox. We went to bed, supposing that the coal would eventually burn out, but about 12 o'clock the whole family had to get up and sit on the fence.

Finally a man came along who had been brought up among coal stoves, and he put a wet blanket over him and crept up to the stove and turned the proper dingus, and she cooled off, and since that time has been just as comfortable as possible. If you buy a coal stove you want to learn how to engineer it, or you may get roasted.

A COLD, HEERLESS RIDE

PROBABLY the most cold blooded affair that ever occurred took place at a certain summer resort a couple of weeks ago. There was going to be a picnic, and a young man and the girl he was engaged to be married to started in a rowboat to cross the lake, taking an ice cream freezer full of frozen ice cream for the picnic. Just before arriving at the picnic the boat capsized. The boat was bottom side up, and the young man helped the girl on to the ice cream freezer, and he got on the boat, and after floating for half an hour they were rescued.

The girl did not complain at the time she was put on the freezer, as she was glad enough to get on anything that would float, but after they got ashore, and she had a chance to reflect on the matter, and talk with the other girls, she concluded that his getting on the boat, which was nice and warm, and putting her aboard the ice cream freezer, which was so cold and cheerless, was a breach of etiquette that would stamp any man as being a selfish, heartless villain, and she refuses to speak to him, and has declared the engagement off.

He is very much mortified over the affair, and tries to explain that he was more accustomed to a boat than she was, while he reasoned that she would naturally be more familiar with an ice cream freezer. It certainly looks to us to have been a cold-blooded transaction, and while the young man might have been rattled, and powerless to grasp the situation as he would if he had it to do over again, the girl is certainly justified in being indignant.

An ice cream freezer is a cold and cheerless companion even when empty, but filled with congealed cream and pounded ice, and in water, it cannot but have been an Arctic exploration on a small scale. Besides the ice, it is a notorious fact that ice cream freezers are made of zinc, the coldest metal in the world, if we bar women's feet.

"Sheridan's Ride" has been spoken of in poetry and in song, but it pales into insignificance by the side of this girl's ride on the ice cream freezer. If the young man had exhibited foresight, and had a side saddle buckled on to the ice cream freezer, the experience would have been robbed of much of its frigidity, or if there had been a thick blanket under the saddle, but he failed to take even that precaution.

As it is, we do not blame the girl for breaking off the engagement. In addition, we think any court would decide that he should pay for the ginger tea and cough lozenges that she had to take to cure her cold.

SOME TALK ABOUT MONOPOLIES

We know it is fashionable for people to talk about the great monopolies, the railroads, and show how they are sapping the life-blood from the farmers by arranging facilities for transporting wheat worth forty cents a bushel in store pay, without railroads, to a market where the farmer realizes nearly a dollar a bushel in cash.

Demagogues ring the changes on these monopolies, tell how the directors ride in palace cars and drink wine, from the proceeds of the millions of dollars invested in railroads, though they never mention the fact that the railroads have made it possible for farmers to give up driving ox teams and ride after horses that can trot in 2:40.

We presume that railroad managers like to get a pretty good dividend on their investments, but do they get a better dividend than farmers do on some of their investments? Do you know of any farmer that ever complained that his produce was selling too high? If you complain at paying eight dollars for a jag of crow's nest wood during a snow blockade, does he argue with you, to show that he is a monopoly, or does he tell you that if you don't want the wood you needn't have it?

Now, talking of railroad men manipulating stock, and taking advantage of a raise, how is it about eggs? Within the last two months there has been the worst corner on eggs that the world has ever seen, and the dividends that farmers have received on their investments have been so enormous that they must blush for shame, unless they are a soulless corporation.

Now, for instance, a farmer paid twenty-five cents for a good average hen the 1st of December. Before the 1st of February that hen has laid five dozen eggs, which are worth two dollars and a half. Take out five cents for feed, two cents for the society that the hen has enjoyed, and there is a clear profit of two dollars and forty-three cents, and the farmer has got the hen left. Did any railroad wrecker ever make a greater percentage than that? Talk about watering stock, is it any worse than feeding a hen, to make her lay four-shilling eggs?

We have it from good authority that some farmers have actually gone so far as to bribe legislators with eggs, to prevent their passing any law fixing a rate for the sale of eggs. This is a serious charge, and we do not vouch for it. It is probable that farmers who are sharp enough to get a corner on eggs, by which they can be run up to a fictitious value, are sharp enough not to lay themselves liable for bribery by giving eggs directly to the members, but there are ways to avoid that. They can send them to the residences of the members, where they are worth their weight in gold, almost.

Rich railroad owners have submitted to this soulless monopoly of the egg business as long as they can, and we learned that they have organized a state grange, with grips and passwords, and will institute subordinate lodges all over the State to try and break up this vile business that is sapping their life blood. Already a bill has been prepared for introduction into the legislature to prohibit any manipulation of the egg market in the future. "Shall the farmers of the State be allowed to combine with hens and roosters and create a famine in eggs, an article of food on which so many people rely to keep soul and body together?" they ask.

Our heart has bled, in the last sixty days, as well as our pocket-book, while studying this question. We have seen men of wealth going about the streets crying for an egg to cool their parched tongues, and they have been turned away eggless, and gone to their palatial homes only to suffer untold agonies, the result of these unholy alliances between farmers and hens. They have tossed sleeplessly on their downy beds, wondering if there was no balm in Gilead, no rooster there. They have looked in vain for compassion on the part of the farmers, who have only laughed at their sufferings, and put up the price of eggs.

The time has arrived for action on the part of the

wealthy consumers of eggs, and we are glad that the State grange has been formed. Let a few determined men get together in every community, and swear by the bald-headed profit that they will put down this hen monopoly or die, and after they have sworn, let them send to us for a charter for a lodge—enclosing two dollars in advance—and we will forward to them the ritual of the order.

If this thing is allowed to go on for five years these farmers will be beyond the power of the government to control. This is a grave question, and if the wealthy people do not get relief we might as well bid farewell to our American institutions, as the liberty for which our forefathers fought will not be worth paying taxes for.

THERE is no person in the world who is easier to overlook the inconsistencies that show themselves on the stage at theaters than we are, but once in a while there is something so glaring that it pains us. We have seen actors fight a duel in a piece of woods far away from any town, on the stage, and when one of them fell, pierced to the heart with a sword, we have noticed that he fell on a Brussels carpet. That is all wrong, but we have stood it manfully.

We have seen a woman on the stage who was so beautiful that we could be easily mashed if we had any heart left to spare. Her eyes were of that heavenly color that has been written about heretofore, and her smile as sweet as ever was seen, but behind the scenes, through the wings, we have seen her trying to dig the cork out of a beer bottle with a pair of shears, and ask a supe, in harsh tones, where the cork-screw was, while she spread mustard on a piece of cheese, and finally drank the beer from the bottle, and spit the pieces of cork out on the floor, sitting astride of a stage chair, and her boot heels up on the top round, her trail rolled up into a ball, wrong side out, showing dirt from forty different stage floors.

These things hurt. But the worst thing that has ever occurred to knock the romance out of us, was to see a girl in the second act, after "twelve years is supposed to elapse," with the same pair of red stockings on that she wore in the first act, twelve years before. Now, what kind of a way is that? It does not stand to reason that a girl would wear the same pair of stockings twelve years. Even if she had them washed once in six months, they would be worn out. People notice these things.

What the actresses of this country need is to change their stockings. To wear them twelve years, even in their minds, shows an inattention to the details and probabilities of a play, that must do the actresses an injury, if not give them corns. Let theater-goers insist that the stockings be changed oftener, in these plays that sometimes cover half a century, and the stockings will not become moth-eaten. Girls, look to the little details. Look to the stockings, as your audiences do, and you will see how it is yourselves.

A BALD-HEADED MAN MOST CRAZY

LAST Wednesday the bell to our telephone rung violently at 8 o'clock in the morning, and when we put our ear to the earaphone, and our mouth to the mouthaphone, and asked what was the matter, a still small voice, evidently that of a lady, said, "Julia has got worms, doctor."

We were somewhat taken back, but supoosing Julia was going fishing we were just going to tell her not to forget to spit on her bait, when a male voice sad, "Oh, go to the devil, will you?" We couldn't tell whose voice it was, but it sounded like the clerk at the Plankinton House, and we sat down.

There is no man who will go further to accommodate a friend than we will, but by the great ethereal, there are some things we will not do to please anybody. As we sat and meditated, the bell rung once more, and then we knew the wires had got tangled, and that we were going to have trouble all day. It was a busy day, too, and to have a bell ringing beside one's ear all day is no fun.

The telephone is a blessed thing when it is healthy, but when its liver is out of order it is the worst nuisance on record. When it is out of order that way you can hear lots of conversation that you are not entitled to. For instance, we answered the bell after it had rung several times, and a sweet little female voice said, "Are you going to receive to-morrow?" We answered that we were going to receive all the time. Then she asked what made us so hoarse. We told her that we had sat in a draft from the bank, and it made the cold chills run over us to pay it. That seemed to be satisfactory and then she began to tell us what she was going to wear, and asked if we thought it was going to be too cold to wear a low neck dress and elbow sleeves. We told her that was what we were going to wear, and then she began to complain that her new dress was too tight in various places that she mentioned, and when the boys picked us up off the floor and bathed our temples, and we told them to take her away, they thought we were crazy.

If we have done wrong in talking with a total stranger, who took us for a lady friend, we are willing to die. We couldn't help it. For an hour we would not answer the constant ringing of the bell, but finally the bell fluttered as though a tiny bird had lit upon the wire and was shaking its plumage. It was not a ring, but it was a tune, as though an angel, about eighteen years old, a blonde angel, was handling the other end of the transmitter, and we felt as though it was wrong for us to sit and keep her in suspense, when she was evidently dying to pour into our auricular appendage remarks that we ought to hear.

And still the bell did flut. We went to the cornucopia, put our ear to the toddy stick and said, "What ailest thou, darling, why dost thy hand tremble? Whisper all thou feelest to thine old baldy." Then there came over the wire and into our mansard by a side window the following touching remarks: "Matter enough. I have been ringing here till I have blistered my hands. We have got to have ten car loads of hogs by day after to-morrow or shut down."

Then there was a stuttering, and then another voice said, "Go over to Loomis' pawn shop. A man shot in"—and another voice broke in, singing, "The sweet by and by, we shall meet on that beautiful"—and another voice said—"girl I ever saw. She was riding with a duffer, and wiped her nose as I drove by in the street car, and I think she is struck after me."

It was evident that the telephone was drunk, and we went out in the hall and wrote on a barrel all the afternoon, and gave it full possession of the office.

Mr. Peck was recently extended an invitation to be present at a meeting of the Iowa Commercial Travelers' Association, at Des Moines, and respond to the toast: "Our Wives and Sweethearts, and Little Ones at Home." He couldn't be present, but he responded all the same, in the following manner:

"That is the sweetest toast that man was ever called upon to respond to. Very few traveling men, who have good wives, loving sweethearts, and dear little children at home, sending loving messages to them, often ever stray very far from the straight and narrow path. There is no class of men on earth that has greater temptations and better opportunities to be 'cusses on wheels' than the traveling men of the Northwest; and when I say that they stand up under it a confounded sight better than the same number of ministers or editors would, I don't want you to think I am giving you any confectionery from my sample case.

"Through snows of winter, mud of spring and fall, and heat of summer, the traveling man makes his connections and sends in his orders, and seems to enjoy religion with the best of them. But the happiest days for him and the shortest are those he spends at home with his wife, the children or sweetheart. There can be more tears brought to the eyes of the traveling man by a little child putting its arms around his neck and saying, 'My dear, precious papa,' than could be brought out by any other press I know of, however powerful.

"I know there is occasionally a traveling man who always has his sign out ready to be mashed. but he never neglects his business for any foolishness. He would leave the finest country flirt that ever winked a wink to sell a bill of brown sugar on sixty days' time.

"It is said that the average traveling man will keep a whole seat in a car, and never offer to give half of it to a man, when, if a handsome woman comes in, he will fly around and divide with her. Well, who the deuce wouldn't? That shows that his heart is in the right place. A man can go into the smoking car and sit on the wood box, but a woman has got to sit down, at least that is the way I should explain it.

"Boys, may the trips become shorter each year, and the visits to the dear ones at home be extended, so that in time you may be detailed to stay at home always, with an increase of salary or an interest in the business; and, I am sure, when the time comes you will be the happiest fellows that ever had thousand mile tickets punched, and when your time comes to attend the grand banquet above, and you appear before St. Peter at the gate, and begin to open up your samples, he will simply look at your business card and turn to the clerk and say, 'Give these boys all front rooms, and see that there is a fire escape and plenty of towels, and that the rooms are aired, and then step down to the box office and reserve them some seats for the sacred concert this evening. Pass right in now and get a check for your overshoes.' "

ACCIDENTS AND INCIDENTS AT THEATERS

SOMETIMES our heart bleeds for actors and actresses, when we think what they have to go through with. The other night at Watertown, N. Y., Miss Ada Gray was playing "Camille," and in the dying scene, where she breathes her last, to slow music, an accident occurred which broke her all up. She was surrounded by sorrowing friends, who were trying to do everything to make it pleasant for her, when the bed on which she was dying—an impromptu sort of a bed got up by the stage carpenter—tipped partly over, and the dying woman rolled over on the stage, tipped over a wash-stand filled with tumblers and bottles of medicine, and raised a deuce of a row. It would have been all right, and she could have propped the bed up and proceeded with her dying, had not the actress got rattled.

Most actresses get lost entirely when anything occurs that is not in the play, and Miss Gray was the sacredest female that ever lived. She thought it was a judgment on her for playing a dying character, and thought the whole theater had been struck by lightning, and was going to fall down. To save herself was her first thought, so she grabbed her night-dress—which was embroidered up and down the front, and had point lace on the yoke of the sleeves—in both hands and started for the orchestra, the wildest corpse that ever lived.

The leader of the orchestra caught her, but not being an undertaker he did not undertake to hold her, and she fell over the bass viol and run one foot through the snare drum, and grasping the fiddle for a life-preserver she jumped into the raging scenery back of the stage which represented a sea.

They had to pull her out with boat hooks, and it was half an hour before she could be induced to go to bed again and proceed with her dying.

Actresses are often annoyed at the remarks made by foolish fellows in the audience. A remark by a person in the audience always causes people to laugh, whether the speaker says anything smart or not.

Recently, in the play of "Cinderella at School," a girl came out with a sheet over her, as a ghost, to frighten a young fellow who was "mashed" on her. He looked at the ghost for a moment, and kept on lighting his cigarette, when a galoot up in the gallery said, so everybody could hear it, "He don't scare worth a damn!" and the audience went

NEATSFOOT OIL FOR ONE.

fairly wild, whilo the pretty girl stood there and blushed as though her heart would break.

Such things are wrong.

Probably one of the meanest tricks that was ever played was played on Mary Anderson. It will be remembered that in the play of "Ingomar," Parthenia and the barbarian have several love scenes, where they lop on each other and hug some—that is, not too much hugging, but just hugging enough. Ingomar wears a huge fur garment, made of lion's skin, or something. One day he noticed that the moths were getting into it, and he told his servant to see about the moths, and drive them out. The servant got some insect powder and blowed the hair of the garment full of it, and scrubbed the inside of it with benzine.

Ingomar put it on just before he went on the stage, and thought it didn't smell just right, but he had no time to inquire into it. He had not got fairly into his position, before Parthenia came out on a hop, skip and jump, and threw herself all over him. She got one lung full of insect powder, and the other full of benzine, and as she said, "Wilt always love me, Ingomar?" she dropped her head over his shoulder, and said in an aside, "For the love of heaven, what have you been drinking?" and then sneezed a couple of times.

Ingomar held her up the best he could, considering that his nose was full of insect powder, and he answered:

"I wilt," and then he said to her quietly:

"Damfino what it is that smells so!"

They went on with the play between sneezes, and when the curtain went down she told Ingomar to go out and shake himself, which he did.

It was noticed in the next act that Ingomar had a linen duster on, and Mary snoze no more.

There was another mean trick played on a comedian a short time ago. In one of the plays he comes into a room as a tramp, and asks for something to drink. There is nothing to drink, and he asks if he may drink the kerosene in the lamp, which is on the table unlighted. The lamp has been filled with beer, and when he is told that he can slake his thirst at the lamp, he unscrews the top, takes out the wick and drinks the contents. Everybody laughs and the idea is a good one.

At Chicago recently, some friend took out the beer and filled the lamp with a liquid of the same color, but the most sickish tasting stuff that ever was. The comedian drank about three swallows of the neatsfoot oil before he got onto the joke and then he flew around like a dog that had been poisoned, and went off the stage saying something like "Noo Yoick.

He has agreed to kill the fellow that loaded that lamp for him.

ALL ABOUT A SANDWICH

THE time for getting to the Michigan Central depot at Chicago was so limited that no regularly prepared supper could be secured, and so it was necessary to take a sandwich at the central depot. There has been great improvement made in the sandwiches furnished in Chicago, in the last ten years. In 1870 it was customary to encase the sandwiches in pressed sole leather. The leather was prepared by a process only known to a Prussian, and the bread and ham were put in by hydraulic pressure, and the hole soldered up.

About four years ago, the Prussian who had the secret said something unkind to a pitcher of a baseball club, and the pitcher took up one of the sandwiches and pitched it curved at the Prussian's eye. His funeral was quite largely attended, considering that he was a man who was retiring, and who made few acquaintances; but the secret of making the soles and uppers of railroad sandwiches died with him.

It was about this time that corrugated iron shutters were invented, and that material was at once utilized to make lids for sandwiches, while the under jaw of the appetite-destroying substance was made of common building paper, the whole varnished with neatsfoot oil, and kiln dried in a lime kiln.

One object in eating one of the sandwiches, was to transfer, if possible, the headache to the stomach, on the principle that the quack doctor cured a patient of paralysis by throwing him into fits, claiming that he was not much on paralysis, but he was hell on fits. The entrance of the piece of sandwich into the stomach—that is, the small pieces that we were able to blast off with the imperfect appliances at hand in the tool box of a wrecking car—was signaled by the worst rebellion that has been witnessed in this country since 1860. The stomach, liver, lungs, spleen and other patent insides got up an indignation meeting, with the stomach in the chair. In calling the meeting to order the stomach said unaccustomed as it was to public speaking, it felt as though the occasion demanded a protest, and that in no uncertain tone, against the habit the boss had of slinging anything into the stomach that came in his way, without stopping to consider the effect on the internals.

The chair remarked that it had heretofore had a good many hard doses to take, notably, army bacon, and later some black bread that the boss had shoved in while hunting out in Minnesota in 1876, and again last year when a pan full of beans from Bill Wall's Wolf river boom boarding house was sent down without any introduction, the stomach said it had felt like throwing up the "sponge," and drawing out of the game, but it had thought better of it, and had gone on trying to digest things till now. But this last outrage, this Chicago sandwich, was too much.

"See here," says the stomach, holding up a piece of the iron lid of the sandwich so the liver could see it, "what kind of a junk shop does he take this place for?"

The liver got the floor and suggested that the stomach was making a terrible fuss about a little thing, and told the stomach it had evidently forgotten the good things that had been sent down from above in times gone by.

"You seem to forget," says the liver, becoming warmed up, "the banquets the boss never fails to attend, the nice dinner he sometimes gets at home, and the wild canvas-back duck he sends down when he goes to Lake Koshkonong, as well as the Palmer House dinners that occasionally surprise us. I move that the stomach be reprimanded for kicking and trying to get up a muss, and that this meeting adjourn and we all go about our business."

The stomach tried to get in a word edgewise, but it was of no use, and the thing was about to break up in a row, when we went to sleep in one of the elegant Michigan Central sleepers, and in the morning the stomach was coaxing for something more, and didn't seem to care what it was.

TWO GIRLS AT A PICNIC

No YOUNG man should ever take two girls to a picnic. We don't care how attractive the girls are, or how enterprising a boy is, or how expansive or far reaching a mind he has, he connot do justice to the subject if he has two girls. There will be a clashing of interests that no young boy in his goslinghood, as most boys are when they take two girls to a picnic, has the diplomacy to prevent.

If we start the youth of the land out right in the first place, they will be all right, but if they start out by taking two girls to a picnic their whole lives are liable to become acidulated, and they will grow up hating themselves.

If a young man is good natured and tries to do the fair thing, and a picnic is got up, there is always some old back number of a girl who has no fellow who wants to go, and the boys, after they all get girls and buggies engaged, will canvass among themselves to see who will take this extra girl, and it always falls to this good natured young man. He says of course there is room for three in the buggy.

Sometimes he thinks maybe this old girl can be utilized to drive the horse, and then he can converse with his own sweet girl with both hands, but in such a moment as ye think not he finds that the extra girl is afraid of horses, dare not drive, and really requires some holding to keep her nerves quiet. He tries to drive with one hand and console his good girl, who is a little cross at the turn affairs have taken, with the other, but it is a failure, and finally his good girl says she will drive, and then he has to put an arm around them both, which gives more or less dissatisfaction the best way you can fix it.

If we had a boy who didn't seem to have any more sense than to make a hat rack of himself to hang girls on in a buggy, we should labor with him and tell him of the agonies we had experienced in youth when the boys palmed off two girls on us to take to a country picnic, and we believe we can do no greater favor to the young men just entering the picnic of life than to impress upon them the importance of doing one thing at a time, and doing it well.

A YOUNG couple from Green county stopped at a Janesville hotel on their wedding tour, and when they went to bed they were in a hurry and blew out the gas instead of turning it off. In the night a terrible smell was heard around the house, and suspicion naturally pointed to the bridal chamber. The door was pounded on but there was no response, and the people feared the young folks had gone to heaven, so the door was broken down. They had not gone to heaven, but they were both senseless, and were dragged out into the open air, with little ceremony and less clothes. They were brought out of the stupor, when they looked at each other in a reproachful manner, and as they pulled on their clothes they each acted as though if they had known the horrors of married life they would have remained single all their lives.